NO

NO LONGER LONELY

A story of hope

Michelina Zugor

HODDER AND STOUGHTON
LONDON   SYDNEY   AUCKLAND

British Library Cataloguing in Publication Data

A catalogue record for this book is available from the British Library

ISBN 0-340-58816-0

Published by Hodder & Stoughton, a division of Hodder & Stoughton
Ltd, Mill Road, Dunton Green, Sevenoaks, Kent TN13 2YA
Editorial Office: 47 Bedford Square, London WC1B 3DP

Typeset by Phoenix Typesetting, Ilkley, West Yorkshire

Printed in Great Britain by Cox & Wyman Ltd, Reading

DEDICATION

To all my friends at the Vicarage Garden for their constant encouragement and irresistible sense of humour

" . . . and God shall wipe away all tears from their eyes, and there shall be no more . . . sorrow, nor crying . . . for the former things are passed away . . . behold, I make all things new."

Revelation 21:4–5

— 1 —

Warm sunlight squinting through the curtains touched my eyelids and gently roused me into semi-consciousness. Outside, the persistent twitter of birds disturbed my drowsiness still further and a moment later I was wide awake. Had it been a normal Saturday, I would have rolled over and tried to go back to sleep until Mum came up to see if I had washed, but it wasn't a normal Saturday, it was a very special one and I didn't want to waste a minute of it.

Quickly pushing back the covers, I slid out of bed and rushed over to a small chair by the window. Carefully draped over the back of it was the new dress Mum and Dad had bought me for this special occasion. I studied it in silence for a few moments and then held it up against me. Temporarily forgetting Mum and the fact that I *hadn't* washed, I began to twirl round and round, watching the full skirt swirl out in front of me. I had not completed many twirls, however, before the inevitable happened.

"Lindsey, have you washed yet?" Mum called from downstairs. Without answering, I quickly threw the dress on my bed and dived into the bathroom. As the door closed behind me, I heard Mum mounting the stairs and her footsteps approaching my room. For a moment they stopped and then, obviously satisfied that I *was* washing, they disappeared downstairs again. I grinned with satisfaction and turned to look at myself in the mirror above the sink.

"I'm six years old," I whispered excitedly to myself. "Today's my birthday, and I'm six years old!" I grinned again and began to run the tap as I remembered what had been planned for this special day.

Last night, Mum had told me that we would be going to the sea-side. This, in itself, was news enough. I loved the beach and had already accumulated a large collection of shells, seaweed and oddly-shaped pebbles from previous visits. But even more exciting was the news that we were going to a part I had never been to before and would have to take a train to get us there.

After a rather hurried wash, I raced back to my room, almost unable to contain my mounting excitement. I had never been on a train in my life, but had often stood peering through the black railings surrounding the station, watching the trains snaking their way out like giant green caterpillars and imagined what it might be like to ride in one myself. About an hour after breakfast, on that special Saturday morning, my imaginings were at last becoming a reality and, as we jerked into motion, I almost wanted to clap my hands for sheer joy. It was going to be a wonderful day and perhaps, for just a little while, I would be able to forget the things that sometimes happened on the days that weren't "special". But, although we might have looked like a normal, happy family, having a day out together, beneath the veneer there was little to substantiate the perfect image that we portrayed. Nevertheless, today was my birthday and nothing else mattered. This was my first-ever train ride, and I was going to enjoy every minute of it!

I sank back happily into the soft, velour-covered seat, my legs sticking straight out, unable to touch the floor, and pressed my nose against the grimy window-pane. Hundreds of tall grey buildings flashed past outside, followed a moment later by rows upon rows of tiny, match-box houses with identical back gardens and what seemed to be identical washing hanging upon their identical washing-lines. Then, quite suddenly, the world outside was plunged into total darkness. I jumped a little in surprise, feeling suddenly afraid, and glanced quickly at Mum and Dad for reassurance. But, as I did, my fear was immediately replaced by a familiar knot of anxiety somewhere in the pit of my stomach. Although they sat together, they seemed somehow to be strangely apart. As if oblivious to each other's presence, they stared vacantly out of opposite windows at the black nothingness that echoed the lack of expression in their faces. That anxious knot inside me drew a little tighter and I heaved a deep sigh.

Mum and Dad were people I simply couldn't understand. Sometimes they would go for several days, hardly speaking a word to each other. Then, they would suddenly break their silence and speak to each other far too much and in voices much louder than was really necessary. Occasionally I found such behaviour upsetting, at other times vaguely amusing, but always confusing. After all, my friends' parents didn't carry on like this. In fact, I could almost believe they liked each other. Some of them held hands when they came to our Sports Days and open evenings, and I even saw Jenny's mum and dad kiss each other when they thought no one was looking. But my mum and dad weren't like that. They never seemed to hold hands or sit close together and I had only ever seen them kissing once. As I watched them now, I wondered if *they* liked each other, but from what I could see, it didn't seem at all likely.

All at once, brilliant sunlight flooded our carriage as we emerged from the oppressive blackness. I blinked a little as my eyes adjusted to the sudden brightness and tried to shrug off my former thoughts. Maybe they would feel happier when we got to the beach, I told myself and turned to look through the grimy window-pane once more.

It seemed only a few minutes later that we stepped on to the cobbles, strewn with black seaweed and tar. I stood silently gazing at the glistening waves and felt the tingling, salty spray against my face. Although still aware of that vague uneasiness deep down inside, the sparkling waters and high-pitched call of the seagulls were enough to revive my flagging spirits. I couldn't wait to get my costume on and rush into the foaming waves, but all at once Mum's voice seemed to call me back from a pleasant dream.

11

"Oh no!" she exclaimed in dismay. "I've left Lindsey's costume at home." I glanced quickly at Dad, who frowned but said nothing, and wondered if we would have to turn around and go home. Then, just as a large lump had come to my throat, he spun round to face me.

"Well, go on, then," he said quickly, throwing his hand in the direction of the receding tide. "Go and have a paddle."

"Mike!" protested Mum. "She's got her new dress on."

"Go on," he repeated, as if he hadn't heard her. "Go and enjoy yourself." I glanced quickly from one to the other, unsure which to placate and then, throwing off my white plastic sandals, I ran off before he could change his mind.

It was a glorious summer's day and the tide was well out, leaving behind a glistening carpet of wet sand. I walked slowly towards the shallow, rippling waves, feeling it squeeze between my toes and stopping occasionally to examine the small shells that lay on the surface. As the sparkling, salty water lapped around my ankles and the gulls screeched overhead, I wondered why this beautiful day had to be spoilt by yet another of Mum and Dad's disagreements. After all, it was my birthday and . . .

Quite suddenly, a high-pitched squeal of laughter interrupted my thoughts, followed by a cry of: "No, no, I don't like it!" But the tone of such obvious delight made it plain that the opposite was true. I spun round quickly to see a young girl, probably the same age as myself, being swung through the air by her parents and I smiled despite myself. After a few minutes, however, I turned to look in Mum and Dad's direction and my smile faded. Although sitting together, they still seemed, in some strange way, to be apart. Even from a distance, I could sense that they weren't happy like the couple I had just been watching and knowing this made me feel very sad inside. Today of all days they should have been happy, but they hadn't been for quite some time. After a few moments, I turned to face the receding tide and my former excitement seemed to have been washed away on the shallow crest of its rippling waves.

As the afternoon drew to a close, even the thought of a train ride home could not rally my deflated emotions and I seemed somehow to have lost my initial affection for the long metal caterpillar. Indeed, it now seemed to be an enemy, rather than a friend, dragging me away from the wide open freedom of the sea-side to a house that was fraught with discord and tension. Of course, they hadn't intended it to be that way. In fact, they seemed to try so hard to make me happy. But why, I wondered, didn't they ever seem to make each other happy?

That night, I lay awake, listening to a low rumble of voices in the room below mine. It was fairly quiet at first, like distant thunder, too far away to be of any real danger, but gradually it came closer and closer. The voices became louder and more clearly defined. Now they seemed to whip each other, like opposing winds of gale-force intensity, each trying to outdo the other in volume. Then, finally, in one frenzied mad flash, the thunder-clap broke immediately overhead, shattering the darkness into a thousand jagged fragments. I held my breath, wondering what was happening downstairs, but too frightened to get up and actually find out. I pulled my covers round me a little tighter and waited, but there were no more thunder-claps that night. The commotion was replaced by a deathly hush, like the calm descending after a storm, and all those shattered fragments settled silently in the darkness. I lay awake for a while, listening to the sound of my own regular breathing until it, too, faded into the black stillness and I fell asleep. The following morning, I awoke from a dream no more comforting than the previous night's reality, with the strange notion that something was very wrong.

It was Sunday – not a day I particularly liked because of its tiresome morning ritual. For some reason, it always seemed important that I wore my best clothes and had my hair tied with a white ribbon into a high ponytail. Mum, similarly smartly dressed, would encourage me to eat a

13

hasty breakfast and then we would embark on the marathon walk to church before Dad woke up. The journey itself was bad enough as Mum set off at a speed beyond the capability of my small legs. In the end, I had abandoned my attempts to walk more quickly and had invented a method of half jumping from one paving-slab to another without stepping on the lines that separated them. This not only enabled me to keep up with Mum more easily, but also introduced a slight element of fun into an otherwise joyless task. But, tiresome as it was, the journey paled into insignificance when we finally reached our destination.

"Church!" I thought to myself as I sat on the hard wooden pew. I didn't even know what the word meant, except that it was a place where hardly anyone smiled and where little girls were expected to sit very still and very quiet for what seemed like an eternity. I was vaguely under the impression that following this ritual every Sunday was supposed to make me a nicer little girl, pleasing to those around me and somehow more acceptable to the Supreme Being often referred to during the service as "God". But it didn't make me any nicer. In fact, going to church only made me irritable. After all, it seemed to me that "church" was what caused most of Mum and Dad's rows. The very mention of the place would send Dad flying into a temper which, in turn, would make Mum terribly upset. For this reason, we would always try to leave the house on a Sunday morning before Dad woke up. Over the years, this had become such a regular ritual that I often felt I could have performed it in my sleep. But this Sunday morning was different.

Ready for another rushed breakfast, I was more than a little surprised to find the table unlaid and Mum nowhere in sight. I stood in the doorway for several moments, wondering what to make of the situation, and eventually decided that she must have overslept.

"Better go and find her," I told myself and tip-toed quietly out of the deserted kitchen towards her room. It never occurred to me until years later how strange it was that Mum and Dad should have separate rooms. I simply presumed that this was quite normal behaviour for mums and dads. Moreover, I was very well aware that Dad's room was "out of bounds" and, though I came and went quite freely in and out of Mum's room, I had only ever been in Dad's room three times. In view of this, I was astonished to find that his usually closed door had been flung wide open. Forgetting my original mission of "finding mum", I stopped suddenly in my tracks and stared through the open door, wondering what it meant.

Everything seemed to be in order – Mum and Dad were both tidy people – if anything the bed looked too neat to have been slept in. The covers showed not so much as a wrinkle, and the pillow lay as plump and unruffled as ever. As I stared silently into that unfamiliar room, I remembered the night before and suddenly it all fell into place. Turning quickly, I burst into Mum's room, hardly noticing her red eyes and flushed face.

"Where's Dad?" I demanded. She looked up in surprise, and tried hard to smile.

"Lindsey," she said quietly, patting the bed beside her. "Come and sit down here." I stood still for several moments, unsure what to do and then, after a quick glance over my shoulder, I hesitantly went over to her. A moment later, I was on her lap, struggling to understand her words, which were making no sense to me at all. After a while she paused, waiting for my response, but I said nothing.

"Do you want to ask me anything?" she asked eventually. I looked down at my fingers and bit my lip thoughtfully for a few seconds.

"Are we going to church today?" I asked at last. She shook her head slowly.

"No, love, not today." There was another short silence before I spoke again.

"Can I go and play in the garden then?" I asked matter-of-factly.

"Have you had any breakfast?" she queried doubtfully. I shook my head.

"I don't want any. Can I go and play now?" Mum nodded with a weary smile.

"Yes, love, you can go and play."

Once outside, I headed straight for the orchard and clambered up to my little tree-house. It was nothing compared to those that some of my friends had built, consisting mainly of two wooden boards and a piece of carpet that Dad had brought home from work. But to me, it was a palace and I often took refuge there when I wanted to be alone with my thoughts. Today, it seemed particularly inviting, for there was a lot more to think about than usual. Settling down with my back against a large, gnarled branch, I ran through Mum's confusing dialogue once again.

Dad had "gone out", and he wasn't intending to come back – at least that was what she had said. Why he had gone, or even where he had gone, I hadn't been told. He could still be somewhere quite close, or, alternatively, he could be a million miles away. The only thing I knew for certain was that he really had gone!

I pursed my lips and swung my legs to and fro over the edge of my palace floor, wondering how to react to this. At first I wanted to burst into tears, but I wasn't quite sure why, so I decided not to. Instead, I thought everything through again and eventually decided that it wouldn't make much difference one way or another. In fact, things might even improve a little now that he had gone. Maybe now there would be no more thunder-claps during the night and no more silences during the day. And, as for Dad himself, I probably wouldn't miss him too much. After all, I hadn't been with him long enough to really get to know him and, if I was honest, he actually frightened me a little. Sometimes, as he hurled his harsh words at Mum, I had wondered if he would ever turn on me, but he never had. If anything, he seemed to have quite a "soft spot" for his only daughter, but his doting displays of affection confused me still further. If I responded to him, Mum would suddenly disappear into the kitchen, or become very busy with something in the

16

furthest corner of the room. On the other hand, if Mum was on the receiving end of my affections, Dad would suddenly remember that he had promised to meet a friend or that he just had to "pop out" for a while.

At first, it had all seemed a coincidence, but fairly soon I became aware of the emotional tug-of-war in which I was so helplessly caught. Just like the unfortunate piece of rope, I found myself continually pulled in opposite directions. After a while, I began to feel quite uneasy about showing affection to either parent, and though I still responded to some degree, such response became careful and restrained. I soon became quite adept at showing only as much feeling as was really necessary and Mum and Dad seemed quite content with my apparent lack of favouritism. But, while I appeared to be coping with the situation fairly well on the surface, underneath it all, deep down inside, the first seeds of insecurity had been sown.

— 2 —

After Dad left, it seemed, at first, as if things had improved. There were no more rows and upsets, and Mum was a little happier – at least on the surface, but the seeming improvement didn't last for very long.

Now that Dad had gone, I should have felt completely at ease about responding to Mum's affection, but strangely enough, I didn't. Of course, I tried very hard at first, because for some reason I knew I was supposed to be responsive, but adjusting to my new home-life was not at all easy. I soon discovered that I knew Mum about as well as I had known Dad, which was not very well at all. Sometimes I felt as if I were living with a total stranger, and yet was expected to behave as if we were the closest of friends. And, even if I *had* known her better before Dad had left, she was quite a different person now. At first I had thought she might have wanted to cry over the situation, just as I had, but apart from having slightly red eyes on that Sunday morning following his departure, she displayed no such inclination. Instead, she seemed to have pieced herself together again and decided that "the show must go on". This made me think she was actually glad he had gone and I felt I should never ask about him again. But there were times when I wished, more than anything, that I could. When I saw my friends with their dads, holding their hands, or sitting on their shoulders as they strolled through the town, I would stop and wonder what life might have been like if only he hadn't gone away.

Mum, of course, tried very hard to fill the gap that Dad had left. But although she gave generously of her warmth and love and all the other maternal qualities that she so fully possessed, she was unable to provide the strength and stability that a father would have given to his family. Strict though she was, I sensed that she disliked punishing me when I was disobedient and would much rather have had Dad around to do this instead. I gradually realised that if I made enough fuss, I could have my own way whenever I wanted it. At first this knowledge gave me great satisfaction but that quickly gave way to insecurity. With no clear line to over-step, I couldn't tell where the real danger lay. I began to feel like some tiny vessel, tossed to and fro on the stormy waves of emotion that sometimes threatened to overwhelm me. One moment, I would be snappy and irritable, demanding attention in any way possible, and the next, I would become sullen and quiet, not wanting to speak to anyone for hours on end. Obviously concerned by my gradual change of character, Mum would try her best to coax me out of these depressive moods, but she met with little success. I didn't appreciate her concern and only withdrew further and further into myself. I spent a lot of time in my room, staring out of the window at nothing in particular.

So many powerful emotions spun round inside me during those silent hours that I was literally rendered speechless. I felt confused and angry, sad and afraid, all at the same time, but out of them all, there was one emotion that was stronger than all the others. It was very unsettling, like a constant, dull ache, deep down inside and it left me feeling that there was something I desperately needed to find. The trouble was, I didn't know where to look, nor even what I was supposed to be looking for. Where this feeling had come from, I didn't know, but it would descend silently, like a heavy black cloak that covered and stifled me, and only years later would I be able to give it a name.

As the next few years dragged slowly by, I retreated further into my invisible fortress, banishing everyone from my secret, silent world, but never once realising that in shutting others out, I had also shut myself in. Anyone I came into contact with was greeted with complete indifference, and Mum, who was with me day by day, suffered the most. I decided I didn't like her any more. My communication with her degenerated into monosyllables and I did my best to avoid her at all times. Years later I recalled how undaunted she had seemed by my lack of response and wondered where her strength to keep going had come from. But, even then, there were times when I sensed that the load she carried with such apparent ease had become almost unbearable. Maybe she would have crumbled under the weight of it all, had our life not taken a significant turn.

One evening, just before dinner, our bell rang and Mum rushed to open the door. From my vantage point on the upper landing, I caught sight of a man, so tall and broad, that he seemed almost to fill the doorway with his huge frame. His thick grey hair, streaked with occasional threads of black from years gone by, was swept back from a high forehead and he reminded me very much of a big fisherman. Whoever he was, he seemed to know Mum very well, giving her a big hug before following her into the lounge.

By this time, my curiosity was definitely aroused and I crept quietly down the stairs. Mum and the stranger were holding such an animated conversation that they hadn't even bothered to sit down, but stood just inside the doorway, completely caught up in their chatter. Eager to hear what they were saying, I crept a little further forward, balancing my back against the edge of the door and began to swing it slowly from side to side as I listened. After a few moments the big man turned around and was obviously surprised to find a small spectator, viewing him from a great way down with such studied indifference.

"Well, hello, young lady," he boomed and folded his big arms across his chest. "You must be Lindsey." His dark, deep-set eyes twinkled merrily at me from beneath his bushy brows and almost made me want to smile as he did, but I forced myself not to and simply stared at him.

"Lindsey," smiled Mum, "this is my brother Tom. He's your uncle." I looked up at the big man for a few moments longer, still maintaining my unresponsive attitude. Then I turned and walked quietly out of the room, leaving Mum to apologise on my behalf. To my amazement, the stranger didn't seem surprised or upset by my lack of response. Instead, he broke into a gruff laugh and his reply filled me with confusion.

"She's a sweet little girl," he said with a chuckle. I hesitated on the landing for a moment and then rushed into my room. After closing the door firmly behind me, I jumped up on to my bed and sat staring out of the window yet again.

"Sweet?" I thought to myself. "No I'm not! I'm *not* sweet! I'm nasty and horrible and . . . and I'm not sweet!" Suddenly, I felt angry at the big man downstairs for accusing me of such a heinous crime as "sweetness". Furthermore, I was rapidly losing my patience with the scores upon scores of people that also told Mum how sweet I was.

But it wasn't Uncle Tom, or anyone else that was the real cause of my anger. Its roots ran far deeper than I ever suspected. So many jumbled emotions and confusing voices continually spun round inside me that I often felt as if I were in a crowded room, with hundreds of people, all shouting at me at the same time. Even though I spent long hours alone, in complete silence, I had forgotten what it was like to be really quiet inside. Now, yet another strange and powerful emotion, second only in intensity to that heavy, black feeling, had joined the crowded room – it was guilt. Deep down inside, underneath the surface anger and resentment, I felt guilty about my attitude towards other people and, most of all, towards Mum. Apart from the occasional, frustrated outburst, she had never seriously reprimanded me for my thoughtless, selfish behaviour, but had maintained an open, forgiving attitude towards me the whole time. If she *had* got angry and shouted at me, or even hit me, I might have felt better. But she never did and it was her ever-patient attitude that made my guilt weigh upon me even more heavily.

Sometimes I would think about it all at school and spend the whole afternoon determined that when she collected me I would throw my arms around her and kiss her cheek and maybe even tell her that I loved her. But when I saw her waiting in the car-park, the thought suddenly vanished and I wouldn't even offer her a polite "hello". After a while, I began to see myself as a nasty, malicious and spiteful person and wondered why people always had to insist that I was "sweet". When those doting old ladies (and even men) would take my round face in their hands and inform Mum that I was "such a pretty little girl", I wondered how they could be so taken in by such a skin-deep façade.

In order to blot out of my mind their complimentary accusations, I constantly told myself that I wasn't "pretty" – inside or out. I was full of horrible, hateful thoughts and I was a horrible, hateful person and I wished everyone would just go away and leave me alone! But, deep down inside, far deeper than all the angry thoughts and bitter frustration, were silent tears, carefully locked up and brought about by the fact that, underneath it all, I wanted, more than anything, to really be a "sweet little girl". I wanted so much to be kind and loving towards Mum, but somehow, I couldn't; for some strange reason, I couldn't.

Suddenly, a male voice from downstairs interrupted my thoughts and I remembered who it was that had set them in motion – Uncle Tom. Just what kind of a person *was* Uncle Tom, I wondered? As I sat wondering, my stomach persuaded me that it was dinnertime and I reluctantly made my way downstairs.

I hated mealtimes, as much as I had hated Sunday mornings. They were strained, anxious affairs during which Mum would try desperately to coax me into some kind of conversation but, eventually defeated by my lack of response, she would give up and we would finish in silence. This had been the pattern for some time now and I went downstairs anticipating yet another uncomfortable meal. However, I was in for a surprise.

Uncle Tom was like no one I had ever met before. He seemed to bring with him such an atmosphere of freshness and vitality that I almost found it difficult to maintain my sulky expression. He and Mum kept up a lively conversation throughout the meal, which pleased me immensely. All the time they kept at it, I could relax and enjoy my dinner in peace. Of course, their discussion was of little interest to me, but that didn't matter, at least I wasn't being called upon to make conversation, and that suited me very well. In fact, I felt I might even get to like having Uncle Tom around if it meant that Mum would leave me alone a bit more. The truth was that Uncle Tom was going to be around a lot more than I could ever have imagined, but not quite in the way that I had hoped. To my great surprise, he stayed the night at our house and, the following morning, the reason for his visit was revealed.

"We're going to live with Uncle Tom, Lindsey," explained Mum as she started packing cups and saucers into a cardboard box. "He owns a farm, just like the one we see on the way to school."

"I've got lots of animals there, Lindsey," added Uncle Tom, with a persuasive smile. "You'll have lots of fun playing with them, especially Ben – he loves little girls!" Despite my determination not to show any emotion about this unexpected news, I couldn't help feeling a little curious as to who Ben might be.

"Who is he?" I asked eventually, in as flat a voice as I could manage. Uncle Tom winked and his smile widened.

"Well, I'll keep him a surprise until we get there," he chuckled. Slightly offended by his teasing response, and feeling that I had already shown far too much interest in "Uncle Tom's farm", I disappeared silently into the garden, leaving him and Mum to finish the packing.

Once outside, I headed straight for the orchard and clambered up to my palace for what would be the last time. Then, just as I had on that Sunday morning, years ago, I turned this latest piece of news over in my mind.

After a few minutes, I had come to the same conclusions about this event as I had about Dad's disappearance – it probably wouldn't affect me in the slightest. But, when I tip-toed back into the house some time later, my feelings suddenly changed.

Apart from the larger items of furniture, everything had disappeared. I ran quickly up to my bedroom, hoping to find at least a few of my things still intact, but there was nothing except my old and rather grubby teddy-bear, slumped on the floor by the window. As I ran to pick it up, I noticed how my footsteps echoed with an eerie resonance in that enormous, empty room and that irritating urge to burst into tears swept over me again. Much as I had come to dislike living there, I couldn't help feeling sad as I saw the empty shell that our little house had become. All my childhood memories had been packed into tiny cardboard boxes and, although they would be re-assembled when we reached our destination, I wasn't sure that they would ever fit together in quite the same way again.

— 3 —

Uncle Tom had never married and, as I gradually became aware of him as a person, I often wondered why. Even though he was getting on in years, there was no doubt that he must have been very handsome in his younger days. Even with grey hair and a slightly weather-beaten face, he was attractive. In addition to this, his large, powerfully-built frame gave one the impression that he would always be equal to any task, no matter how old he became. But Uncle Tom wasn't just attractive physically, he possessed an equally attractive nature. It was this that earned him instant friendship wherever he went, but it was also because of this that he frightened me a little. Right from the start, I had determined to treat him in the same way as I treated Mum and everyone else, but his warm, unpretentious manner made this task quite difficult.

The day following our arrival at the farm, while Mum started on the unpacking, Uncle Tom had taken me on a guided tour. He kept up an enthusiastic commentary the whole time, despite my lack of response, stopping occasionally to introduce me to the animals. There was Skippy the cat, Henrietta the cow, Randolph the goat, and many others that had no names. But, without a doubt, it was Ben that I liked best of all.

Ever since I had heard of this mysterious being that "loved little girls", I was curious to find out who or what he was and perhaps Uncle Tom had kept his "surprise" until last because he knew what my reaction would be.

After quite some time, our tour ended in some sort of back yard. Here, Uncle Tom stopped and gave a long, low whistle and I looked up, wondering what was about to happen. A moment later, I only just managed to stop myself squealing in delight as a very young and bouncy English sheepdog puppy bounded round the corner. His small white ears flapped up and down as he ran and I thought he was the cutest thing I had ever seen. Eventually, he bounced to a halt at Uncle Tom's feet and I feasted my eyes upon him in delight. He had a solid little body of silky white fur, with a tousled white mop of a head sticking out the top. Obviously as excited as I was, he let out a high-pitched "yap, yap" of a bark, jerking his head from side to side as he did so. I clasped my hands tightly together, trying hard not to smile as Uncle Tom crouched down to pat him.

"Hello, boy," he said with a chuckle. "Been having fun?" Once again the little puppy let out his high-pitched bark and then, to my joyful surprise, he held up a small, silky paw. Uncle Tom took it in his large, rough hand and shook it gently up and down.

"Like him, Lindsey?" he asked with a smile. "I only bought him last week, so he's almost as new to the farm as you are." I bit my lip to keep myself from smiling and continued to study his white, furry face. A small black blob of a nose poked out of his fur and his sparkling blue eyes seemed to be laughing at me.

"In case you haven't guessed already, Lindsey, this is Ben," smiled Uncle Tom and I noticed that, upon hearing his name, the little puppy held up his paw again. As Uncle Tom shook it once more, I could contain myself no longer.

"Can I shake hands with him too?" I asked quickly.

"Of course you can," beamed Uncle Tom. "Here, come over here." I stepped forward until I was beside him and awaited instructions.

"Just hold out your hand and say 'paw'," he advised me. Feeling suddenly self-conscious, I took a step backwards and bit my lip again.

"Come on," coaxed Uncle Tom. "He won't hurt you."

I hesitated for a moment and then reluctantly stepped forward again and held out a shaky hand.

"Paw," I said in a very small voice. The little creature jerked his head in my direction and a tense moment passed while I awaited his token of acceptance. Then, quite suddenly, he held out his paw once again. A thrill of excitement ran through me as I grasped it and shook it gently up and down. But, exciting though this was, there was more to come. Suddenly, the little creature bounced forward and licked the side of my face with his little pink tongue.

I jumped back in surprise, rubbing my face with my hand as Uncle Tom laughed merrily.

"He likes you, Lindsey," he smiled. "That's his way of saying so." Once again, I tried very hard not to show how excited I felt, but was conscious of a warm, cosy feeling, deep down inside. That evening, after dinner, I crept out to the back yard and did something that was to become a regular ritual for several years to come. Looking around carefully to make sure no one was watching my uncharacteristic display of emotion, I sat down quietly beside the dozing puppy. Finally convinced that no one could see, I put my arms around his soft, stubby neck and laid my cheek against his ear.

"I like you too, Ben," I whispered fervently. "I like you very much."

From that day forward, Ben and I became almost inseparable and every evening after dinner, I would sit on the back step with my arm around his neck and my head laid gently against his small, furry head. Feeling the warmth of his tiny, fluffy body against my own, I would gaze wonderingly into the clear blue sky above us and dream. At first, I had tried to keep this exercise a secret from Mum and Uncle Tom and was quite annoyed when they eventually discovered it. But, after a while, it didn't seem to matter. Uncle Tom would only ever smile and wink at me whenever he saw me with Ben and Mum, for some reason, pretended not to notice. Sometimes I would sit with the little puppy until late into the evening, watching the sunset colours melting

27

slowly away until, at last, the silver-studded mantle of deep-blue velvet fell across the sky. At other times, we would go for long walks over the hills that surrounded the farm and I would pour out to him my deepest longings, certain that my secrets were safe with him.

It was probably thanks to Ben that I settled into my new home so quickly. Had it not been for him I might have found my new environment even more uncomfortable than the previous one, and the main cause of my distress was that infuriating man – Uncle Tom! He was always so warm and friendly and so kind to Mum that just being around him made me painfully aware of how wrong my own attitude was. It seemed to me that his life was a brilliant shaft of light penetrating my invisible fortress, revealing all those bitter, angry thoughts that I tried so hard to keep concealed within its walls. Because of this I tried to avoid him as much as possible, but, at the same time, I found myself irresistibly drawn to this strange man who never seemed to have a bad word to say about anyone, and something inside me began to wish, more than anything, that I could be like him.

But that was impossible, I told myself. After all, it wasn't as if I hadn't tried to change – I had, several times, but each attempt had been a dismal failure. In the end, I decided that it was impossible for me ever to be anything except the selfish, introverted individual that I was, no matter how much I wished I could be.

Over the years that followed, I watched Ben change from an excitable, bouncy puppy into a huge, shaggy dog. His bright-blue eyes were now almost completely concealed by two curtains of long white fur and the paws that he still held out for me to shake became large and heavy. And, as I, too, began to grow up, maintaining my resolve never to show any feeling or emotion in front of other people, I opened up to the shaggy dog more and more during our solitary walks. My depressions became deeper and my moods more frequent, until I almost forgot what it was like to be really happy. But it didn't matter, I told myself. I didn't want to be happy anyway, it was much easier to be miserable and moody. One day, however, a strange thing happened, which revealed very graphically how much the opposite was really true.

I was sitting on the back step, playing with a rather irritating toy. It was a small, transparent box, sealed on all sides. Inside it there were three tiny silver balls and a coloured piece of plastic, punched with three minute holes. The idea of the game was to make all three balls come to rest in the holes that were just a little too small to hold them. I had made several unsuccessful attempts at this when Mum called me from the kitchen to help with preparing the lunch. I put down the little box and sighed. Irritating though it was, I would much rather have continued with my tortuous game than had to help Mum. This was not because I particularly disliked cooking, but simply because she would insist on making me talk to her whilst I did it. With very bad grace, I peeled the potatoes and set the table and was eventually allowed to escape to my room with Ben. Closing the door firmly behind me, I slumped on to the floor, with my back resting against the side of my bed and Ben curled up beside me. As I again thought about how tiresome life was, I heaved another deep sigh and shut my eyes – and it was then that it happened.

At first, I saw only the usual, patchy blackness as my eyelids closed. But then the darkness seemed to be slowly receding to the edges of what would have been my scope of vision, had my eyes been open, and a vivid picture began to develop behind my closed lids.

In the picture, I saw a girl, quite young, but at the same time, a good deal older than I was then. She wore a thick, roll-neck jumper, blue trousers and green wellington boots, and I knew, beyond all doubt, that the girl was myself. It was difficult to believe this at first, for her cheeks glowed with some obvious, inner joy and a radiant smile wreathed her face. She seemed to be in some peaceful, wooded place and, from the surrounding scenery, I deduced that it was autumn. The trees all around her seemed to have been set on fire and turned into glowing torches of blazing orange, yellow and red. The girl was walking briskly up a hill through the colourful woodlands, swinging a bucket in one hand and, from the movement of her lips, I realised that she was singing.

As the vision continued, I entered into it more fully, almost feeling the fresh breeze that blew her hair gently around her shoulders and hearing the birds' shrill accompaniment to her singing. But, most of all, I could feel the sheer joy that seemed to course through her being and which had put that merry spring into her step. As I continued to watch her, I wondered where that beautiful place might be or, indeed, if it really existed. It never occurred to me to be frightened or upset by this strange happening, for I was far too caught up in the sheer beauty of what I was seeing. Then, all at once, I opened my eyes and shook my head, startling Ben with my sudden movement. As I surveyed my familiar surroundings and remembered my former depression, I suddenly wanted to get back into that beautiful place again. Quickly, I shut my eyes in a desperate attempt to regain the vision, but it had gone – although not for ever.

"Ben," I whispered, stroking his huge, shaggy head, "she was happy, really happy. One day, Ben, *I'm* going to be that happy too, I know I am!" But then, as I looked round again, and remembered how wretched and miserable I was, my conviction faded, just as the vision had. Instead of trying to pursue that fleeting hope of blissful joy, I decided to continue with the discipline of keeping myself to myself. The only problem was, the more I tried to succeed at this task, the more it seemed as if Mum was determined to stop me doing so.

The further I drew away from her, the more set she seemed on regaining my affection. Sometimes, she seemed almost desperate to be near me and to touch me or, worse still, to kiss me. But I didn't want to be touched. I didn't want her near me. I wanted her to go away and leave me alone! But, when she did go away, I wanted more than anything for her to come back. Such were my feelings one day, when I returned home from school in very low spirits.

It had been a particularly tiresome day and I hadn't been able to concentrate on any of my lessons. All I could think about as the hours dragged slowly by, was returning home and taking Ben out for a long walk. To my dismay, however, I bumped into Mum just as I pushed through the back door. Sensing that she was about to question me on my more than usually long face and sullen attitude, I rushed quickly past her without saying a word. But she had no intention of ignoring my obvious distress and, just as I flopped down on my bed, I heard her footsteps on the landing outside.

A moment later, she quietly pushed open my door and stepped into the room. My first impulse was to rush downstairs, but she was blocking the doorway, making it impossible for me to escape. Tensing every muscle, I continued to stare silently out of the window, hoping desperately that she would just go away.

"Lindsey?" she said softly, taking a few steps towards me. I held my breath and made no response. "Is there something wrong?" I shook my head quickly without turning around, but instead of giving up, she came closer and placed a hand on my shoulder.

"Lindsey, if there's something on your mind . . . "

"No, there isn't," I replied quickly and jumped up from my bed.

"Lindsey . . . " she called after me, but I was already half way down the stairs, stopping only to grab Ben's lead from its hook by the back door. A few minutes later, we were alone, walking once again over those silent hills. I walked quickly, not turning around once until we came to my favourite, most secluded spot. Finally certain that the farmhouse was well out of sight, I sat down, burying my face in his long, white mane and cried bitter tears of frustration.

"I didn't mean to do it, Ben," I sobbed, grabbing handfuls of his snowy fur in my hands. "I just can't help

31

it. I want to love her, really I do. But I can't Ben . . . I can't." Ben was a great connoisseur of emotions and seemed able to understand when I felt really sad. He let out a low, mournful whimper and licked my face with his rough, pink tongue.

"I don't understand it, Ben," I continued, still sobbing. "I don't understand myself any more." He lowered his shaggy head on to his paws and I stroked it thoughtfully. "You're a really good friend, Ben," I said sincerely. "But sometimes I don't think you understand either." He shuffled a little from side to side as I stroked the furry bridge of his nose.

"But it's not your fault," I continued. "You're only a dog. Sometimes, Ben, I wish there was someone I could talk to – I mean *really* talk to . . . a special friend, of my very own."

Anne handed me a rather dog-eared red rose, to which was attached a small blue card, bearing the words:

With this flower I give to you
all my love, my whole life through.

I stared at it in surprise as I tried to take in its touching message.

"I told you," sniggered Anne as she read the card over my shoulder. "I said he liked you, didn't I?"

"Don't be ridiculous," I snapped. "Of course he doesn't."

She clicked her teeth and sighed.

"But he does, Lindsey – really. He's going to ask you out next."

I looked up at her in amazement. "What? How do you know?"

"It's obvious," she replied, with the air of one who was addressing a complete imbecile. "And in any case, he told me so."

"When?"

"When he asked me to give you the flower." Just then, I glanced over to the school building and noticed the subject of our discussion in the corridor, peering intently at us through the window.

"Well, you can tell him before he does," I said, defiantly pushing the faded flower back into her hand. "I'm not interested!"

"But Lindsey . . . "

"I'm not interested," I repeated firmly and walked

quickly towards the entrance. Just as I pushed through the door, my amorous admirer was making his way out. He stopped suddenly, pinning me to the edge without the slightest intention of letting me pass.

"Hello, Lindsey," he said dreamily. I shot a threatening glance at Anne and managed a noncommittal "Hi", before pushing past with my bag of books. As I sat at my desk that morning, trying desperately to concentrate on my studies, I was aware of a certain young man, looking often in my direction.

Adolescence was turning out to be a very troubled time for me. By the age of fifteen, I was more aware than ever that Ben was "only a dog" and my desire for a "special friend of my very own" began to dominate my thinking. More than anything, I longed for someone with whom I could share my innermost feelings. Someone who would not only listen, as Ben did, but who would respond as well. Someone who, perhaps, would even go beyond superficial response and who would be genuinely interested in my secret dreams and ambitions. And then, maybe, just maybe, they would be interested in me, as a person, as well.

But the final stage was the most difficult to believe in. Because of the opinion I had formed of myself during childhood, I found it very difficult to believe that anyone would ever really be interested in me as a person. It seemed such an impossibility that I couldn't even bear to tell anyone about it. Only as I rambled over those hills with Ben did I ever come close to hinting at what my deepest longing was.

Underneath it all, I wanted more than just "interest". If the truth were known, what I really wanted was love. The "someone" that I was looking for would not only like me, or be interested in me, they would love me as well. Of course, I knew that Mum loved me, but I told myself that this was only because she was related to me and expected my affection in return. Uncle Tom seemed to love me too, but I quickly explained this away. He was only so nice to me because he wanted to please Mum, I told myself. And in any case, he couldn't possibly *really* like me. No, the person

I was looking for would love me for no other reason than because I was me. But it was almost impossible to believe that such a person could exist.

In some respects, however, life had become a little easier. I now attended secondary school, which was much bigger than my small primary school had been and accommodated children from many different backgrounds. Many of them were also from single-parent families, which made me feel much less of a mis-fit. Also, although I had never lost my self-deprecating attitude, I had almost learned to live with it and came across as a quiet, rather shy and slightly introverted youngster. But this hadn't stopped me making friends. Many of the other pupils had similar backgrounds and problems to my own and I was, therefore, quite readily accepted as one of the crowd. After only a short time, I even began to like my new school as it provided a welcome escape from the pressures of living at home. I gradually built up a small circle of friends who accepted me as "the quiet one" and never put pressure on me to be anything else. Of course, I never allowed my friendship with them to go beyond the surface aspects of life and they all seemed quite happy with this arrangement. But there were two areas in which they found me just a little out of the ordinary. The first was my attitude towards the opposite sex. As classes for the morning ended and we made our way across the playground to the canteen, Anne raised her eyebrows and shrugged in desperation.

"C'mon Lindsey, what's the matter with you?" she pleaded. "That's the third person that's asked you out. Don't you want a boyfriend?"

"No, I don't!" I replied defiantly. "There's more to life than boys!" But even though it sounded outwardly convincing, underneath I had quite a different opinion. The truth was, I very much *did* want a boyfriend. In fact, it was the one thing I wanted more than anything else. But it was too bad, I couldn't have one, no matter how much I wanted one – Mum wouldn't let me!

This was another thing that I added to her list of failings. Why did she have to be so old-fashioned and archaic about the opposite sex, I wondered? Indeed, I got the impression that she regarded men and boys as dangerous monsters who should be avoided at all costs. Furthermore, she would not hear so much as a word on the subject of boyfriends. When a visitor to the farm had one day informed her that I was a "nice looking kid" and was probably "breaking hearts at school", she had replied, very firmly, that I wasn't interested in boys and that, in any case, I was far too young to be thinking about such things. *That*, I told Ben, as we went for our evening walk, was how much she understood me anyway!

From her behaviour I decided that she was deliberately holding out on me and trying to spoil my fun. It never occurred to me that her attitude might be a product of her own unfortunate experience with Dad. I simply believed this was her way of getting back at me and it made me extremely cross.

But I was not only angry about the restrictions placed upon me; for some reason, I was terribly ashamed about the whole business. I was worried that my class-mates might regard me as being a little odd because I wasn't allowed out with boys and so I determined to keep this fact a secret at all costs. One day I would be old enough to make my own decisions about such things, I told myself, and until then, I would just have to pretend I wasn't interested.

At first, I thought my indifferent attitude would stave off any would-be admirers, but had soon found the opposite to be true. Rather than putting them off, many of the boys interpreted my attitude as shyness or "playing hard to get" and I was even once informed that I "brought out the protective in a guy". Upon hearing this, I had replied, with more than necessary vehemence, that I was quite capable of looking after myself and didn't need "protecting"! But inside, I felt completely the opposite. As I watched the other girls with their boyfriends, often holding hands or arm in arm in the playground, I wondered what it must be like to feel a comforting arm around my shoulder and indeed have someone to protect and care for me.

But it was no use thinking about such things and maybe, in spite of it all, Mum was right. I tried to convince myself that perhaps fifteen *was* a little young to be thinking about such an important relationship. But, on the other hand, I had in some ways grown up far too quickly and my expectations of a boyfriend were vastly different from those of the other girls. All they seemed to be after was a good night out and having fun and coming home late. I was looking for safety and security and a sense of belonging that I hadn't felt for so long.

But, even if Mum was right, her over-protective attitude made me feel more and more restricted and I began to see the farm as some kind of open prison, rather than the tranquil retreat from outward pressures that it had once been. The extent of my supposed incarceration became apparent one awful Saturday afternoon.

I was sitting looking out of my bedroom window when I noticed, with extreme horror, a familiar form at the front gate. It was one of the boys from school, whose amorous advances I had spurned several times and who seemed unable to take "no" for an answer. Sudden panic set in as I watched him making his way down the drive and I anticipated the outcome of his visit. I had never mentioned my "admirers" to Mum and was certain she would think I had put him up to it just to spite her.

A moment later, the door-bell rang and I rushed on to the landing just in time to see Mum answer it. As the poor lad explained to my very overbearing mother that he had come to ask me out, I cringed and could hardly bear to continue my eavesdropping. In fact, it was hardly necessary to do so, for I knew already how the conversation would go. Mum informed the unfortunate boy, in no uncertain terms, that I was far too young for a boyfriend and that he really ought to run along.

That evening, I walked Ben for much longer than usual, unloading on to him all my pent-up emotion. Why, I asked

37

him angrily, couldn't Mum treat me like a reasonable young adult? Why didn't she trust me the way my friends' mothers trusted them? Why did she have to treat me like a child all the time? Well, I would show her, I told him, and everybody else, that I could run my life quite well without their interference. One day I would be old enough to go my own way and I would make a better job of running my life than they ever could! For now, I had no choice but to live at the farm, but my presence there was purely physical. In my heart and mind, I had left already.

The other thing that set me apart slightly from the other girls was my complete lack of interest in pop music. Mum and Dad had never allowed it to be played in our house. Their small record-player, which Mum had since given to me, had only ever been used for playing soft, "country" music and even then, at such a low volume that it was virtually impossible to hear anyway. Because of this, I had grown up believing that modern music was little more than jangling, nonsensical gibberish and I might have continued to think so, but for one reason.

The girls I had fallen in with were as enthusiastic about the modern music scene as they were about boyfriends. Indeed, apart from the latter, their lives seemed to consist of little more than records, discos and posters of their latest pop idols. When the conversation steered round to such subjects, as it inevitably did, I suddenly felt isolated and unable to maintain my position as one of the crowd. The things they talked about sounded like double-dutch to me. I didn't know any of the very famous names they mentioned, neither was I exactly sure what the "charts" were – let alone an LP! After a while, I realised that anyone who was anyone at school was into pop music and that, in order to really fit, I ought to get into it too. I began this task almost by accident one Friday morning before registration. Anne was sitting at her desk, next to mine, reading an article in the latest issue of *Melody Maker* and I couldn't help noticing the opposite page. On it, seated at a piano, in a dazzling suit of some shimmery material, was a young man. Outrageous though his clothes were, however, it was not them, but his face that attracted my attention. There was something about the sadness in his eyes and the seriousness of his expression that I immediately identified with, although I wasn't really sure why. Almost without thinking, I leaned over and nudged Anne's arm.

"Hey, Anne, who's that?" She looked at the picture and apathetically threw out yet another obscure name.

"Does he sing?" I asked. "Or just play?" Obviously surprised by my uncharacteristic show of interest, she became a little more enthusiastic.

"He's a singer. I've got some of his records." She looked at me enquiringly. "Want to borrow one?"

I looked again at the serious face and nodded. "Yes, okay."

She folded up the magazine as our teacher entered the room with the morning register under his arm.

"I'll bring one at lunchtime," she whispered.

That evening, I returned home with the promised record in my bag and dashed up to my room, feeling as if I had just smuggled a ton of cocaine into the house. Once the door was firmly closed behind me, I pulled the slim package out of my bag and studied the sleeve.

The clothes worn by the singer were no less dazzling than they had been in the magazine, but once again, it was his face that was the main attraction. His eyes seemed to reach out to me with some kind of desperate hollowness and his face was as serious as my own. In spite of his obvious success and popularity, his expression betrayed the fact that he wasn't completely happy. There was something missing from his life and, once again, I felt a sudden kinship with this strange man whom I had never even met.

As I positioned the stylus and watched the small black disc complete one silent revolution, I wondered what kind of song this man would sing. Once or twice, I had caught snatches of the rather rowdy, jarring music played on Radio One and I fully expected the same sound to suddenly blare out from my record-player. When the music began, however, I could not have been more surprised. Instead of the raucous noise I had been expecting, the song began with two bars of gentle, fluid piano music, sensitively played and reminding me slightly of the rippling brook that ran alongside the farm. Then, as the gentle musical stream gathered momentum, the voice began. It wasn't harsh, or even very loud, but soft and melodious and tinged with the same sadness displayed in the owner's face. The words were deep and meaningful, perfectly rhymed and timed and seemed to verbalise so perfectly the things I felt, deep down inside. In some strange, indescribable way, they brought to the surface and expressed for me the things that I, myself, would never have been able to put into words. As I continued to listen to the sad, sweet melody, I left behind the pressures of my life and escaped, for a few, short minutes, into a world of soothing fantasy.

Eventually, the record ended and I jumped up suddenly, feeling as if I had woken up from a dream that was sweet and bitter all at the same time. Almost involuntarily, I set the needle in position again . . . and again . . . and again.

It was my first "shot in the arm" and, from that day forward, I was hooked. Music now became another means, alongside Ben, of relieving the complex emotions still so tightly bottled up inside. When I wasn't out walking with the big, shaggy dog, I was shut in my room with my record-player turned up rather more loudly than it should have been. After only a short while, I, too, owned hundreds of records, just like the other girls at school, and I, too, was able to recite the Top Twenty, without stumbling once over those formerly unfamiliar names. The pretty floral wallpaper in my bedroom was soon covered with posters of the latest pop idols that I, too, now worshipped as a fully-fledged disciple of the current pop scene. Now, I even liked that loud, jarring music that I had once hated with such a vengeance and whenever I wanted to, I could escape from outward pressures into a fantasy world of glitter and noise.

My ability to do this was further strengthened when I was asked to choose an instrument to learn during music

40

lessons, and I immediately chose the guitar. In only a few short months I was able, not only to listen, but also to play along with the many records I now possessed and to enter more fully than ever into the deceptive and surrealistic world I had found.

Mum, of course, was not at all pleased by my new interest and was full of disparaging remarks but, perhaps frightened that she would alienate herself from me still further if she put a stop to it, she permitted me to continue listening to my records. In addition to this, she grudgingly allowed me to watch "Top of the Pops" on a Thursday evening. Some time ago, I had refused to go to church with her and Uncle Tom any more and, therefore, I was also able to listen to Radio One quite freely on a Sunday.

In spite of such leniency, however, she still maintained certain limitations. If ever I broached the subject of going to discos with my friends, she would refuse this with as much vengeance as she had refused my request for a boyfriend. At first, I had been blazing mad about this but, true to type, I kept my feelings carefully concealed and found my own way of thwarting her restrictive desires.

Every so often, the sixth-formers would get together and organise an after-school disco in the assembly hall. Since beginning the run-up to my "O" levels, I had fallen into the habit of staying behind after school studying or doing homework. Mum, therefore, had got quite used to me not arriving home until some time after five, quite rightly believing that I had spent the time in the library. It wasn't long, however, before I realised that I could attend these after-school discos without her suspecting in the slightest where I had been or, indeed, what I had been doing. On the relevant day, I would pack some ordinary clothes into my school bag and change into them, as the other girls did, in the school cloakroom. Then we would congregate in the large hall that had been blacked out for the purpose and leave the real world behind for an hour or so.

For me, this was the ultimate experience in escapism. The flashing lights and pounding music drowned out, at least temporarily, those clamouring voices that still tormented my mind and, for a short space of time, I became a completely different person. The music I had once disliked so much now seemed to hold some kind of transforming power that I failed to find in anything else and was second only to Ben in its ability to provide a release from my conflicting emotions. My friends had taught me all the latest dances and we never just stood and "swayed" as some did. Instead, we would make up a team and perform our intricate dance routines in the centre of the floor, often causing the others to stop and watch our energetic performances. One evening, the sixth-former turned DJ suddenly stopped the music and leaned forward over the microphone.

"Hey, you," he shouted. "The girl in red." In the darkness, it was impossible to see who was wearing what colour, but as the spotlight hit me I remembered that I was wearing skin-tight red jeans and a red top.

"Yeah, you," he continued, looking straight at me. "Catch." I raised both hands, just in time to catch the package that he threw in my direction.

"Best dancer prize," he shouted, with a dazzling smile and then started up the music again. I clutched it in amazement, hardly able to believe it was really meant for me as Anne nudged my shoulder.

"And to think you used to hate this stuff," she shouted through the blaring noise and flashing lights. I laughed myself and then began to dance again, losing myself even further in the pounding, pulsating blackness.

It was exciting, wonderful, exhilarating – while it lasted! But eventually, the music stopped and the curtains were drawn back. Dusty, tubular shafts of real, harsh daylight flooded the room, catching us out in the sudden brightness like worms that had just crawled out from underneath a stone. As we blinked at each other, feeling slightly dazed, it became apparent that this bright, flashing world amounted to little more than a rather disorderly school hall and a pile of worn-out records. Reality was a difficult concept to embrace.

For a short while, as we walked part of the way home together, we tried to hang on to the excitement and exhilaration we had felt, but eventually we would split up and go our separate ways. It was then that reality, for me, really began to take its toll. Now there were no flashing lights or pulsating music to hide behind. Now I was alone, face to face with myself and those tireless voices that I could never really silence. And it was then that the oppressive black cloak that I had managed temporarily to shake off, would settle upon me more heavily than ever. It made me feel sick and stifled and strangely empty, all at the same time. Often, as I made the long journey home, it would become so heavy that I would be unable to continue walking. Instead, I would sit for several minutes on the grass verge with my head in my hands as the devastating truth filtered slowly through my mind. I wasn't one of the crowd, in spite of my desperate attempts to appear so. I wasn't carefree and happy-go-lucky like the other girls were. I was afraid and angry and so desperately alone.

Suddenly, almost suffocated by that dark, heavy mantle, I wanted to stand up and shout at someone – anyone who would listen – that I needed help, that I felt hopelessly trapped in a prison of my own making. But it would have been futile. There was nothing I or anyone else could do as far as I could see. The lock had rusted over many years ago and I would just have to keep up the charade – perhaps for the rest of my life. Eventually, feeling as if I were carrying a great burden, I would get up and finish the journey home and never let anyone know of the double life I lived.

Another thing that assisted me quite considerably in the exercise of escapism was study. Having left behind the frightening first year, the rebellious second and the undecided third, I had entered my fourth year in a much more serious frame of mind. All at once, the words " 'O' levels" were on everyone's lips. The awareness hit me that these final years at school were of vital importance and that I was actually working towards some kind of crucial culmination. More and more, thoughts about the future began to fill my mind and I began to realise just how much hinged on these important exams. So it was that, although I maintained my enthusiasm for discos and pop music, I became equally enthusiastic about my studies and grew into a serious, hard-working student. Very soon, the results of my diligence showed up in my work and put me into the top streams in all subjects but maths. This was the one subject I had never excelled in, no matter how hard I tried, but my success in all other subjects more than made up for this deficiency. Indeed, I occasionally surprised myself at some of the results I achieved.

One morning, our English teacher began the lesson by announcing that I had won the Morrison cup for English Literature. She then asked me to read out my latest essay. As I nervously obliged, I thought how ironic it was that this essay, which had gained me the award, should be a three-page exposition on the different types of love depicted in Shakespeare's *Romeo and Juliet*. As I read my carefully written notes, I was aware of my teacher gazing admiringly at me, obviously wondering where my understanding of "love" had come from. And as I continued reading, I was aware, also, that I didn't have the faintest idea what I was talking about.

In this way, my final years at school slowly passed, for time did pass very slowly at the farm. Its gentle pace and day-to-day sameness began to bother me more and more and I longed to escape from its claustrophobic structure. Often, when returning from my evening walk with Ben, I would stand on the bottom rung of the five-bar gate and throw my thoughts as far as they would go into the fragile, unreal distance. All kinds of exciting worlds lay beyond those fresh, green hills and, with everything in my confused young heart, I determined to venture forth one day and experience the life that, as yet, was still only a wonderful dream. I was tired of life at the farm where nothing exciting ever happened, deliberately choosing not to remember the exciting moments I had experienced. I carefully buried the memory of holding a fluffy young

44

chick in my hands as a child, the flurry of delight that had raced through me when I had taken Ben's paw in my hand for the first time, and the way I would eagerly rush to the cowshed through the early morning dew to stroke the velvet nose of the new-born calf. They were stupid, "cissy" things to get excited about, I told myself. The girls at school would laugh at me if they knew about my life at the farm. I wanted *real* excitement. I wanted to get away from this rural existence and live a life of my own, full of glitz and glamour. I wanted to go to discos and have parties and friends, lots of friends. But most of all, I wanted one friend who would be special to me alone. Then, I told myself, my life would *really* begin.

In the midst of the quiet sameness, however, there was one noteworthy event that took place and which was to hold great significance in the years that followed. One Monday morning, Anne seemed rather more than usually excited by something in her latest copy of *Melody Maker*.

"Hey, Lindsey," she called enthusiastically. "Look at this." I peered at the page she held open and suddenly felt as thrilled as she did. It was my favourite singer, the one with the sad eyes and solemn face. Since I had first listened to him, I had become a fan of many groups and other solo artists, but, without a doubt, he was still my favourite. Whenever I felt really down, and wanted to relieve my fraying emotions, it was his music that I played and he was given pride of place amongst the posters all over my bedroom walls. The article informed us that he would be giving a concert in London the following month and the other girls had already decided to go.

"Are you going to come, Lindsey?" asked one of them. Without thinking about all the implications, I nodded eagerly.

"You bet," I smiled. "I wouldn't miss that for anything!"

Lessons were difficult that day and I could hardly concentrate on any of my studies. Instead, my mind kept drifting into the wonderful daydream of seeing my favourite artist in real life at last. We spent all break that morning

45

plotting our best way of obtaining tickets and catching a train to London. By the time I got home that evening, the matter was signed, sealed and settled. At least, it was as far as I was concerned, but I hadn't at all accounted for Mum.

"You're not going, and that's final!" she had informed me most emphatically. I stared at her in stunned silence, feeling like a child whose favourite toy had been suddenly snatched out of its arms.

"And in any case," she continued firmly, "it's being transmitted live, so you can watch it on television." As she turned to leave the room, I wanted to jump up and down and shout at her and tell her she was making my life a complete misery. But I wasn't going to do it. Showing emotion was beneath me and I wasn't going to give her such satisfaction! I walked silently out of the room, calmly climbed the stairs and slammed my bedroom door as hard as I could. Then I put on a record and turned the volume up much louder than usual in an attempt to drown out once again the angry voices that spun round in my mind. Much as I hated accepting Mum's charity, however, I was still determined to see my idol in action and was overjoyed when she and Tom announced that they would be going out on the evening of the concert. This meant that I would have the house all to myself and could turn the music up as loud as I liked.

Armed with a cup of coffee and with Ben curled up at my feet, I turned out the light and waited impatiently for the credits and introductions to finish. Why, I wondered with more than a little irritation, did there always have to be half an hour of mumbo-jumbo before we got to the good stuff? At last, the final credit dipped below the screen and the concert began. As the camera scanned quickly round the vast audience gathered there, I searched eagerly for the faces of Anne and my other friends, but it was impossible to pick them out of the vast ocean of expectant, up-turned faces. Not a moment too soon, the lights dimmed, the curtain rose and the opening notes of some sad, sweet melody echoed out from the darkened stage. I snuggled back into my chair and listened for the first sound of his voice. A moment later, however, the music stopped abruptly, the Man himself rose from the piano seat and stepped into the small shaft of light on the centre stage. The audience waited expectantly, wondering what he was about to do, but not at all prepared for what took place. Instead of bursting into song, or even giving a message of greeting and welcome, the Face, serious at the best of times, struggled now to keep its composure. His message was far from expected.

"I'm bored, and I'm lonely, and I need someone in my life," he said clearly and simply. Then, gathering up his glittering jacket, he walked slowly off the stage, leaving an astonished audience behind. Indeed, I too was stunned, but for a completely different reason to them. Suddenly, that strange, searching expression in his eyes had been explained – he was lonely. And explained also was my feeling of kinship with the man. For the first time, I understood what that dull ache and constant searching in my own heart was – I was lonely too. At last, I could put a name to that heavy, black cloak that had almost permanently come to rest on my shoulders. It was loneliness: sharp, cutting, soul-destroying loneliness. As it all suddenly became clear, I wanted to jump up and shout at the empty stage: "I know! I know how you feel! I feel like that too . . . I'm lonely too!"

But if I had felt better about identifying my problem, the feeling didn't last for very long. All at once it seemed as if I had fallen foul of some dreadful disease for which there existed no cure, or as if a Supreme Judge had found me guilty of some heinous crime for which there was no reprieve. Discovering what the problem was had seemed to compound and complicate it still further and, for the first time in my life, I wished I had never heard of the sad singer.

The incident had a profound effect on me and would, in years to come, mark one of the greatest turning-points in my life. But for the moment, it was too upsetting and

I wanted to bury it deep inside, along with all the other painful memories. I never wanted anyone to know that I was lonely. They might start to pity me, and if there was one thing I hated, more than anything else, it was pity. I didn't want people looking at me and calling me a "poor little thing", like the teachers at my primary school used to. Neither did I want sympathy, or people trying to be nice to me. No one must ever know how I felt inside and, in any case, I told myself, one day I would meet someone who would stop me feeling lonely. It would all turn out all right then, and I would live happily ever after.

By the time I left school, my diligence in studying had been well rewarded and I passed my exams with flying colours. Such qualifications, I was informed, would place all kinds of exciting career prospects at my feet. Talks, films and visiting careers officers had filled my mind with all kinds of wonderful ambitions, any of which, I soon realised, would be a stepping-stone out of the farm and into a life of my own at last. Having discussed all the possibilities, it was the career of "Shorthand Court Reporter" that really captured my imagination. Already my tastes in fiction were heavily dominated by the writings of Conan Doyle and Agatha Christie and I was immeasurably drawn to anything that contained an element of mystery and suspense. The thought of actually being involved in real, live court cases was, therefore, very appealing.

"It's very demanding," Mrs Harper, my careers adviser, informed me. "For instance, you won't even be considered if you fail to achieve one hundred and forty words per minute shorthand at college." But, far from dampening my spirits, her comments only whetted my appetite still further. Underneath the quiet, retiring surface lay a stubborn and determined spirit. More than anything, I wanted to be an achiever, to succeed. The last thing I wanted was to be "ordinary".

As I was caught up in dreaming and scheming about the future, I was able, to some extent, to push away that niggling emptiness that lurked just under the surface, but there were times, especially at the weekends, when it would get the better of me. It was during those times that I reached out for Ben, who alone seemed able to provide me with some degree of relief. After facing up to his limitations as a "confidant", I had stopped sharing my feelings with him in quite the same way as I used to, although we still went out for long walks together. But on the occasions when things really got on top of me, I would revert back, just for a short while, to the young girl that used to sit with her arm around his shaggy neck, believing that he really did understand.

"I'll meet him one day, Ben," I whispered against his floppy ear one Sunday evening. "One day I'll meet someone who really loves me and who'll want to be with me for ever." I looked down at the round black nose that poked out from his fur. "Then I won't have to pretend any more, Ben," I whispered, with just a note of urgency in my voice. "Then . . . then I'll be able to be me again." Suddenly, Ben sneezed and I jolted upright, withdrawing my arms from his neck and realised that I had revealed openly my deepest and most secret longing. Suddenly afraid in case anyone had overheard, I jumped up quickly and brushed some grass off my jeans.

"But it's a secret, Ben. No one must ever know." The great beast lumbered to his feet and I pulled him in a homewards direction, glancing furtively all around, hoping desperately that no one had overheard my revealing confession.

— 5 —

Uncle Tom stood with one foot on the bottom rung of the gate and his arms folded across the top ridge.

"Well, I could tell her, Lindsey," he said, with a hint of sad disapproval in his voice. "But I think it would be better if you told her yourself." He paused for a moment and tilted his head. "Don't you?" I shifted my weight nervously and stared down at the ground.

"I suppose so," I conceded at last. "But ... well, I always find it so difficult to talk to Mum." There was a short, awkward silence before he spoke again.

"Don't you think it's time to put an end to this silent feud, Lindsey?" he asked softly. The answer was obvious. Of course it was, and I wanted to, more than anything, and especially now, in the light of recent events. But I didn't know how to, or even if I could. Seemingly ignoring his question, I kicked away a large stone and shrugged.

"I'll tell her later," I replied casually and ran up to my bedroom. Once inside, I tried, yet again, to escape from reality by turning on my record-player, but was unaware of which record I had left on the turn-table. It was one of the sad singer's and, far from helping the situation, it only made things worse. The song was about a young boy, leaving home. I had listened to it often, but never before had it been so meaningful. It echoed perfectly my own, most recent decision and brought to the surface the same conflicting emotions experienced by the boy of whom it told.

Having attained the grand age of eighteen, and with numerous certificates proclaiming my academic achievements, I had decided it was time to seriously pursue my chosen career. Mrs Harper had been very helpful and had provided me with the names of several local colleges. They ranged from the large, glass-constructed Polytechnic that dominated the town, to a small and exclusive secretarial college, situated in a narrow back-street on the outskirts. But none of them had been acceptable to me, for my intention was not merely to pursue a career, but a new life, completely independent of those around me. A local college would be too close to all I would try to forget and I wanted to move as far away as possible.

"Are you sure?" Mrs Harper had asked anxiously. "I mean, going to college is very different from school, and even sixth-form. You might be glad of your parents' support when ... " I quickly interrupted before she could continue.

"I'm quite sure," I said definitely. She studied me in bemused silence for a few moments and then heaved a sigh of defeat.

"All right," she said eventually. "I'll see what I can find."

At our next meeting, she produced numerous leaflets and information about colleges in the north of England. At the same time, we discussed grants, accommodation and other relevant details and I walked out of her office with my head spinning. All at once, what had always been just a wonderful dream, was now fast becoming a reality. When it had seemed so out of reach, I had felt nothing but excitement about the whole thing, but now that it was within grasping distance at last, I began to wonder if I really could go through with it after all. Ben had been the first to know of my decision and then I had told Uncle Tom. My main motive for telling him so quickly was in order to ask him to break the news to Mum, but his response had not been very favourable.

As the record turned tirelessly on the turn-table, and the young boy was at last flying into a distant sunset, I looked out of my window and saw Mum in the garden. She stood with her head bowed and her shoulders slightly stooped, aimlessly throwing crumbs for the birds. A sudden tremor of remorse ran through me and all at once I wanted to run downstairs and throw my arms around her and let her scoop me up and hold me tight. I wanted to tell her how sorry I was for the way I had treated her and then let her kiss me as she had wanted to so many times. Suddenly I saw her, not as the legalistic, over-bearing matron I had come to regard her as, but as a heart-broken woman, whose own dreams of true love had been cruelly shattered. I realised then that she had only tried to protect me from the same sorrows and given all she had left into bringing me up and giving me some sort of home.

But it was no use. It was too late now. I couldn't possibly tear down in five minutes what I had built up over so many years. Much as I wanted to break out of my self-made prison, I quite truthfully didn't know how to. Indeed, the key was held in another hand, much greater than my own. I believed that hand to belong to a man who would one day provide me with the stability and security that had vanished from my life as a young child. That man would enable me to overcome my self-abhorrence by declaring his undying love for me, in spite of what I was, and promising to take care of me for ever. Little did I realise that my theory was, indeed, correct, although the practical working out would not be quite as I had imagined.

Eventually, the young boy had reached his destination and the needle stopped in the final track. Feeling strangely weary, I replaced it in its holder, switched off the machine and watched the spinning black disc grind slowly to a halt. It was now or never, I told myself, and I might as well get it over with.

Mum looked round, obviously surprised that I should approach her voluntarily as it was my custom to avoid her as much as I could.

"I . . . I've got something to tell you," I began hesitantly, carefully avoiding the use of the word "Mum".

"Oh yes?" she enquired, throwing down another handful of crumbs.

"I'm leaving home," I said quickly, meeting her eyes for only a second before looking away. She seemed stunned for a moment by the impact of my words.

"Oh . . . I see," she returned, flatly, throwing the last of the crumbs to the ground. "Thanks for telling me." She looked up at me for a moment, with a sad, painful expression in her eyes and then disappeared quickly into the house. I stared after her, feeling completely paralysed. This wasn't how it happened in all the good books, I told myself. There should have been lots of back-slapping and congratulations and excited questionings, not to mention the promise of a slap-up farewell party. But there again, I reflected, my life was hardly the stuff that good books were made of!

My admission that day marked the point of no return and I immediately began the exhausting task of applying for a job. Much as I wanted to pursue my glamorous career, I had, quite sensibly, decided that I would greatly benefit from some financial backing. College grants were far from generous and there would be all kinds of expenses that I had never considered whilst living at home. In view of this, I had decided to go out to work for a couple of years before enrolling at a college. I had plenty of time, I assured myself, and would feel much better if I were financially secure. In addition to this, Mrs Harper had agreed with my decision and informed me at the same time that college lecturers preferred more mature students to those fresh out of school. Accommodation also had to be found and over the weeks that followed, my life became a hectic cycle of activity. Several times, the thought that I might be making a terrible mistake had crossed my mind, and I had seriously considered calling the whole thing off. But it was too late now, I kept telling myself. The deed was as good as done and, in any case, Mum and Uncle Tom would probably be glad to see the back of me!

Outwardly, I was able to convince myself that they were in fact relieved I was going, as they managed to keep up a fairly cheerful countenance about the whole thing. They showed great interest in everything I did and were very supportive of any new development that transpired. Never once did they allow me to witness their personal sadness, neither did I then know of Mum's private tears as she watched her child slip further and further out of her reach.

One week, two letters, bearing good news, flapped through the letter-box. One informed me that accommodation had been found by the agency with which I had registered. The other was a response to one of my job applications, inviting me to an interview. I made hasty preparations to attend a week later and returned home with the news that I had been successful. At last, there was no more to be done and a final date was set for my departure. Up until then, I had been so caught up in the excitement of planning a new life that it hadn't completely dawned on me that I was really going. But, on the evening before I left, the truth finally sank in.

After helping Uncle Tom load my bags into his vehicle, I went for a final walk around the place that had been my home for so many years. Slowly, I made my way round the familiar grounds, stopping to gaze wistfully at the mounded hills that held my deepest secrets in their cushioned, green vaults. Once or twice, I paused as I came across the animals that I had made friends with. Skippy the cat lay curled up in her favourite haunt, just outside the hen-house. Randolph the goat had died some time ago and had been replaced by another goat that I had never liked quite as much. Henrietta the cow was still as strong as ever, although she moved rather more slowly than she used to. I stopped in front of her and thought how sad her soft brown eyes looked as she blinked at me from beneath long lashes. Silently, I reached out and stroked her soft, velvet nose.

"Goodbye, Henrietta," I whispered softly, and then turned quietly away.

Slowly and thoughtfully, I passed the old out-buildings and piles of straw, stacked tidily in various corners, wondering if I really could leave it all behind. My step was deliberately slow and reluctant as I knew, deep down inside, that my last stop would be the back yard. Eventually, however, it could be avoided no longer and I came to a halt in front of the huge dog, lying in his favourite position with his front paws outstretched and his head resting on top of them. I quietly sat down next to him and draped one arm over his shoulders. Now, as usual, he seemed to sense my sadness and let out a low, pathetic whimper. All at once, I was a very young child again, sitting in my palace for the last time.

"Ben," I whispered, "I've got to go now, but I'll come back and see you, really I will. Then we can go for long walks again, and chase rabbits over the fields and . . . " Suddenly I could contain myself no longer and I drew both arms around his neck, burying my face in his long, white mane.

"I'm going to miss you, Ben," I sobbed. "I'm going to miss you so much." Again, the huge creature let out a mournful whimper and his tongue lapped at the air in front of him. I lifted my head and allowed him to lick the side of my face. Then I buried it in his long fur once more and cried as if my heart would break.

The following day, I stood with Mum, Uncle Tom and Ben on the cold station platform, trying to make some meaningless conversation about the ageing structure of the old country station. This was proving more than a little difficult, however, as Mum appeared to be searching for something in the bottom of her bag that seemed to be so well hidden I doubted that it would ever be found. At the same time, Uncle Tom had become preoccupied with imaginary specks of dust on the sleeve of his jacket. The atmosphere was so tight and strained that I was quite relieved when I noticed the train's yellow face advancing slowly upon us from way down the line. Its colour and structure had changed quite considerably since that first journey years ago, but my feelings for the great metal caterpillar were still the same.

As the cold January wind whipped mercilessly around us, sending my long hair flying in all directions, a sudden, gushing wave of sadness swept over me. The childhood years that had flown past far too quickly, rushed through my mind, one by one. But in all those years, I could remember nothing to equal the sadness that now engulfed me as we stood together for the last time. I glanced quickly at Mum and Uncle Tom's slightly averted faces and knew they felt it too.

The only one of our sad gathering that seemed to be coping a little more easily with the situation was Ben. He darted to and fro, running circles round the birds that pecked at crumbs on the platform and seemed, at least outwardly, totally unaffected by what was happening. As he continued his game, the train came closer still and I drew a deep breath.

"Here it is," I volunteered as steadily as I could.

"Oh yes," agreed Uncle Tom, unnecessarily. "Have we got all your bags here, Lindsey?"

"Yes – and my guitar."

"Right then," he said definitely, turning to look for the big dog. "Here, Ben . . . here boy." Ben looked round with a slightly mystified expression on his face, not quite certain why he had been summoned, but somehow sensing that this was a very important moment.

"Here, say goodbye to Lindsey," said Uncle Tom.

All the time, the yellow face was advancing down the track with alarming speed, like a long-awaited executioner, coming to take me to my fate. I bent down and allowed my face to be licked by the big, shaggy dog and kissed his head in return. How grateful I was that we had said our emotional farewell the night before.

"Goodbye, Ben," I said, struggling to keep my voice steady. "Look after Skippy and Henrietta."

The train pulled up noisily and Mum abruptly abandoned her search for the elusive object and stood behind me, next to Uncle Tom. I looked round at them awkwardly for a few seconds and then Uncle Tom suddenly leaned forward and kissed my cheek. Mum did the same thing a moment later, but even then, I was unable to respond and quickly looked down at the ground. As doors began slamming all around me, I turned sharply and pushed my bags on to the train. Once they were safely boarded, I slammed the door and leaned out of the window. Uncle Tom stood next to Mum with a big, brotherly arm around her shoulders. They tried to smile, but their eyes were strangely glazed and their faces looked tight and strained as the train jerked into motion.

"Goodbye," I shouted, as we pulled away. But, as they echoed their response a sudden rush of panic surged within me. All at once, I wanted to say the many things that I had kept locked up inside for all those years.

"I love you," I wanted to shout above the train's clatter. "Thank you ... thank you for taking care of me." But even if I had, they were well out of earshot now, just two stationary blobs, merging into the grey background, with only the red of Uncle Tom's tartan scarf to indicate where they stood.

As the train began to gather speed, my sense of panic increased. Suddenly, I was gripped by a mad desire to hurl myself out of the moving carriage on to the verge opposite, like the slapstick heroines of old. I would rush back to where Mum and Uncle Tom had courageously climbed the embankment, waiting for my imminent escape. Then, all three of us, and Ben, would return to the little farmhouse in the country and have supper together. Then I would start all over again. I would be a different person. I would love Mum, and respond to Uncle Tom, and stop being selfish and spiteful, and let them get close to me and ... but it was no use. The deed was done. This was the moment I had longed for and dreamed about for so many years. This was the chance I had always wanted to begin a new life of my own and I mustn't think about turning back now. I shut the window and flopped back into my seat, telling myself that I had to go forward and forget what was behind. I had done it once, as a very young child – I was certain I could do it again.

Completely oblivious to my inner turmoil, the train clattered on into an increasingly unfamiliar landscape, taking me further and further away from all that had once been home. Outside, the world flashed past in a mass of blended colours and I struggled with mixed emotions of guilt and remorse. As I stared through the grimy pane, just as I had done years ago, those two sad figures and the mis-shapen, shaggy bundle of white fur beside them came again to my mind and blotted out the unfamiliar landscape. A cold, clammy feeling of despair engulfed me and, had I been alone, I would have broken down uncontrollably in tears. But I mustn't. Those days of crying on Ben's shoulder were over. I was an adult now, about to begin a new life, as a new person. No one would know me in the north of England, and no one would suspect what a deeply hurt, badly scarred person I was. Not even I suspected just how deep the scarring had gone.

Darkness had well fallen by the time I peered through the window and a lit-up sign on the platform told me I had arrived. The great metal caterpillar shrugged to a halt as I pulled my luggage down from the ceiling rack and pushed open the window. A few moments later, as I moved with the sea of bodies that made their way slowly through the ticket-barrier, I felt very much part of a crowd. We were moving together, with one purpose, to a common destination. A few moments later, however, when I was left standing on the cold, dark pavement, I suddenly felt alone – more alone that I had ever felt in my life. Shivering slightly, I fumbled in my bag and pulled out a folded piece of paper with the words "41 Albert Avenue" scrawled on one side. I had been assured that this old house, converted into bed-sitters, was "just a stone's throw" from the station, and a simple map on the back showed me how to get there. By the time I reached it, however, my arms felt twice their normal length from carrying my cases and I began to wonder what kind of super-human being could throw a stone *that* far!

Squinting at the numbers in the light of the yellow street lamp, I eventually found number 41. It was flanked by a tall beech hedge, separated in the middle by two grey stone pillars. The steps beyond them led up to a dismal front porch, and a black door that looked as if it had never been opened. I thought how cold and uninviting it looked as I turned the main key in the lock and, to my surprise, the door brushed open. A single light-bulb lit up the dingy hallway and I noticed on one wall a key-board. There, underneath the number 11, hung a key, bearing the name "Miss L. Fairweather" on the small plastic tag. I stared at it for a few moments before pushing it into my pocket. Then, picking up my cases once again, I began to mount the stairs.

I had already been informed that the other residents of 41 Albert Avenue were all elderly women, either spinsters or widows. This, it seemed, had been taken into account when the landlord had allocated my room, as it was at the very top of the house – four floors up! Obviously, he had thought that my young legs would be better suited to the summit climb required to get there than would those of the older residents. However, upon reaching it with my laden cases, I began to doubt his sense of judgement.

Pushing open the door, I surveyed the limited contents of what was to be my room. They were basic, to say the least, and in stark contrast to my room at the farm, with its pretty floral curtains and matching bed-clothes. A plain, green cover was draped over the hard-looking bed in one corner. Next to it stood a low bedside table with a small lamp, so faded and covered with dust that I was a little surprised to find that it actually worked. A sink and small cooker stood in the opposite corner and I presumed that the door in the wall would, in time, reveal a built-in wardrobe. Apart from a small table, one easy chair and a gas fire, fixed to the wall, there was little else of real substance.

As I put down my cases, I noticed a small, pink envelope on the carpet, bearing my name in Mum's familiar hand.

Inside was a welcome card, depicting a large English sheep-dog and a simple message that read: "Welcome to Albert Avenue. All our love, Mum and Tom."

My eyes swept round the room, taking in every detail once more and then returned to the dog on the card. He reminded me so much of Ben. Dear old Ben. How I longed to put my arms around his shaggy neck and bury my face in his long mane, just once more. If ever I wanted to feel his warm, comforting frame, it was now. As I read the short message again, my thoughts drifted to Mum and Uncle Tom and what they might be doing now. I wondered if they would be missing me as they sat beside their open log fire. Maybe they really *had* been sorry to see me go, I thought, as their sad faces came again to my mind. Suddenly, waves of homesickness swept over me and I longed to be back with them at the farm. Now I realised, perhaps for the first time, just how much they had been to me during those traumatic years. But, once again, I pushed the thoughts away, reminding myself that I couldn't afford to look back now. With great effort, I drew a deep breath and promised myself that things would, undoubtedly, look better in the morning.

6

"Just go straight ahead and turn left at the end. It's a red and white building called Harrington's," smiled the kind old gentleman I had stopped. After carefully following his directions, I found myself outside the local music shop a few minutes later. It was my last stop on the way home from my first shopping trip into the little town in which I now lived. Things had, indeed, looked better on the morning following my arrival and I had spent quite an enjoyable two hours exploring my new surroundings.

It was quite a pleasant town, with a noticeable number of old people. This, however, was fairly well balanced out by the young people. Most of them were clad in jeans and drifted along the narrow streets with the semi-glazed, aimless expressions peculiar to people of their age. On my travels that morning, I had managed to locate the village green, a large area of grass, surrounded by numerous cherry trees. They were not yet in bloom, but I painted an imaginary picture of how it would look in spring, when they were covered with delicate pink blossoms. Such was my vision of the glorious splendour that was to come that I felt I might grow to like the place after all.

"Not from round 'ere then?" inquired the shop assistant as he handed me some guitar strings.

"No, but how . . . ?"

"Accent, love. Sounds like you've been to public school or somethin' like." I blushed slightly, not quite sure whether I had been paid a compliment or served a rather subtle insult.

"Any road, there's strings. Nowt else?"

"Er . . . no, that's all, thanks." As he fumbled in the till for some change, I pondered his former statement. I hadn't ever considered my accent before. Indeed, there had never been any reason to, but it seemed, now, to be important and to set me apart in some strange way. I stepped out on to the pavement, aware of feeling, just slightly, an outsider. But it was not a matter for undue concern, I assured myself, and quickly turned my feet homeward.

Having to fend for myself was such a novel experience that I quite forgot how I had felt the night before and arrived back at Albert Avenue in a much better frame of mind. This was just as well, as I was about to have my first encounter with one of the other residents of number 41. As I pushed through the door with my heavily-laden bags, I saw a woman studying the key-board. She had her back to me and I noticed that she was slightly built, with steel-grey hair, neatly swept up into a bun. She turned around to reveal a pleasant, but badly-crinkled face, which smoothed out quite dramatically as she smiled at me.

"Hello, dear, you must be Miss Fairweather," she said, extending her hand.

"Yes," I said, shaking it a little nervously.

"And what does the 'L' stand for?" she asked brightly.

"Lindsey," I replied, not at all prepared for her gushing response.

"Oh, what a pretty name – and a pretty owner too. It'll be so nice to have a fresh, young face about the place." She leaned forward and lowered her voice to a confidential whisper. "We're a bunch of old codgers, you know," she grinned, with a wink of one eye. "I'm Miss Peters – that's 'Miss', not 'Mrs'. I'm not married, never have been,' she finished, with just a note of defiance in her voice.

"Oh, I see . . . er . . . pleased to meet you," I stammered nervously, sensing that it was my turn to volunteer some information. "I'm in room 11, right at the top."

"Well, rather you than me, dear. My legs aren't what they used to be. Anyway, I must let you get on, you look as if you're going to be busy. If you need anything, give me a knock. Room 9, Miss Peters," she repeated. I smiled and thanked her and then began the marathon climb to my room.

She had seemed a pleasant enough character, I thought, but I was certain I would never condescend to ask her for help, or anything else for that matter. Not for a moment did I suspect that I would, in the future, be more than grateful for her obliging attitude and previous nursing experience.

After a few days, I had more or less adjusted to my new environment – at least physically. The bed was, perhaps, a little harder than I had been used to, and it would have taken a lot to beat Mum's cooking in any circumstances. But these things paled into insignificance when compared with the other adjustments I was required to make.

At first, I had thought that it would be easy to shake off the many hang-ups that had been so much a part of my character until then. I constantly reminded myself that I was a new person, beginning a new life. But, however hard I tried, I could not keep my mind from drifting back to the little country farmhouse. I often remembered the big, shaggy dog that had been my most faithful companion for so many years. The times we had spent walking together over those peaceful hills were still so fresh in my mind, but somehow, the world beyond them didn't seem nearly so exciting as it had promised my impressionable young heart that it would be. Then, with the remembrance of Ben, would come the remembrance of Mum and Uncle Tom. Never before had I appreciated how much they had given to me in terms of love and security during my rebellious teenage years.

At such times, great, gushing waves of homesickness would sweep over me and I would long to be back with them again. But I was certain I could never go back, not after the way I had behaved. And it was then that I felt that stifling black mantle descend upon me more heavily than ever. It settled upon my young mind like a dense, clammy fog, obscuring my vision and numbing my senses until all I could do was curl up, very still and quiet, and hope that the raging storm in my mind would soon pass.

In a valiant attempt to counteract such feelings, I deliberately blotted out of my mind all thoughts of Mum and Uncle Tom and dear old Ben. The welcome card was too vivid a reminder of my old life but I felt unable to destroy it. Instead, I hid it in the bottom of my suitcase, determined never to look at it again. Then, I penned a quick letter, informing them that I had settled in and giving a brief description of my new surroundings. As I pushed it through the letter-box on the corner, I decided it would be the last contact I ever made with them. In this resolute frame of mind, I turned up at my chosen place of work on the pre-arranged Monday morning, feeling more than a little nervous.

The place I had chosen to begin my working life was a large, family-run department store, two floors high, and which spread outwards rather than upwards. My interview of a month earlier had been a very rushed affair and I hadn't, therefore, been able to see the "Fashions and Millinery" department, where I was to work. It had sounded quite glamorous at the time, and I had imagined rows upon rows of dazzling designer clothes. My dreams, however, were soon to be shattered.

Following my instructions to appear at the main door and show a card, signed by the manager, I was confronted by a rather surly-looking doorman. His jet-black hair was so heavily greased that it divided into furrows where his comb had passed. This, coupled with his pale complexion, suggested that he would have felt more at home in a conventional horror film, than in a family-run department store. After examining the card, he opened the door just wide enough for me to squeeze through and muttered something that vaguely resembled "Good morning". A little dampened by his uninviting attitude, I tried to rally my deflated feelings as I mounted the slatted staircase. The girls in the Fashions department were sure to be a lot friendlier, I assured myself as I reached the top and stood surveying the countless rows of coats, dresses, skirts and jackets.

"Looks a bit frumpy," I thought to myself. "Maybe there's a 'Young Persons' Section' somewhere." Just as I was about to begin a search for the said section, I was stopped in my tracks by a clipped voice behind me and spun round to see a small, exceedingly well-groomed woman, probably in her late forties.

"Good morning," she began. "You must be Miss Fairweather." Being addressed in such formal terms had taken quite a bit of getting used to. No longer was I just "Lindsey", another name on a school register, but I was now "Miss Fairweather", an individual and an adult. When addressed as such, I felt obliged, for some reason, to respond in a mature and adult manner. Now, faced with this obviously important woman, who seemed to be addressing me as an equal, I made my first attempt at responding as such.

"Yes," I said, shaking her hand as firmly as I could. "But please call me Lindsey." She looked me up and down for what seemed like a full minute and then smiled stiffly.

"Follow me if you please, Miss Fairweather," she replied and began to march briskly towards a long glass counter. I obeyed in dumb silence, feeling like a deflated balloon. My first grand attempt at maturity had failed miserably!

"My name is Mrs Jarvis," continued the imperious woman. "And I'm the buyer for Fashions." I glanced quickly round the sales floor as she spoke, but no "Young Persons' Section" had yet become apparent. When she paused in her brisk, introductory dialogue, I decided, therefore, to carry out some subtle investigation.

"Is this where I'll be working?" I asked as unsuspiciously as I could.

"Yes," she replied, pushing open a door behind her. "I'll show you round in a moment. Now, just put your coat and handbag in here."

Having deposited my belongings, I then endured a half-hour lecture about what I was supposed to do and what I was definitely *not* supposed to do. My rapidly sinking heart was only kept from completely drowning by her mentioning that the "girls" would be in soon. At last, her inaugural speech was over and she disappeared into her buyer's office, leaving me dusting coat rails with a faded yellow duster.

Already, only forty-five minutes into my new job, I felt like handing in my notice. The woman had come across as so domineering and officious that, far from feeling like the adult that I was now supposed to be, I felt more like a naughty schoolgirl who had committed some dreadful misdemeanour. But I mustn't let it get to me, I told myself, fighting hard to keep my spirits up. The girls were sure to liven things up a bit and I might even meet some nice young people in the staff room at the ten o'clock tea-break. But I was not permitted to pursue my train of thought for very long, as I caught sight of a rather heavily-built woman, with tight, curly hair, making her way towards me. I froze on the spot at the prospect of confronting my first customer and then, clearing my throat, I advanced at a discreet pace. I hated it myself whenever I was pounced upon by sales assistants and I didn't want to be guilty of doing the same to anyone else.

"Good morning," I began, as confidently as I could. "Can I help you with anything?" The woman broke into a relieved smile and nodded.

"Yes love, just 'ol' this for a second, will you?" She handed me a large, brown parcel and removed her coat. "There, that's better, all fingers 'n' thumbs this mornin' I am. Now then, you must be Lindsey." I felt my face flush as I saw my mistake and realised that this was one of the "girls". At last, my heart completely sank as I realised what a terrible mistake I had also made about my "glamorous" new job.

" . . . and by sounds of it," she continued, " . . . 'ere comes crew." A wave of raucous guffawing and laughter floated up the stairs, followed a moment later by three more ladies, similar in age to the first one. All of them sported the same tight head of permed hair, although in slightly varying shades of grey and their entrance was something akin to jubilant football supporters returning from a winning game. A moment later, however, the noise stopped suddenly on their seeing a young stranger standing in the middle of their Fashions department.

"Oh, hello dear," they all began at once. "You must be Lindsey." Several smiles and several hand-shakes later, the introductions were concluded by one of them informing me that it would be so nice to have a "fresh, young face around the place". Upon hearing this, I felt that if one more person made the same comment, I would pull a grotesque grimace and keep it intact for the rest of the day! But, by this time, I had neither the nerve, nor the energy to do anything so daring and returned to my dusting, hoping that ten o'clock would be soon in arriving.

When the greatly anticipated tea-break did arrive, however, I found that I had been as mistaken about this event as I had about the Fashions department. There, seated at a rustic, wooden table, half-heartedly drinking a cup of black coffee, was the surly doorman. Also present were a couple of porters of about the same age and a vast assortment of men and women. None of them came anywhere near myself in age, except for one girl, two years my senior. She had failed to gain any academic qualifications at school and was, therefore, quite happy to accept the status of sales assistant as a life-long prospect. I groaned inwardly and sat down, determined not to say a word, but this proved to be impossible. Once again, my misplaced accent attracted much attention and I was poked and probed about it for the entire ten-minute break until I eventually escaped to the staid quietness of the Fashions department.

Over the weeks that followed, I tried to convince myself that it wasn't so bad and that I really would get to like it after a while. I had committed myself to at least two years at work before starting college, but began to wonder now if I would even make two months. The job itself was boring, to say the least, and during the course of one day, no more than seven or eight customers would wend their weary ways up the slatted wooden staircase, only to be pounced upon by the entire floor staff, excepting myself. Then they would be bundled mercilessly in and out of any number of weird and wonderful outfits. As I hung back and let the women divide their prey, I often wondered if the poor, unsuspecting soul had purchased that completely unsuitable garment simply as a desperate means of escaping from their clutches.

It was, perhaps, the endless hours of undistracted boredom that highlighted more clearly than before the degree to which I was inwardly hurt. This, of course, was not immediately apparent to those around me as I had, over the years, cultivated my quiet, imperturbable image to perfection, and never ceased to be amazed at how easily people fell for it.

One day, I had taken a parcel down to Despatch and, as I handed the form to John, the despatch officer, we had exchanged a few words. I then waited patiently as he went through the arduous task of checking the paperwork and making out a receipt. Most people, I had noted, would often become rather irritated by this protracted process, drumming their fingers on the counter and huffing under their breath. I, on the other hand, found it a welcome escape from Mrs Jarvis and the girls and was quite happy to stand and stare blankly at the opposite wall whilst John completed his task. At last, the receipt was ready and he handed it to me for signature.

"You know something, kid?" He smiled as I scribbled my name in the relevant box. "Either you've got a lot of cool for a youngster . . . or you're a damn good actress!" He paused for a moment and winked at me. "But I hardly think that's likely." I smiled at him feebly, without the slightest intention of enlightening him as to the truer judgement. Then I walked calmly out of his office, wondering, just as I had years ago, how anyone could be taken in by such a thin disguise.

Outwardly, it seemed foolproof, but underneath, it was a different story altogether. Far from disappearing, those powerful feelings of anger and guilt that had always hovered dangerously close to the surface, only became more intense now I had left home. This came as something of a shock to me, since all the outward causes had now been removed. Mum was no longer around to make me feel angry, nor Uncle Tom to make me feel guilty. But it would take some time before I finally realised that my problems could not be blamed on outward circumstances and people, but existed instead on the inside. In addition to this, the relentless feeling of loneliness that I had identified during the televised pop concert set in more strongly than ever before. It seemed as if a huge, yawning chasm had opened up inside me and was getting bigger and more empty as each day passed.

In spite of it all, I forced myself to continue with the charade. I was bound to feel a little homesick, I assured myself, but I would get over it soon. And anyway, being lonely wasn't such an unusual event. There were hundreds of people who felt the way I did, but it would eventually work out all right. I was bound to meet that special Someone that I had pinned all my hopes on soon. Then I would look back and laugh about how bad I had once felt. In the meantime, all I had to do was to try and keep my mind off the farm and Mum and Uncle Tom, but this proved to be much more difficult than I expected.

As the job itself offered few distractions with which to discipline my mind, I turned my attention towards the girls. At first I had decided to keep a safe distance from them, as they frequently asked me about my family and where I had come from, going over all the things that I had decided to forget. Eventually, however, the endless hours of pacing to and fro between coat rails persuaded me to attempt some kind of superficial conversation with them. After a while, I even began to find some of their stories interesting. They spoke of family life, of their children and grandchildren and, inevitably, of their husbands. It all sounded so safe, so secure, so much all I had ever wanted and eventually, my rapidly mounting interest turned to jealousy.

This was rather surprising at first. After all, *they* should have been jealous of *me*. I was young, free, had my whole life before me and could do anything I pleased with it. They, on the other hand, had lived theirs already and all they had to show for it was a dead-end job in the frumpy fashions department of a local store. Nevertheless, the fact remained, they had something *I* was jealous of. They belonged, and the longer I listened, the more I was convinced that I didn't. What they had may not have been glamorous, or even exciting, but it was real and safe and I felt I would have changed places a hundred times over, with any one of them, just to find a place where I, too, belonged.

In this way, the days turned into weeks and the weeks into months, during which their words painted fairytale pictures on the canvas of my mind. I imagined the warm, secure houses that they lived in and all the homely, "ordinary" things that went on in them. Sometimes I could almost feel myself sinking into their plump, over-stuffed armchairs and the warmth of the roaring log fires they described. And then, my thoughts would again drift back to the farm where, had I chosen to, I could have enjoyed the family life that Mum and Uncle Tom had tried so hard to provide for me. I often remembered Uncle Tom and his warm, unguarded way of reaching out to me, and wondered why I hadn't opened myself up to him and allowed him to fill Dad's place. But "Dad" was a word I had lost faith in long ago. Instead, I felt certain I could take care of myself very well without anyone else's interference. But my theory was turning out to be very wrong. In spite of my gallant efforts to forget them, the couple would spring back to my mind and the memory of their sad, concerned faces would bring a lump to my throat and cause tears to prickle the back of my eyes.

It was at such times that I would rush back to my room after work and rummage under my bed for the suitcase containing the welcome card that had greeted my arrival at Albert Avenue. I wanted to take it again in my hands and study the soft, sweet face of the dog that reminded me so much of Ben, or run my fingers over Mum's flowery writing and wonder what things might have been like if I had behaved differently. On all such

70

occasions, however, the case remained unopened. Just as I was about to rip up the small metal clasps, I would freeze on the spot and could only stare at it from a safe distance, as if it contained some dangerous device that would explode at the slightest touch. Then, I would quickly push it back under my bed and straighten out the faded, green cover with trembling hands.

At first, I had managed to confine such emotional weakness to my private life, but eventually, it seeped into my life at work too. I began to suffer severe bouts of black depression, far worse than anything I had ever experienced at home and my concentration level hit an all-time low. I became very forgetful and made embarrassing mistakes, one of which muddled up a whole day's stock-taking. The near perfect image was already showing hairline cracks and I wondered if perhaps I wasn't such a "damn good actress" after all. One Tuesday morning, I let myself in for something that caused it to almost disintegrate completely.

My break in the rustic staff-room was proving rather more trying than usual as Jill, the unacademic girl from Haberdashery downstairs, had found her mission in life persuading me to have a night out.

"Why don't you come?" she had asked for the third time. "You'll really enjoy it." I sipped my coffee thoughtfully and wondered if I would, any longer, find a disco enjoyable. At one time, it would have taken wild horses to keep me away, but now, at liberty to do just as I pleased, they had somehow lost their appeal. In fact, it had been some time since I had even listened to the music that had once been so much a part of my life, as it seemed to stir up too many painful memories.

"I'm not sure discos are my thing really, Jill," I replied eventually. "And anyway, I won't know anyone there."

"Of course you will," she countered enthusiastically, "I'll be there."

Despite my grave misgivings, I had left the room agreeing to meet her outside the appointed place at seven o'clock the following Friday night.

Trying to look relaxed, I leant against the outside wall and kept my eyes peeled for Jill as dark silhouettes brushed past me and disappeared through the door. As it swung open for a few seconds to admit them, I caught the sound of raucous laughter and blaring music, together with a strange mixture of heady perfume and cigarette smoke. Just as I was willing her not to turn up so that I could go home, one of the shadows stopped in front of me and my heart sank into the pit of my stomach. I had anticipated a night out with Jill, but I hadn't accounted for her boyfriend.

The sum total of the evening was that they drifted off to the dance floor, leaving me sitting at a table in the corner, trying to look as if I were actually enjoying myself. After a while, the blaring music made my head pound and I wondered how I had ever enjoyed it so much. To make matters worse, the drink Jill had bought me stung the back of my throat in a most unpleasant way and I began to feel quite sick. In the end, I sneaked out and caught the bus home. It was my intention after that to avoid Jill and so not have to explain my disappearance, but this proved to be unnecessary as she had obviously decided to drop me anyway. So it was that our friendship was over before it had really begun.

The women in Fashions were slightly less pushy than Jill had been, but they seemed to have an insatiable desire to know if I would be "doing anything exciting this weekend". I would always brush the question off by declaring that I reserved weekends for shopping and catching up on "odd jobs" that I didn't get round to during the week. But, in reality, weekends were the days I dreaded most. They were the days I would end up sitting in my room, trying desperately not to think about the case under my bed and that cold, empty feeling, deep down inside. They were the days I would take off the mask that I had worn to such perfection for five days of the week and examine again the frightened, feature-less being that lay hidden underneath. And they were the days during which I struggled not to admit to the loneliness that was eating its way so relentlessly into my life.

Although I *did* make a brief shopping trip into town for my weekly provisions, the rest of the time was spent doing virtually nothing. There was nowhere to go, and no one to go with even if there had been. After the disastrous episode at the disco, I decided it would be better to keep myself to myself and this view, it seemed, was shared by the world at large. Apart from Miss Peters, I had hardly seen or spoken to any of the other residents of Albert Avenue. The women at work were superficially friendly, but I suspected that they found it quite a strain to even hold a conversation with such an unresponsive and introverted character as myself. And as for Jill, the one person in the entire building that I might have been tempted to form a friendship with, she had obviously decided that I was a "southern snob", who thought herself superior to those around her, and this must have been her explanation for my sudden disappearance that Friday night.

The more I thought about it, the more I convinced myself that no one was really bothered that I existed at all. Of course, there was Mum, and Uncle Tom, but I had, by then, decided that they couldn't possibly be concerned about me now, not after the way I had treated them. But I had no conception of how badly affected I had become by such thoughts until they came to a head, rather violently, one dismal and exceedingly wet weekend.

I had been sitting in my room, trying to read a book, but the endless patter of rain against the small sky-light window had become increasingly distracting. Eventually, I closed the book and drew back the flimsy net curtain. Rows upon rows of purple-slated roofs stretched as far as the eye could see, forming a harsh, jagged outline against the lowering grey skies. So different, I reflected, from the softly sweeping outline of the mounded hills against the clear blue skies at the farm. In contrast to those gentle curves, the slates looked treacherous and slippery as the rain cascaded over them in swirling, oily rainbows and gurgled noisily into the black plastic gutters. Suddenly, it occurred to me how easy it would be to climb out on to them and hurl myself to the ground below. I held the thought quite dispassionately. After all, such a spiteful, selfish person as myself didn't deserve breathing space anyway!

Then, all at once, I shuddered, as if suddenly awakened from a deep sleep, and the thought was gone, as quickly as it had come. But it had left me badly shaken. As I sat down again, I wondered how I had come to be thinking such thoughts. Where had they come from? More importantly, where could they lead? Hastily, I picked up my book once again and began reading in order to distract my mind, but I noticed that the pages trembled slightly as I held it in my cold, clammy hands.

Had it not been for one thought that I deliberately focused on during those dark, dismal days, I might have caved in completely. It was the only faint glimmer of hope in my seemingly hopeless existence – college. When I started college, I told myself, everything would be all right and my life would begin to take on meaning again. I was sure all the young people there would be enthusiastic about life and their enthusiasm would, undoubtedly, rub off on me. And then maybe, just maybe, I would meet there the man of my dreams, and live happily ever after.

It was the only thing that kept me from utter despair. Or so I thought. For then, I had not yet begun to perceive the unseen hand that had already completed the vague outline of what was, one day, to become a beautiful picture. I believed only that I was still completely in control. Still too blind to see the futility of trying to plan my life with my own wisdom. Still convinced that I could get by alone.

7

Shaky, but determined, I merged with the crowd that pushed its way through the tall wrought-iron gates on to the college campus. At last, after two dismal years which I wanted very much to forget, I had arrived. This, I was certain, was the new beginning I had always dreamed about. Marching resolutely forward, I chose not to remember that my life was already so full of "new beginnings" and assured myself, instead, that the bad times were behind me for good. Already, my heart had been cheered by the hundreds of young people that swarmed everywhere, like excited honeybees, and I noticed that even some of the lecturers had fresh young faces. Now I was certain that the days of wanting to pull horrible grimaces were over.

The classroom number shown on my college form was located without too much difficulty and was already half full of girls, talking excitedly amongst themselves. I stood in the doorway for a moment and noticed how relaxed and easy they seemed with each other. In contrast, the thought of approaching them and attempting some kind of conversation made me feel decidedly queasy. I would much rather have slunk over to one of the empty desks in the farthest corner of the room, but I mustn't, I advised myself. After all, I was a new person and this was my first chance to prove it. Taking a deep breath, I stepped into the room and approached three girls seated by the window.

"Er ... excuse me, is this Mrs McNeil's room?" I asked as confidently as I could, even though I knew the answer perfectly well already. The girls stopped chatting and looked at me rather curiously for a few moments before one of them responded.

"Yes, I think she's supposed to be here at nine."

"Oh, right," I said, feeling horribly conspicuous. "Mind if I sit here? My name's Lindsey."

"Not at all, go ahead. I'm Sandra," said the girl who had spoken first. "This is Jane."

"And I'm Tracy," finished a rather stocky, bespectacled girl. Feeling just a little more relaxed, I pulled up a chair and sat down.

"You're not from round here then?" commented Jane. My mind flashed back to the morning after my arrival at Albert Avenue and the man in the music shop who had asked the same question. Suddenly, I recalled that uncomfortable feeling of being an outsider and began to feel nervous all over again.

"No," I replied, a little hesitantly. "I'm from down south – right on the coast actually." The girls looked interested.

"Like it up here?" they wanted to know. I thought quickly. If the truth were known, it had been the worst two years of my life and I had hated every moment, but I daren't let them know as much in case they drew the wrong conclusions. Thankfully, however, I was spared from having to make a suitable reply by the classroom door swinging open to admit a prim, motherly-looking woman, carrying a large pile of books. These she slapped unceremoniously on a desk at the front and turned to face us with a stilted smile.

"Good morning, girls," she began briskly. "I'm Mrs McNeil and I'm your year tutor." A vague rumble of "good morning" rolled round the room in a tone of such obvious apathy that I deduced the other girls were as disappointed as I was. Where were all the fresh-faced lecturers that I had seen entering the staff rooms on my way in, I wondered. Why did we have to be lumbered with an older woman who reminded me only too well of those I had just left behind?

"Now then, let's have some names and ages," she continued and then went systematically round the room with this rather kindergarten method of obtaining the necessary information. From what was said, I ascertained that I was the oldest in the class and the only southerner. Once again, that strange outsider feeling crept over me, but I consoled myself with the fact that I was, indeed, a "mature" student and was certain to secure a special place in the affections of my tutor because of this. I could not, however, have been more mistaken.

It was, of course, utter foolishness to believe that I had shaken off overnight the depth of depression I had sunk into during the past years, but I convinced myself, at least initially, that I had done so. However, not only was I soon to learn how deeply it had affected me, but I would also come to realise that a change in geographical location could not guarantee a change in my inner state. Little wonder, then, that once the novelty of my first few weeks at college had worn off I found that, underneath it all, I was still exactly the same person.

My efforts to be a "new person" had failed as miserably as my efforts to appear an equal, when confronted with Mrs Jarvis. Far from fitting in with the other girls, it became obvious that we were, in fact, poles apart. They were lively and ambitious. All of them had boyfriends, or even fiancés, and they would often make up a group of even numbers during break times. I, on the other hand, was still the depressed, introverted person I had always been. Of course, they were nice enough, and I suspected that some even pitied me. But never did their concern become strong enough for them to draw me into their exciting world. They simply left me alone. Most of my break times were spent sitting on the grass verges, apparently studying for my lessons, but in reality, I spent the time staring at meaningless black blobs on a white page.

Much as I hated to admit it, I was right back where I had started, but now the situation was even more hopeless than before. College had been the proverbial straw clutched at by the drowning man, but now it had snapped and I was sinking fast. It was hardly surprising then, that far from my "maturity" endearing me to my tutor, my lack of concentration and interest in my studies did much to alienate me from the woman. Indeed, it seemed as if her only way of coping with such an unrewarding pupil was simply to pretend I wasn't there, concentrating instead on those that responded with good results and were less of a challenge than I was. But, beneath her cast-iron exterior, she was flesh and blood after all and her patience ran out one Monday morning, following one of my typical, lonely weekends.

I had woken up without the slightest inclination to go to college, but I had gone anyway. By lunchtime, I was wishing I had stayed at home and everything that could possibly have gone wrong had done. At least, so I thought. As the typing lesson drew to a close, I decided I couldn't face any more lectures that day and would dash off home instead. Hurriedly, I gathered up my typed papers, stapled them together and slapped them on Mrs McNeil's desk. Feeling that my task had been successfully accomplished, I dashed back to my place and began to gather my things. Suddenly, my name reverberated round the room as all other activities ceased and silence descended. I stood rooted to the spot, unsure whether to turn around or run out of the door.

"Lindsey Fairweather!" it persisted. "You're not going to get away with this – look at it!" She was behind me now, brandishing the offending papers in front of her like a badly-dealt pack of cards, for not only myself, but the entire class to behold. I suddenly turned hot and cold as I realised the cause of her distress. Not only had I stapled the papers face to face, with the blank sides outermost, but I had also stapled them upside-down. I could only bite my lip and say nothing.

"I don't know why you're on this course," volunteered the irate woman when sufficient time had elapsed for me to feel really humiliated. "You're in Fairyland, all day long!" With that, she slapped the papers on my desk and marched back to her own. Not a sound was heard as we all began a tense clear-up and then dispersed for lunch.

"Sure seems to have it in for you," volunteered Jane, once we were safely out of earshot. "That's the third time today, and it's only twelve-thirty!"

When it came to run-ins with Mrs McNeil, the girls were undoubtedly on my side and often encouraged me to give as good as I got. Now I sensed that they were waiting for some kind of response, but I said nothing. This was not because I possessed latent martyr-like qualities, but simply because there was nothing *to* say. What I had been accused of was true. I had become so depressed and distracted that I was hardly in touch with reality at all. Finally realising that I was not about to deliver a rousing Churchillian speech, the disillusioned girls drifted slowly away in little groups, leaving me standing in the corridor.

I sat down on a conveniently-placed wooden bench as hordes of students pushed past me, like stampeding buffaloes, none of them in the least bit bothered that my life-long ambitions were being shattered into a thousand tiny pieces. Moments later, they had all disappeared and the corridor became deathly quiet. I clutched my books close to my chest, gripping them so tightly that my knuckles turned white, and tried desperately to suppress the feeling of hopelessness that swept over me. At that moment, I wanted, more than anything, to throw it all in and catch the next train back to the farm. But I was still convinced that I could never go back. To do so would be to admit failure and defeat, and I would never be able to handle the gushing sympathy that it would undoubtedly warrant from Mum and Uncle Tom. But there was also another reason for my determination to succeed. In spite of my aloofness from Mum, underneath it all, for some strange reason, I wanted her to be proud of me. I wanted her to see that I had turned out all right after all. And I wanted her, one day, to be able to look at me and tell herself that it had all been worth it in the end.

79

Valiantly blinking back the tears that threatened to surface at any moment, I told myself, yet again, that I couldn't give up. I had to keep going, no matter how bad things seemed. Then just at that moment, an unfamiliar voice interrupted my thoughts.

"No one's going to steal them, you know," it advised me. I looked up, slightly dazed, to see a tall, dark-haired young man smiling down at me.

"I'm sorry?" I replied fuzzily.

"The books," he said. "Looks like you're clinging on to them for dear life." I smiled, mostly with embarrassment, and stood up.

"Maybe I am," I said quietly and walked off down the corridor.

College was situated four miles from Albert Avenue, but I chose to walk home that day. Wearily placing one foot in front of the other, hardly noticing where I was going, I reflected on how badly things were turning out. I told myself over and over that I must pull myself together and get on with my life. And then I asked myself what on earth for. What *was* it all for anyway? So what if I *did* become a court reporter, if underneath it all I was empty and lonely, just like the sad superstar I had listened to years ago?

I continued my slow, systematic step, occasionally looking up at the people who pushed and jostled all around me; all with their set, determined faces, each one intent upon arriving at their own particular destination. Gradually, my thoughts began to gather momentum. Now they reached beyond my life at Albert Avenue, my studies at college and the predetermined plans I had made for my life. Perhaps for the first time, I wondered what it really was all about. What *was* the purpose of life? What meaning did it really hold? Suddenly I realised that I, too, was a part of that crowd, chasing colourful rainbows that were, in reality, nothing more than a trick of the light.

By the time I reached Albert Avenue, I was exhausted mentally and physically, and had come to the conclusion that life had no meaning or purpose whatsoever. As far as

I could see, it was a complete and utter waste of time.

Such thoughts persisted with ever-increasing intensity as my first year at college dragged slowly to an end. I often wondered why I bothered to continue my studies at all, if life really was as futile as I then believed it to be. Perhaps it was my belief that I no longer had a home at the farm, or a place in the hearts of Mum and Uncle Tom that forced me to keep going. Or maybe I was afraid that if I didn't surround myself with enough activity, I would look further into the terrifying chasm that had opened up at my feet and give life to the same thoughts I had had whilst surveying those slippery slates that wet weekend.

Whatever the reasons I did carry on, but my waning enthusiasm soon began to show up in my results. By the end of the year, all the other girls had passed their exams with flying colours, but I had only just managed to scrape into the pass bracket for the following year. The fact I had achieved as much as *that* surprised me considerably. And it positively irritated Mrs McNeil, who would now be faced with another year of teaching this unresponsive and worthless student.

Her fears were well founded and the second year began in much the same way as the first had ended. I had lost interest entirely, not just in my studies, but in life as a whole. Sometimes I wondered how it had all happened and searched deep inside for any trace of the headstrong, ambitious young girl who had once held the reins of her life so confidently. But she had disappeared long ago. If only I knew where I had gone astray. If only I could find the wrong turning that I must have taken, I might be able to retrace my steps and then, perhaps I could start again.

Yes, that's what I would do, I would start again. But then I remembered – I had already "started again" so many times before. Never for a moment did I suspect that there was one more new beginning for me to experience. I wasn't aware that plans had already been made for my life by Someone with greater wisdom and understanding than I myself possessed. On the contrary, I continued to endure futile hours at college and increasingly lonely weekends at Albert Avenue. But, out of the many weekends that rolled endlessly into each other, there was one that stood out as different from all the rest. It was the one during which I met the Angel. At least, that was my first impression of the young man I met in town that Saturday afternoon.

Just about to return home from my weekly shopping trip, I remembered that I needed a new pen for college. Having found a suitable shop, I was intently studying the display in the window when my thoughts were interrupted.

"Excuse me, could I offer you one of these?" asked an unfamiliar voice. I knew, even before turning around, that the speaker was smiling, and I was curious to discover what "one of these" was.

"What is it?" I asked, glancing from the stranger to the small leaflet in his hand and back to him again. He was tall and blond, with intense blue eyes that held my gaze so steadily I had to look away.

"It's a tract," he said, smiling.

"A tract?" I had never heard the word before and my curiosity was aroused even further.

"Yes, about the second Oliver Cromwell."

"Cromwell?" I searched desperately through my subconscious, hoping to find there some dregs of the history I had learned at school that might remind me who the *first* Oliver Cromwell was, let alone who the second might be!

"Actually, it's not about Oliver Cromwell at all really," he volunteered. "It's about Jesus Christ."

As he spoke the name, I felt just as I used to when I had been with Uncle Tom, only far worse. Once again, it seemed as if that piercing shaft of light had penetrated my deceptive disguise, showing up all the horrible, hateful things that lay hidden underneath. All at once, I wanted to turn around and run away, but at the same time, there was something about that unfamiliar name to which I felt irresistibly drawn, just as I had been to Uncle Tom. Why I should feel this way about someone I had never even met,

I wasn't at all sure, but before I could wonder further, the smiling young man continued.

"Did you know He came and died for you so that you could have eternal life?" he asked. As he spoke the word "life", the constant question in my mind was suddenly answered. All the time he had been speaking, I had been trying to fathom what it was about him that was so captivating. All at once, I realised – it was "life", he had life. I glanced surreptitiously from his face to those of the other people milling around us. In comparison to his, their faces looked drab and expressionless, and even those that were smiling didn't have the same brightness about them that his had. Yet, even though there was something appealing in what he said, and in spite of my feelings of failure and hopelessness, I still believed that I could handle my life perfectly well by myself.

"Um . . . no, I suppose I didn't know that," I replied rather nervously. "But I really do have to be going now. Sorry I can't buy a tract but . . . "

"Oh that's okay, it's free. In fact the whole package is free; salvation, redemption, the whole lot. Here, take it, everything's in there. We're holding meetings at the address on the back every Thursday and twice on Sundays. You're very welcome to come whenever you want to. Bye."

A moment later, he was gone, not quite in a puff of smoke, but just as quickly. I glanced briefly at the small leaflet before pushing it into my shopping-bag and returning my attention to the display in the shop window.

I supposed I should never see the smiling young man again and, in a few hours, he had vanished from my mind. But other things that I would gladly have forgotten were all too apparent; the empty room at Albert Avenue, my rapidly deteriorating studies and the growing preoccupation with my feelings of guilt and loneliness. Those were the things that I dearly wished *would* disappear in that puff of smoke. Instead, they became more unbearable as each day passed until my resistance finally broke.

Friday had been a long day and I should have been tired, but as the evening closed in, I felt no inclination to go to bed. I sensed that I wouldn't sleep even if I did, because, for some reason, I felt unusually awake and alert. Instead, I sat in my easy chair in front of the gas fire, and glanced round the room, just as I had done on the evening of my arrival. Apart from the welcome card, everything was in exactly the same place. Nothing had changed and it was as if, in that small room, time had stood still. The only difference was that everything somehow appeared to be more clearly defined. All the corners and angles seemed to meet in razor-sharp edges, casting crisp, clear shadows on the walls and even the dingy, nondescript colours of the wallpaper and carpet seemed to stand out with a greater vibrance than before.

Gradually, the strange clarity began to penetrate my own being, clearing aside the thick darkness that had been so heavily clouding my mind for so long. Once again, I questioned the meaning of the word "life". But now it was not being questioned in the muddled confusion of a darkened mind, but in the clarity of dazzling light, that enabled me to see, in intimate detail, what I was examining.

It was a strange word, "life", and held so many different meanings. To some, it meant ski-ing holidays on the snowy Swiss mountains. For others, it was a healthy bank balance that would enable them to indulge every whim and fantasy. But better than that, there was life in the new-born lambs that stumbled clumsily after their mothers in the fields back at the farm. There was life in the glistening snowdrops, those heart-warming "heralds of spring", informing the world that the long, harsh winter was over and that brighter days were up ahead. And then there had been life in the face of the young man I had met in town a few weeks earlier. He had spoken of life too, but a kind of life that I had never considered before. "Eternal life" he had called it and, for a few moments, I had wanted to ask him what it was all about. Finally, there was the life that I knew, my own life, that didn't seem like

84

life at all. As the light continued to shine ever brighter, I remembered what the young man had said.

" . . . He came and died for you so that you could have eternal life." I looked across at the wardrobe, where I had put my shopping-bag containing the little tract and tried to recall our brief conversation. He had mentioned a name, an ancient leader, a conqueror of some kind. Cromwell! That was it, Oliver . . . no, that wasn't it, it was the other name that was important, the name that made me feel hopeless and yet hopeful, all at the same time – Jesus.

As it returned to my mind, the mixed feelings that it had stirred up inside me rose to the surface. Once again, I wasn't sure whether I wanted to run away and never hear the name again, or risk reaching out and making contact with it, even if I were turned away for doing so. I hovered between the two options for several moments and then I remembered how I had felt as the young man in town had spoken the word "life". I had known by the expression in his eyes and the tone of his voice that he spoke of a different kind of life from the one I had known so far. Now I was certain that I, too, wanted what he had. All at once, I decided to take the risk. Even if I was turned away, I simply had to find out who Jesus was and why I felt so sure He could make sense of my confused and conflicting emotions.

In sudden haste, as if the moment might pass, I slid back the wardrobe door and seized the bag. A moment later, most of the contents had been emptied on to the floor in a frenzied search for the small piece of paper. At last, it was in my hands, badly crumpled, but still in one piece. As I sat down and smoothed it out on my lap, my eyes came to rest on the most beautiful words I had ever read: "Unto Him that loved us and washed us from our sins in His own blood."

I was arrested immediately as both the statement and the answer to my two greatest longings were summoned up in those few, poignant words: my desire to be loved and my desire to be clean inside. Almost all my life, I had been convinced that the answer to the first would be found in a human man and in getting married. To the second problem, however, I wasn't sure there existed any answer at all. Indeed, I often wondered if I would ever be free from the burden of guilt and condemnation that I had carried for so long. And at times, I also wondered whether marriage really would solve all my problems. Maybe natural, human love would not be strong enough to deal completely with the things I felt inside. Such wonderings were nearer the truth than I could have imagined at the time, but until then it had seemed as if there was no alternative. Now, summed up in those few, meaningful words, I wondered if there might be one after all.

Still clutching the small leaflet, I read the words again and again and, as their significance slowly filtered through my mind, tears began to well up in my eyes. I brushed them away with the back of my hand, only to find them replaced by more, and more, until the dam finally burst. I had shed many tears before, it was true, but they had been tears of anger and frustration and perhaps sorrow at saying goodbye to Ben. But these were different. They came from much deeper inside than any I had ever cried before. They were tears of relief, such as a lost child might cry when it had at last been found by its parents. And they were tears of release. In them, all the bitter anguish and confusion I had kept locked up inside for so many years finally rose to the surface and gushed over the edges of my being, in a swirling cataract of released emotion. They flowed for some considerable time, as if making up for all those years of being locked inside, only ever allowed to escape for a few moments as I walked across those secluded hills with Ben.

How long it all lasted, I wasn't quite sure, but when I eventually stopped crying, I felt a quiet stillness, just like the calm that would descend after a raging storm, and that the room was filled with a warm, comforting presence. It was only slight at first, like the sweet sense of well-being experienced when waking on Christmas morning and knowing that good things are in store. But gradually it became stronger and stronger, seeming to warm the air all around me until I knew, beyond all doubt, that I was not alone. Slowly and gently, the serene presence flowed into my weary soul, bidding all other voices to keep silence. For the first time since I could remember, my mind had become completely quiet. Then, in that peaceful silence, a new voice spoke. It wasn't harsh and compelling like all the other voices that had tormented my mind for so long, but calm and gentle. Where it came from, I didn't quite know. It could have come from somewhere deep inside, or from all around me, but it echoed, with unmistakeable clarity, the same sentiments I had just read. Over and over, it assured me that I was loved, in spite of all that I had been and done. I had convinced myself over the years that I was unlovely and unloved, even when the opposite truth was staring me in the face. Indeed, Mum and Uncle Tom had loved me dearly, but I had been unable to believe that they were genuine – or that anyone ever could be. Now, the comforting presence continued to penetrate my being, causing me to see for the first time where my fears and insecurities had their earliest beginnings: I had never been able to believe that I was loved and, from this primary root, all the others had sprung up. Now, in that beautiful silence, those three, simple words: "I love you" seemed to echo through the inner chambers of my soul.

I had heard them often, it was true. They were spoken by couples as they walked hand in hand beneath the silvery moon. By parents to their children at bedtime and vice versa. But, tonight, the King of kings and Lord of lords, Maker of the world and everything in it, had spoken them directly to me. I ran them through my mind over and over, as if I had tasted of a cup so sweet and soothing that I wanted to lift it to my lips again and again. Slowly, I felt the warmth of His love, far greater than any human love, reaching deep into my soul. For the first time since I could remember, I let down the defence and allowed myself to be loved. But, much more than that, suddenly I wanted, with everything in me, to respond and to speak the words that had begun to form in my mind.

"Jesus?" I began, a little uncertainly. "I'm not really sure what I'm supposed to say to you but, well I . . . I never realised before that you love me. I thought you only loved nice people, like Uncle Tom." The silence deepened and I knew, beyond all doubt, that He was listening. "But I'm not like that. In fact, I'm really quite a nasty person, and I've been so horrible to people – but I really didn't want to be. I tried so hard to be good and kind, like . . . like Uncle Tom. And I've been trying so hard to make something of my life, but it's all gone hopelessly wrong. I know it's not a lot to offer you, but if you want it, please take over, because I just can't do it any more." It was the best I could do for a first conversation with this Supreme Being, but I meant every word, and I knew He had accepted them.

A moment later, my mind was a mixed-up jumble of new emotions: joy, laughter and peace, things I had never experienced before. I felt like an excited child with a new friend who wanted to say everything all at once, even though He knew it all already. And then, when it was all said, I just sat quietly soaking up the healing waters of His love, like a thirsty sponge. Finally filled to overflowing, I spoke the words that I had never allowed to pass my lips, but which I had wanted so many times to say to someone.

"Lord . . . I love you." They were the words I believed I would never speak to anyone and even Ben, who had been the recipient of my most heartfelt affections, had only ever received an earnest "I like you very much", that night on the back step. Now, as I allowed them to pass my lips for the first time, the master key turned slowly in the rusty lock of my formerly impenetrable fortress.

— 8 —

I woke up late the next morning from what seemed like a beautiful dream and that warm sense of well-being was still as strong as it had been the night before. Slowly, I looked round the room at the unusual state of disarray. My shopping bag lay slumped against my easy chair, its former contents strewn untidily all around it and tipped over on its side was a half-empty box of tissues. Finally, my eyes came to rest on a folded piece of paper, displaying the words: "Second Oliver Cromwell" and immediately I remembered – I wasn't alone any more.

My first thought was to rush into town, it being a Saturday, and, as breakfast at such a late hour seemed inappropriate, I obeyed my instinct. Half an hour later, I found myself standing in the local bookshop, surveying row upon row of Bibles. I had only ever seen one type of Bible before. It used to lie on the pulpit in Mum's church and was big and black and forbidding. Now I was faced with hundreds of all shapes and sizes. There were red ones, white ones, short ones, tall ones, Bibles with strange-sounding names, Bibles that informed me they were "parallel" and one that declared emphatically, in big, gold letters that it was "Living"! I was completely bewildered as to which I should choose. In the end, however, my penchant for poetry won the day and I bought a traditional King James Version, simply because I was delighted with the flowery language and quaint Old English phrases.

Once back in the sanctuary of my room, I began to devour it as hungrily as I devoured my late lunch and, in no time at all, I was hooked. From that day forward, I spent every spare moment reading this wonderful book and as I continued to do this, I discovered that a whole new world was now within my grasp. On almost every page, I was reminded that I was loved by Someone who died for me and who had promised never to leave me. I had hope of being with Him for ever, not only in this life, but also in the life to come. Although it was still almost too wonderful for my finite mind to take in, I was just able to grasp what that part of it meant. But there were other things that left me more than a little confused. As I read the New Testament, I came across such phrases as "The Family of God", or "The Body of Christ". Then there were some words that I was vaguely able to understand, like "Brethren" and "Fellow Soldiers", but still others that I definitely didn't understand, like "Elder", "Apostle", "Pastor" and many others. It seemed as if the Bible was full of these people, but I hadn't met one of them yet. After a while, I began to wonder if they still existed, or if they were just around at the time of the Early Church. As the days passed, I became more and more aware of wanting to talk these things over with someone of like mind and, more than anything, to find the "Church" that was described on the pages of my Bible. This feeling became stronger and stronger until one day, in desperation, I fished out the little tract and remembered the young man's invitation to go along to a meeting.

This word also left me a little confused. What on earth *was* a meeting, I wondered, and several ideas about what kind of an affair this might be began to run through my mind. Perhaps there would be crowds of people in long robes, with sandalled feet. Or maybe they would be long-haired, "left-over-from-the-Sixties" types, with frayed jeans and Flower Power slogans emblazoned across their shapeless T-shirts. In the end, probably because I was on a business course at college, the final picture of smart individuals, in business-like suits, was the one that stuck. Plucking up all my courage, and the little tract, I ventured forth on Sunday evening, nursing the vague hope of meeting at least one of the characters that seemed to appear on almost every page of the New Testament.

Finding the place was difficult enough, but when I at last located the street mentioned on the back of the tract, I was convinced I had made a mistake. Subconsciously, I had been expecting some kind of ornate church building, complete with stained-glass windows, heavy wooden doors, and all the other paraphernalia that I had always associated with "religion". Instead, I stood in front of a large house, quite similar to my own, but with a much bigger garden and set further back from the road. It seemed to be the typical style of house for that area of town and many had been converted into bed-sitters by money-spinning developers. This one, however, had been left untampered with and retained its original identity as a large, rambling mansion.

As I stood in front of the gate, I had a sudden attack of "nerves", so bad, in fact, that I almost forgot the idea there and then. I had never walked into a strange house before, with nothing but a tract to explain my appearance. But after a few minutes, I decided that the worst they could do was to turn me away, or direct me to the correct address. Taking a deep breath, I gingerly walked up to the front door and pressed the bell-button. As I waited for what seemed an eternity, I began to wonder just what I was letting myself in for. Eventually, the door was opened by a young man wearing blue cords and an open-necked shirt.

"Hello," we volunteered simultaneously.

"I've come . . . "

"Have you come . . . ?" We both stopped and laughed as our words clashed again.

"Hold on," he said, smiling. "You speak, I'll listen." His warm friendly manner reminded me very much of the young man I had met in town a few weeks earlier and made some of my nervousness disappear – but not quite all of it.

"I met someone in town a few weeks ago," I began. "He gave me this." I held up the tract for his inspection.

"He said I could come along to a meeting. Is this . . . ?"

"That's great, you're very welcome. Come on in." I obediently stepped into the hallway and tried to reconcile my surroundings with my idea of a "meeting".

"So what's your name?" he asked as he closed the door behind us.

"Hmm? Oh . . . er . . . Lindsey, Lindsey Fairweather," I said, reluctantly withdrawing my gaze from the ornate wooden staircase that swept up to the next floor.

"Don't come from round here with an accent like that, do you?" Strangely enough, I didn't feel threatened or condemned by the all-too-familiar question.

"No, I'm from down south, right on the coast actually."

"Like it up here?" he asked, pushing open one of the heavy, oak-panelled doors that confronted us.

"Yes, at least . . . " I remembered fleetingly how dismal the first three years had been. "I'm beginning to like it better now."

"Grand stuff! We're not such a bunch of old dragons up here really. In fact, some of us are quite human when you get to know us."

He led me through the doorway into a magnificent room. A large piano, made of some rich-looking, dark wood, stood against one wall, with a tall rubber plant flanking one side. But, although this looked very impressive, it was the chairs that really caught my eye, for I had never seen so many packed into one room. A large three-piece suite, exquisitely covered in floral material, was given pride of place in the centre of the floor. Behind that was a row of ordinary, hard-backed chairs, and even further back, some easy chairs had been pushed into corners and crevices. As if that wasn't enough, there was a miscellaneous array of low stools, children's chairs and bean-bags strewn around wherever they would fit.

"What time does the meeting start?" I asked, a little nervously.

"Around seven-thirty. People should be arriving soon. Here, make yourself at home. Sit anywhere, I'll be back in a minute." With that, he disappeared and left me with the daunting task of choosing a seat.

Feeling increasingly nervous, I headed for a large easy chair in the most secluded corner of the room, right in the back row. As I sat down, I noticed that my stomach had tied itself into any number of knots and that I was becoming more uneasy with every passing moment. The large grandfather clock in the corner faithfully ticked away minutes that seemed like hours, while I wondered again, just what this meeting was going to be like.

As I sat, staring round the room, I realised that my expectations had been sadly off beam. I had imagined a large, polished table, in the centre of an equally large, but sparsely-furnished room. Around the table would be seated several aged men in dark, pin-striped or charcoal-grey suits, with yellowing shirts and un-colourful ties. They would each have a large Bible open in front of them and would spend the evening expounding deep and curious scriptures. The only women present would be their wives, who would be dressed in a manner suitably sober for such an occasion and whose hair would be an exact copy of Miss Peters'. I was, therefore, more than a little surprised when a young woman, with long, flowing hair, entered the room wearing a prettily-printed dress. She deposited a young child in the middle of the floor and, with a brief smile and a quick wave, was gone. Not many minutes later, the others began to arrive, slowly, in ones and twos. I kept my eyes peeled for the man I had met in town, but he didn't show up at all that evening.

Nothing was turning out as I had imagined. Not a pin-striped or charcoal-grey suit was apparent (although there *were* a few rather large Bibles around with numerous bits of paper and book-markers sticking out of them). No one seemed at all surprised at my presence and smiled at me as if I had always sat in the large chair in the corner. The young woman with the flowing hair appeared again, this time approaching each person in turn and planting a kiss on their cheek. I watched with growing apprehension as she came closer to me. What would she do then, I wondered? Worse still, what should *I* do? The question was answered quite simply by her planting a kiss on my cheek too, as if I were some bosom buddy that she had known all her life.

"Hi, I'm June," she said simply. "That was my husband, Peter, that let you in." I smiled in recognition and watched as she continued her rounds, thinking how uncanny the whole thing was. She had never set eyes on me before and yet, here she was, treating me like one of the family. My ideas of a business-like evening had long ago disappeared, but even so, nothing could have prepared me sufficiently for what followed.

Out of nowhere, several guitars appeared and a tuning-up session began. An amply-built woman positioned herself on a tiny piano-stool that seemed to fairly buckle under her weight. Then she began to play a little tune to herself that seemed totally unrelated to anything else that was happening. Tambourines were pulled out of various bags and children were apprehended by parents, who informed them that we were "about to start". Then, quite miraculously, all the discordant strings and unrelated piano keys came together as one, in the strains of the sweetest song I had ever heard. I didn't understand many of the words, which seemed to be about some kind of city, in a place called Zion, but there was something about it that touched me deep down inside and reminded me very much of how I had felt that Friday evening, when I had talked to the Lord for the first time.

Gradually, the volume of singing increased and people began to move around. Some stood up, whilst others remained seated and just raised their hands. Still others began clapping and even dancing up and down on the spot. Nobody seemed particularly bothered by what anyone else was doing (or not doing) and, far from being disorderly, it all seemed, in some strange and wonderful way, to just flow.

As the singing began to gather momentum, so did my nervousness and I began to feel very conspicuous, despite my secluded position in the corner. In contrast to Mum's church, and even Uncle Tom's, there seemed to be no rhyme or reason to what was happening here. At those other churches, everyone had stood up or sat down at the same time, but the people here stood up and sat down as and when the fancy took them and I even noticed that one man opposite me was on his knees. Also, in the other churches I had been to, there had always been someone at the front, directing operations. Here, however, it seemed to be every man for himself and I was completely at a loss as to what I should do.

Just as I was feeling at my most conspicuous, I noticed a man in the opposite corner of the room who seemed to be studying me with immense interest. As our eyes met, he smiled briefly and then, to my great relief, he looked away. Most people, I noticed, seemed to have their eyes closed, but this man had his open most of the time, and was looking round the room, as if monitoring what was happening. From this behaviour, I decided that he was the man that should have been at the front if this had been an ordinary church. But as it was difficult to decide where the front of the room actually was in the random seating arrangement, I concluded that he might as well be in the corner as anywhere else.

Becoming increasingly confused, I glanced nervously round the room at the wide spectrum of society represented there and wondered how they could all flow together in such unforced unity. They were so varied a group of people; young, old, slim and, in the case of the pianist, not so slim, but out of them all, it was a man almost opposite me, in the front row, that secured my attention most immoveably. As I studied him, I completely forgot everything else, for I had never seen so many contradictions dwelling together in such obvious harmony as they did that saintly old man.

He must have been the oldest person in the room, and definitely the most unwell. Thick, blue spectacles concealed his eyes and I noticed a white stick propped up against the side of his chair. His unsteady stance was due to the fact that he wore one built-up shoe and, as if that wasn't enough to contend with, a good half of his right arm was missing. His obvious disabilities, however, were eclipsed by the glowing light that seemed to shine from his face and I thought I had never seen anything so amazing in my life. He should have looked sad, I thought to myself, and his face should have been etched at least with lines of pain, if not anger about what he must have endured throughout his life. But no such things were apparent. Instead, he smiled radiantly, lifting what was left of his arms into the air and whispered gentle words of praise to God. As I continued to watch him, I realised that he possessed what few able-bodied men possessed: joy in the face of adversity, peace in the midst of turmoil, and life in the midst of physical death. All at once, I felt that I would willingly have given *my* right arm to possess the quality of life that he did.

Just then, a sudden movement by the door jolted me back to earth. The man that I thought should have been at the front had stood up and was reading from a large, well-thumbed Bible. Then, when he had finished reading, he began to speak. As he did, I immediately noticed that, in contrast to the cold, monotone voices of the ministers at Mum's church, his voice was lively and convincing. At times, his words provoked laughter in the congregation and I couldn't help enjoying the short message he gave. It was so captivating that it seemed only a few minutes later that he closed his Bible and asked one of the guitarists to "give him an 'E'". This request complied with, he then sang one line of a song and was immediately joined by everyone else who seemed to know it by heart. A moment later, people were jumping to their feet and the dancing, clapping and general noise began again. This time, however, it all carried on for a much shorter time than before and then it seemed as if the meeting had ended. This was not immediately obvious as I had been waiting for some kind of closing prayer, but it never came. Instead, two of the women left the room, some of the musicians put down their guitars and people began to turn and talk to those sitting next to them.

All at once, I felt very lost and more confused than before as to what I should do next. In the end, I decided it would be a good time to make an exit, but just as I was about to get up, the two women returned with a tray of drinks and biscuits. Everyone took something to eat or drink and then huddled in little groups in various corners of the room. As I glanced quickly round, I noticed the man that had spoken heading in my direction. As he made his way towards me, sudden panic swept over me and I shrank back into my seat, wondering what he was going to say. Perhaps he was about to question me on my lack of participation, or maybe throw me out for my insolent lack of response. With growing apprehension, I watched as he wove skilfully through the obstacle course of chairs, coffee cups and miscellaneous musical instruments and finally stood right in front of my chair.

"Hello, I'm Ken," he said pleasantly. "Like some coffee?" I was so relieved that he hadn't intended to probe the inner depths of my soul that I took up his offer without hesitation.

"Sugar?" he asked, holding out a small white bowl.

"Er . . . no thank you, I don't take it."

"Well done, it's bad for you anyway," he said, at the same time as spooning two ample helpings of the damaging substance into his own cup.

"Ever been to a meeting like this before?" he asked, after taking a sip of coffee.

"N . . . no, nothing quite like this" I stammered and as I lifted my cup, I noticed that my hand was shaking. Feeling extremely embarrassed by this, I tried to divert his attention.

"Are you . . . er . . . in charge here?" I asked helplessly.

"Well, I suppose you could say that, although I like to believe that the Holy Spirit's in charge." Suddenly a thought occurred to me and, despite my nervousness, I couldn't help feeling excited.

97

"Are you an Elder?" I asked enthusiastically. He smiled broadly, obviously surprised that I should be familiar with such a word.

"Yes, I am," he replied, smiling even more widely. For a moment, I completely forgot my uneasiness in the excitement of having found a New Testament person.

"Are there any more?" I asked eagerly.

"Yes, but they're tied up tonight. They should be at the next meeting though." He looked at me rather curiously for a moment and I sensed that he was about to begin a more in-depth line of questioning. Certain that I would make a complete fool of myself if he did, I decided it really was time to leave.

"Well, I suppose I'd better be off now," I said, putting down my unfinished cup of coffee. "Thanks for having me."

"It was a pleasure" he said warmly. "Here, I'll show you out, it's easy to get lost in this mansion of a place." After successfully negotiating the obstacle course once again, we eventually reached the front door, but just as I was anticipating the wide open space outside, he stopped suddenly.

"Do you think you'll be coming again?" he asked pleasantly. Recalling my earlier feelings of nervous confusion, I decided that I never wanted to come within miles of another meeting. Just as I was about to say as much, however, I happened to glance through the half-open door and caught sight of the disabled man who had earlier caught my attention. A young child sat on his knee and his face was once more aglow as they held an animated conversation. I looked quickly up at Ken and my premeditated speech came out all wrong.

"Yes, I think I'd like to come again," I replied, to my own astonishment. "If it's all right with you, that is." He smiled warmly.

"Of course it is, we'd love to see you again. But I'd better give you the new address. This is the last meeting we're going to have here," he explained. "Our numbers have grown so much that we're going to hire an old youth club and hold meetings there. It's not far away, but a little off the beaten track. If you have any problems about finding it, give us a ring and we'll pick you up." I took the piece of paper from him, a little surprised that he should so genuinely want me to come to another meeting.

"Thank you," I said, glancing briefly at the strange address. "I'll be going then."

"Okay, Lindsey, see you soon."

As the doors closed behind me, I stood on the step, inhaling deep lungfuls of the refreshing night air and wondered how he had known my name. Maybe Peter had tipped him off, I concluded. Clicking the gate shut behind me, I turned to take a final look at the stately house. What on earth would the neighbours think, I wondered, if only they knew what went on behind those innocent-looking pink curtains. Then, digging my hands into my pockets I began to plod slowly home.

As I walked, I thought over the things I had just seen. The people at that meeting seemed to possess a depth of freedom I had never witnessed before. I could still see the smiling faces, the many uplifted hands and the abandoned dancing for sheer joy. As I remembered, in contrast, how inhibited I had felt, I began to see, perhaps for the first time, the invisible walls that I had so carefully built around myself over so many years. I had gone to such great lengths to keep my emotions and feelings locked up. Now, when I wanted for the first time to let them escape, I realised just how strong those invisible walls had become.

I thought back to the events that had taken place in my room that Friday night. To me, they had been the new beginning of which I had so often dreamed. Now, in the light of how I had felt at that meeting, I wondered if this, too, were just another wild fantasy that would gradually grow dim and finally fade away completely.

As I continued walking, I tried to make sense of what had happened on that Friday evening, weeks ago. Once I had finished my own "praying", I had read the little tract three times over and then recited something printed on the back entitled "Sinner's Prayer". By doing this, the tract informed me, I had "accepted the Lord" and been officially "born again". Before reading this, I had used my own words and was convinced that they had been accepted, but I had wanted to say the printed ones as well, just in case I had left anything out. Now, upon reflection of my lack of liberty earlier that evening, I began to wonder if, in fact, I had. Maybe there *was* something else I had to do. Maybe I wasn't really born-again after all. Maybe it had all been a weird and wonderful dream.

Eventually, I pushed through the door to my room and immediately fished out my Bible. At some point on the journey home, it had occurred to me that I had read something of significance in it that morning, but I couldn't quite remember what or where it was. Thankfully, I had left my book-marker in the right place and had also underlined the words in red so that they caught my eye immediately.

"I have loved thee with an everlasting love . . . "

I read the words slowly several times and then closed my Bible and remembered that evening. As I did, the same assurance of being loved washed over me again, erasing all doubt from my mind. Whatever had happened (or not happened) earlier, it made no difference to Him. He had loved me back then, He had loved me even before I accepted Him, and He loved me now, in spite of how I felt – or didn't feel! The words I now read assured me that His love knew no limits and didn't change according to what I did, or even what I was, it was, quite simply, everlasting. Still a little perturbed by the evening's events, this knowledge was just enough to bear me up above the storm that had earlier raged in my mind and to convince me that this really was a new beginning that would never fade away.

The weeks that followed that Sunday meeting were a fierce conflict of faith and doubt. Sometimes the Lord would seem so real I felt I could almost reach out and touch Him and wondered why I had ever doubted Him at all. But at other times, He seemed so far away that I almost doubted His existence. As time went on, I became more and more convinced that something was wrong and that I needed help. It seemed as if I was fighting with something stronger than myself, although I wasn't sure what it was. One Thursday evening, two months after I had attended that first meeting, I pulled out the little piece of paper with Ken's writing on it and decided to give it one more try.

"At least I know what to expect this time," I told myself
as I walked nervously down the long driveway to the low,
spreading building. It was quite a secluded site, screened
on every side by tall poplar trees and standing in two
acres of lawns and semi-woodlands. The youth for whom
it had originally been designed had forsaken the site for
one that supplied more of the glitz and glamour essential
to a really good night out. It was now let out at reasonable
rates to bingo clubs, pop groups for practice sessions – and
Christians! As I pushed open the door, it was immediately
obvious that I was, once again, mistaken, for nothing
looked as I had expected it to.

Instead of being strewn haphazardly round the room,
the chairs were arranged in three neat rows. There was
a central aisle, at the top of which stood a plain wooden
table. Behind this, three men, one of whom I recognised
as Ken, and one woman were seated. Ken looked up
briefly and smiled a greeting. I smiled back, but was
conscious that I was just as nervous as I had been at
the first meeting. The other three people, I presumed,
were the Elders I had not yet met, but none of them
looked up.

In fact, no one else seemed aware that I had entered the
room at all, as their heads were bent forward, resting in
their hands, and some were even kneeling in front of their
chairs. A general rumble of voices rose from all sides of the
room, sometimes quite soft and low, and at other times
getting louder and louder until it might well have been
described as rowdy. I stood, rooted to the spot, unsure

whether to turn around and go home or stay in spite of myself.

As the volume of noise gradually increased, the soft, low tone disappeared completely and the atmosphere became powerfully charged. More than anything, I wanted to rush back out of the door, but something seemed to prevent me from doing so. Instead, I sat down on one of the empty seats, thankfully in the back row, and clasped my hands tightly together in order to stop them from shaking. Even though no one paid any attention to me at all, I felt sickeningly self-conscious. I couldn't possibly join in with what was going on and decided to concentrate instead on the three new faces at the front.

The first man was tall and lean, with finely-chiselled features and a deeply-furrowed brow. This might have been normal, or due to the fact that he was praying intensely. His right fist was tightly clenched and he thumped it at regular intervals into the palm of his left hand, as if to emphasise what he was saying. I imagined he was probably a few years younger than Ken, and infinitely more terrifying. The other man was much older and more stockily built, and reminded me quite a bit of Uncle Tom. He didn't seem as intense as the other two, but equally serious about what was going on. Then, there was the woman, probably in her mid-forties, who seemed to add a gentle touch to the otherwise intimidating trio. But even so, I wasn't quite sure about her as she struck me as motherly and "mother" was a concept I found it hard to relate to.

The praying continued for quite some time and then gradually faded into silence. At this point, Ken stood up, placed his Bible on the wooden table and gave a short message, although I was far too nervous to take in much of what he said. At the end of his talk, he closed his Bible and concluded the meeting with a simple prayer. Whilst he did this, I noticed fleetingly that, in contrast to the previous meeting, there had been no singing at all tonight. After a respectable pause, people started putting away Bibles, stacking up chairs and apprehending unruly children. I looked around, feeling as lost as I had at the first meeting when, to my great relief, I spotted a familiar face. It was the young man I had met in town.

"Hi, I remember you," he said, smiling. "I'm really glad you made it. My name's Rick, and this is my girlfriend, Melanie." A slim, pretty girl stood at his side and smiled at me in a most encouraging way. We shook hands and I tried my best to appear confident and relaxed, although this proved more than a little difficult.

"Hello, I . . . I'm Lindsey," I stammered nervously and was greatly relieved when Ken rescued me from having to say more by placing a hand on my shoulder.

"Hello, Lindsey," he smiled. "Nice to see you again."

"Oh . . . er . . . thanks," I said, trying to smile and didn't notice that Rick and Melanie had slipped away. Then, the woman that had sat with the three men behind the table came and stood at Ken's side.

"This is my wife, Barbara," he smiled. She extended a hand, which I shook rather cautiously. Close up, she seemed even more motherly than before, and I half expected her to draw me close to her chest in some kind of maternal embrace. However, I was pleasantly surprised when, after giving it a quick shake, she let go of my hand quite quickly and I decided that maybe she wouldn't be so bad after all. We exchanged a few words and then Rick and Melanie returned with three steaming cups of coffee.

"Like one of these, Lindsey?" asked Rick, placing one of them into my hand and so making it impossible for me to refuse. I thanked him as convincingly as I could and tried to hold it steadily. Now it was Ken and Barbara's turn to slip away, leaving me with the two young people. I felt a little awkward at first, and wondered what on earth I was supposed to say, but they were so friendly and out-going that after a few minutes, I was chatting to them without too much difficulty.

Occasionally, as we talked, my eyes flickered round the room as I tried to recognise faces from the first meeting and, more than once, they came to rest on the tall, lean man who had sat at the front with the others. By now I was convinced of the genuine friendliness of most of the other people there, but this man was a little different. His expression was serious to the point of being intimidating and his eyes, which seemed to dart round the room in a ferret-like fashion, had a strange, piercing quality about them. Although I never caught him looking directly at me, I left the hall that evening, convinced that he had made a thorough appraisal of me and that, if required to do so, he could have told me all there was to know about myself.

As I walked home that evening, I tried to make sense of the mixed-up jumble that my mind had become. I had felt about as bad at this meeting as I had at the first and, in view of this, I should have decided never to go to another one. But I did quite the opposite. In spite of my uneasiness, the warmth and friendliness of the people there was irresistible. They seemed to have accepted me, a complete stranger, in spite of my very obvious hang-ups and inhibitions. I might not have taken in much of what was spoken over the make-shift pulpit during those early days, but the attitude of the people there spoke far more to me than any sermon I had yet heard. So it was that I did go back. Not on a regular basis at first, but gradually I began to feel more and more at home with the new friends I had made and it wasn't long before I turned up at every meeting without fail.

This was not to say that going to meetings became any easier. In fact, as time went on, it almost seemed to become more difficult. Each time I went along, I was conscious of how free those people were and, in contrast, how bound I was myself. Sometimes this realisation would plunge me into the blackest depths of despair and I would then vow never to go back again. At the same time, my lack of release caused me to question quite seriously my experience of salvation. If I really *was* a Christian, I told myself, I should be able to sing and clap and even dance for joy as they did. But I couldn't. I should be able to read the Bible and then get up and tell everyone what it had meant to me, just like they did. But I couldn't do that either. Furthermore, they could all pray spontaneously in the company of the whole congregation, but I couldn't imagine myself ever doing such a thing. But, worst of all, I found that, in spite of my first, great step towards freedom, I had not undergone the dramatic overnight change that I had come to expect should have taken place. Underneath it all, I still felt unable to open myself up and respond to the love these people had for me.

On the days when the Lord seemed very real, I never doubted that something had, indeed, happened to me that night in my room. But not all the days were like that. More often than not, He *didn't* seem real and I was greatly discouraged to find that well-worn, heavy mantle of blackness still able to descend upon me quite often. As I continued to watch those around me, I was convinced that their experience of salvation was vastly different from mine. They never seemed to be down and depressed the way I was. Neither were their lives the constant cycle of hills and valleys that mine was, and I desperately wanted to know why.

Sometimes, when it all got on top of me, I would make up my mind to talk to someone about it. But I never did. Talking was not something I did easily at the best of times, and I had certainly never talked to anyone about my innermost feelings – except perhaps Ben. Of course I talked to the Lord about it all, but sometimes He seemed so far away that I wondered if He really had been listening.

So it was that meetings became an intense conflict. On the one hand, I wanted very much to be there, but when I was, I could think of a thousand other places I would rather have been. The quiet meetings were, perhaps, a little easier to cope with and I had cultivated an almost fool-proof method of enduring them without too much difficulty. As always, I would sit in the back row and tip my head forward. This action would cause two curtains of long, dark hair to partly close over my face, leaving only a small piece of my forehead and my nose visible to those around me. In this position, with my eyes glued to my songbook, I sang with the others and got on fairly well as long as we sang the slow, smoochy songs. But not all the meetings were quiet. In fact, most of them were quite the opposite and it was during those meetings that I again felt like rushing out of the room when the singing really got under way. The struggle I experienced at such times was almost unbearable, but, although I had found our own "ordinary" meetings difficult, there was one that made them seem like a picnic in comparison.

Derek, the elder who resembled Uncle Tom, had invited a guest speaker to address our group and, from the moment he walked in, I was certain I had never met a more lively or terrifying person in my life. He led the singing with a large accordion and punctuated the songs by marching back and forth across the room. Then, when he felt we had done enough singing, he gave a simple message that was short and to the point; this being that Jesus died to set us free.

It had already been a difficult meeting for me, but this declaration just about finished it. So He might have done, I thought crossly, but it didn't seem to be working too well for me! Feeling decidedly angry, I sat and fumed through the rest of his message until he finally closed his Bible. Then, throwing the accordion straps over his shoulders once again, he stood up and asked us to do the same. A moment later, he launched into the loudest, fastest, most unnerving praise service that I had ever been to in my life. Everyone – excepting myself – seemed to be instantly caught up and the usual clapping, dancing and even shouting for joy began. This, in itself, was bad enough and made me want to run off somewhere and hide, but if I had known beforehand what was to follow, I would never have gone to that meeting in the first place.

After quite some time of this animated singing, he slowed the pace right down. Then, still playing his accordion softly, he began to speak. There was someone in the meeting, he informed us, that was in need of prayer. He wanted to pray with them, if they would just raise their hand. Suddenly, I turned hot and cold and knew, beyond all doubt, that the someone was myself. As I realised this, I wanted very much to let him pray for me, but at the same time, I was completely terrified. If he did pray for me, I was certain I would make a complete fool of myself. Maybe I would burst into tears, right there, in front of everybody. Or maybe he would uncover some of the deep secrets from my childhood that no one there knew about. Still the man continued to play his accordion softly, asking again for the person to raise their hand. My tension mounted rapidly as the minutes ticked away until I felt I really would have to rush out of the room before much longer. Then, just as my endurance had almost run out, someone raised their hand. I heaved a sigh of relief, assuring myself that it was all over. But I could not have been more mistaken. Several other hands went up and the man prayed for one person after another. Strange, unnerving things began to happen all around me. Some people he prayed for broke down and cried. Others burst into joyful laughter. Husbands and wives embraced and asked each other for forgiveness. But then I realised, with mounting apprehension, that the man was now not only praying for people with their hands up, but seemed to be making his way steadily round everyone in the room – and everyone would include me!

Once again, I turned hot and cold as I watched him come closer and closer until I could stand it no longer. He was now only two people away from me and as he leaned over to pray for one of them, I slipped quickly out of the room, through the main door and out into the cold night air. Almost fearful that someone might come after me, I began to walk quickly in a homewards direction. As I did, the wild fantasy that the accordion-wielding preacher had, indeed, followed me gripped my mind and I broke into a frenzied run. I mustn't stop, I told myself, or even turn around. I had to keep going as fast as I could. As a sharp pain dug into my side, I remembered how I had so often felt like running away from Uncle Tom back at the farm and realised that, deep down inside, I was still, very much, a frightened young child.

Eventually, I reached Albert Avenue and rushed up the stairs to my room. Breathing heavily, I closed the door firmly behind me and stood against it for several moments, feeling my heart beating much more quickly than it should have done. Then, in a final act of desperate anguish, I fell on my knees by my bed and buried my face in my arms.

"Lord," I sobbed, as tears streamed down my face. "You died to set me free. You shed your blood for me so that I don't have to go on living this way. But I'm not free, Lord, I'm bound, hopelessly bound. And Lord, you've got to do something." I pleaded desperately. "Please Lord, do something, because if You don't, nobody else can." Not many days later, my heartfelt prayer began to be answered.

We had just finished a meeting. It had been one of the quiet ones and I hadn't handled it too badly, but I had not yet got over the visiting speaker experience. Feeling quite unable to enter into the pleasant chatter that always followed the service, I stood with one shoulder leaning against the wall and slowly sipped a cup of coffee. To my surprise, Barbara came up behind me without my seeing her.

"So what's it all about this time, Lindsey?" she asked. I turned suddenly, almost spilling my coffee and made an attempt at smiling. I had tried very hard to conceal the struggle I had recently been through and thought I had been making a fairly good job of it. But there was no hiding from the Spirit of the Lord who, infuriating as it sometimes was, had chosen to dwell within those concerned people that I had come to know.

"Oh, nothing much really," I replied, studying my coffee with great interest.

"Okay," she smiled. "Just thought I'd ask." Being able to quickly back off was one quality in Barbara that endeared her to me greatly. It told me that she was able to mother me, but not smother me and, in fact, her attitude often made me want to open up more than if she had tried to force the issue. She squeezed my shoulder quickly and made as if she were going. As she turned, I suddenly decided that I couldn't bear the burden alone any longer and I quickly called her back. She turned to face me again and looked at me enquiringly.

"There is something wrong, Barbara," I said hesitantly. "It's just that . . . " I looked down at my coffee again and wondered why it was always so difficult to talk to people. Barbara said nothing but waited patiently until I began again.

"I've been wanting to talk to someone for ages but . . . well I just can't seem to say it all." I looked up at her quickly, feeling angry with myself for behaving like a tongue-tied schoolgirl and wondered what to say next. She smiled sympathetically and nodded.

"I know, Lindsey," she replied, reassuringly. "We all know you've been struggling for a while now." She paused for a moment and then it seemed as if a thought had suddenly occurred to her.

"Tell you what, Ken and I are going over to Jim's on Saturday. Why don't you come over as well? Maybe we could have a chat then." I flinched slightly as she mentioned the tall, slim man whom I had come to know as Jim. I had spoken to him only a few times since going along to meetings and didn't find him any less disconcerting now than I had done at the beginning. Not that he was unpleasant in any way, but his serious, slightly distant manner always left me feeling a little less than at ease.

"Well, I'm not sure," I replied cautiously. "He hasn't invited me so maybe . . . "

"He won't mind at all – *really*. It's just a friendly get-together and people are always dropping in on Jim and Sally."

"Well, if you're really sure," I finished doubtfully.

"Of course I am," she replied definitely. Before I could say more, our conversation was cut short by the lights going off and our being plunged into complete darkness. In the stunned silence that followed, the culprit was revealed.

"Georgie!" came Sally's voice out of the darkness, followed by a smart slap somewhere on the little boy's anatomy. "How many times have I told you not to do that?" The lights came on a moment later to reveal a tearful Georgie, apologising to his mother.

"Well," grinned Barbara. "If that's all sorted out, I guess that's the cue for home time." I nodded with a smile and then began to help the others stack up the chairs.

By Saturday afternoon, I had almost decided not to go through with the meeting at Jim's house. I felt sure I wouldn't be able to say anything even if I did and concluded that it would be better not to waste their time. However, the Lord had obviously foreseen my lack of resolve and decided that a little divine intervention was needed.

Just after lunch, my bell rang and I rushed downstairs to find Jim's wife, Sally, standing on the doorstep. She was a bright, cheerful young woman in her early thirties, with strawberry-blonde hair and appealing brown eyes. Although mature beyond her years in many ways, the trademark of her character was her childlike openness and infectious sense of humour.

"Sally!" I exclaimed in amazement. She grinned mischievously and bounded towards the front gate.

"Well, come on if you're coming," she shouted over her shoulder.

"But Sally . . . "

"Come on!" she shouted again, jumping into her car. Not even stopping to grab a coat or anything else, I pulled the front door shut behind me and jumped in next to her. As was her wont, she pulled away before I even had time to fasten my seat-belt and took off at an almost criminal speed.

"I suppose I couldn't ask you to explain?" I grinned as she turned the corner sharply.

"Barbara said she'd invited you over but thought you were a bit nervous about gate-crashing," she volunteered.

"So?"

"So Jim told me to drag you over myself."

"You mean he really doesn't mind me coming?"

"No, of course not," she replied casually. "He thought it was a great idea." I breathed an inconspicuous sigh of relief and relaxed back into my seat. Even so, when we approached their house, my stomach fluttered nervously as I wondered what the afternoon would bring.

It was the first time I had ever been to Jim's house, even though it wasn't too far from my own and I took a few moments to look it over while Sally gathered up some toys from the front garden. It was large and detached, with a bay window and a small, lantern-like lamp hanging over the front porch. The ruched curtains, visible through the lead-crossed window, gave the whole thing a very homely, Dickensian look and I could imagine gaily-clad carol singers, standing on crisp snow on their doorstep, singing merrily. But it wasn't Christmas, I reminded myself, and I was feeling anything but merry!

A few moments later, I was sitting in Jim's lounge, together with Ken and Barbara and Jim's two children. The atmosphere was informal and relaxed and, due to the children, rather noisy. In this unfamiliar setting, a completely different side to the restrained, austere Jim was revealed. He spent the first twenty minutes of my visit on all fours, being ridden across the floor by his four-year-old son, George. Jessica, George's senior by one year, squealed with delight as Jim tipped the little boy off his back and heaved her up into the saddle instead. As I watched them, the thought occurred to me that she was almost the same age as I had been when I had stood on the beach, watching another young girl and her parents playing together.

After some time, we stopped for tea and the children were then escorted to bed by Sally. As they left the room, we all breathed a sigh of relief and sat for a few minutes soaking up the welcome quietness that descended.

"And you wanted eight!" said Sally to Jim as she returned.

"Well, why not," he grinned back. "Work it out right and the older ones look after the younger ones and we can put our feet up." Sally raised her eyebrows doubtfully.

"The theory sounds wonderful," she murmured, and we all laughed.

The whole scenario served to convince me that there was, after all, more to Jim than I had thought, and this became more apparent as the evening wore on.

It was the first time he had ever spoken to me for any length of time and, although I still found him a little disconcerting, he proved to possess a gentle tactfulness that I would hardly have believed possible. He was the sort of person, I reflected, that could wield a sword so skilfully, you would hardly feel it touch until it had passed right through your chest. He steered the conversation so subtly round to the reason for my visit that I hardly realised what was happening. Caught completely off guard, I began to share the many doubts and fears that had been troubling me ever since my conversion. In particular, I spoke for the first time about my inability to break out of myself and relate to people around me. We discussed this for a while, then I moved on to my lack of release in meetings.

"I just can't get free like the rest of you," I confided. "Sometimes, it makes me wonder if there's something so wrong with me that even the Lord can't put it right." Jim smiled slightly.

"Of course He can, love, but it might not happen overnight." This was something less than I had wanted to hear. Deep down I had convinced myself that becoming a Christian had signalled the end of all my problems and that all my past fears and failings would instantly disappear.

"Hmm," murmured Jim, when I informed him of my grand expectations. "The theory sounds wonderful," he grinned, mimicking Sally's tone to perfection.

"Actually," he said, leaning forward in his chair and becoming a little more serious. "The theory's right. What

113

Jesus did at Calvary meant that all your hang-ups were laid on Him in one package. But now you have to allow that truth to become a reality in your daily life – and that doesn't always happen instantly. In fact," he continued, "you might find things actually begin to look worse now that you're a Christian."

"Worse? But I thought things were supposed to get better from now on," I remarked in dismay.

"Oh they do, Lindsey," he replied with conviction. "They really do, but you see, when you accept the Lord, He begins to reveal things that have been so deeply hidden inside that sometimes we never even knew they were there ourselves. Shortly after I became a Christian, I began to wonder if I hadn't been a better person before my conversion, there was so much junk He began to reveal. You see, the Lord doesn't do things by halves. He wants to set you completely free from everything that's lurking deep down inside, and in order to do that, He has to reveal it all first."

I flinched a little as he spoke. The thought of having my innermost secrets revealed was a difficult one to contend with. I didn't really want them, or anyone else for that matter, to know what was, indeed, "lurking deep inside". But at the same time, I knew that what Jim said was true. Unless it *was* revealed, I had no hope of ever being set free from it. I struggled with the predicament for a few moments and then decided on a compromise. I would tell them *some* of it, but there was one part that I was still determined to keep to myself. It was my deepest longing for another person to share my life with. I knew I must never tell anyone about that side of things. People might get the wrong idea and in my case, I was still quite young so there was plenty of time for it to happen naturally anyway.

Taking a deep breath, I began to relate the events from early childhood that had caused me to build up those invisible and seemingly unscaleable walls. As I spoke about them openly for the first time ever, I began to see just how powerfully I was held in their grasp and wanted more than anything to be free from their haunting influence. The others waited patiently until it seemed as if I had said it all and then Jim leaned back in his chair.

"Well, Lindsey," he smiled, "we could all talk for a lot longer about the problem, but it would be better to talk about some answers." I looked up at him wondering what on earth he was going to say next. "I think we should pray for you," he continued. "There's a lot in the past that you need to be set free from. There's also no doubt that you've been influenced by other spirits, especially during your childhood years, and you need to be set free from them too. What d'you say?"

I considered his words for a few moments. "Spirits" were something I was only vaguely aware of. To me, they were little more than mischievous imps that ran around in red leggings, some with pitch-forks and others without. But now, I began to wonder if, perhaps, they were just a little more serious than this comic-strip image suggested. Eventually, I decided that there was nothing to lose by giving it a try. After all, I told myself, anything would be an improvement on where I was at the moment. I looked up at Jim again, feeling as if I were about to sign my own death warrant.

"Okay," I replied as confidently as I could.

The four of them placed their hands on my shoulders and began to pray. At first I was dubious that any of it would serve much purpose and my problems did, indeed, have greater prominence in my mind than the answers. But as they continued to pray, I slowly lifted my eyes from the mire at my feet and looked instead at the One who had given His own life to deliver me from it.

Jim had been right. There was a lot I had always believed to be "just me", character traits that I was doomed to live with for the rest of my life. Now, for the first time, I realised that they were quite the opposite. They were nothing to do with the real me at all, but were, just as he had said, "other spirits". Not the mischievous imps that I had once imagined, but powerful, intelligent forces that had eaten their way into my young life all those years ago. Now, finally caught out in the light and seen for what they really were, it wasn't long before they fled their former habitation in the Name that was greater than their own. As they did, a peace such as I could not remember ever experiencing washed over me, and an unspeakable joy flooded my being. For the first time, I lifted my hands and praised Him freely, not feeling in the least bit bothered that anyone was watching. From that day forward, the words "born again" took on greater meaning than ever before. At last, I felt completely clean, for the first time in my life, just like a newly-born child, too young to be tainted by the pollutions of this world.

Slowly, sometimes falteringly, I began to take my first, fragile steps into the limitless ocean of God's love. This was not to say that my problems had disappeared overnight and, just as Jim had said, there were still the days when I couldn't seem to get it all together. But never did I despair to the same degree as before. Now, even during those down days, there was still a faint glimmer of hope in my heart, just bright enough to make me get up and give it one more try. And, after a while, those days were far outweighed by the times when it *did* work, when one small step seemed to me like a thousand miles and I began to experience a release I never dreamed could be possible. Meetings, far from being frightening, were now a tremendous joy. Instead of slinking into the shadows of the back row as I used to, I wanted to be right out front, singing, clapping and even dancing for joy, just like everybody else. My Bible sprang alive and I, too, was now able to stand behind our make-shift pulpit and tell everyone about it.

But my desire to speak about the Lord and what He had done for me was not confined to our own meetings. Something wonderful had happened to me and I wanted everyone to know about it. The girls at college soon learned of my life-changing experience and I also joined Rick and Melanie and some of the others in our "street outreach", which took place on Saturday afternoons. Some people would bring their guitars and Rick would bring his accordion. Then, having selected a suitable street corner, we would sing some of the songs we sang at the meetings. Our performance would last for about twenty minutes and then we would go off in separate directions. Armed with similar tracts to the one Rick had handed me at our first meeting, we would tell as many people as we could about Jesus Christ – the second Oliver Cromwell.

During those early days, I never ceased to be amazed at the uncharacteristic boldness that surfaced during those small street campaigns. Indeed, I would always remember the first time I handed a tract to a Hell's Angel. Feeling extremely nervous, I marched up to the grim-faced man, almost twice as big as I was, and held out the small leaflet. As he towered above me, resplendent in black leather and silver studs, I felt just like David, standing before Goliath. A moment later, however, I realised that he was more afraid of me than I was of him.

"Sorry," he squeaked in a small, falsetto voice. "I can't stop, Mum's expecting me 'ome for tea." I glanced at the tall clock-tower behind him and, as it was barely two-thirty, decided that he was probably trying to make a tactful escape.

Then, of course, there was Mum, and Uncle Tom. I was still very much aware of how badly I had treated them and many voices had condemned me in the past for my selfish attitude. However, they had never provided me with any answers to the problem, but merely threw it in my face and left me floundering. Now, in contrast, the gentle conviction of the Holy Spirit not only brought the situation again to my attention, but also showed me the way to deal with it. Inside, I sensed that it would take some time for my relationship with Mum to be completely restored, but I was able, for the moment, to at least take the first step. Shortly after being prayed for at Jim's, I made a long phonecall, apologising to both Mum and Uncle Tom, for the way I had behaved at the farm. It was a good beginning, and would have an even better conclusion.

As each day passed, I saw barriers come down that I had always believed would be there for life and I began to relate to those around me to a greater extent than I had ever dreamed possible. The times I found it the easiest to do this were on "fellowship teas", hikes through the local woods and barbecues on the beach. When we had finished eating, Rick would produce his accordion and we would sing, sometimes until quite late at night. Those were the times when I would throw my head back and laugh as freely as all the others at the antics of the children – and some of the adults – and catch a fleeting glimpse of the person that I really was underneath all the insecurity and fear that had once been the trademark of my character. A whole new world had begun to open up before me, and I drank in every new experience, just like the desert traveller, suddenly confronted with an oasis that wasn't just another mirage, but a reality at last.

— 10 —

Those first few months as a Christian were the happiest that I could remember. The God that had once been the austere, distant Being, in the church with the hard wooden pews and unsmiling faces had now become a close and personal friend. Wherever I went, I was aware of His presence and, far from wanting to run away, I now wanted to draw close to Him in any way that I could. As I poured out my heart to Him day by day, it almost didn't occur to me that I was praying. That was something we used to do in assembly at school, or in church on Sunday and had always struck me as a boring and painful duty. But talking to the Lord wasn't like that. It was more like holding a conversation with a close friend and something I did simply because I wanted to. And, above all, the tangible awareness of being loved, not only by Him, but by the people around me too, made my life seem more wonderful than ever before. At one time, I had dreaded the dawning of each new day, knowing that it held nothing but emptiness and lack of purpose. Now, each day was a new beginning, a fresh opportunity of getting to know Him a bit better. In my eagerness to do this, I took my Bible with me everywhere, hungrily devouring every word and not in the least bit embarrassed by the odd looks I sometimes received from the girls at college or people on the bus when they saw me reading it. I had so much to learn and I didn't want to waste a moment. Suddenly, my life had taken on meaning and purpose and, even in later years, when the storm-clouds once again gathered overhead, the memory of those early days remained indelible.

At the time, it was easy to believe that my hardest battles were over, but in actual fact, they were just about to begin. Wonderful though it was, accepting the Lord had been only the first step on the road to complete freedom. As time went on, He began, just as Jim had said, to reveal things that really were so well hidden I didn't know they were there. This process began roughly three months after being prayed for at Jim's.

Most of the people in the fellowship were older than me and married. The exceptions were their children, Ted, the disabled man who had secured my attention at that first meeting, and Rick and Melanie. Once again, much as I was accepted and very much loved, I began to feel the odd one out. At first, the novelty of my new relationship with the Lord had eclipsed this fact and I hadn't given it too much thought. But, after a while, just like the newly-wed couple, returning from the honeymoon, I began to settle into the down-to-earth process of actually living with Him on a daily basis. This was not to say that I felt any less excited about being a Christian, but eventually my feet touched the ground again and I began to be more aware of my surroundings. Gradually I realised that I was the only one of the group who didn't actually have "someone of my own". Even Rick and Melanie, the only others who didn't have family relations there, had each other and were planning to become engaged at some point. Of course, there was also Ted, but he always seemed so happy I simply assumed that being without a human companion was not a problem to him. However, much as I hated to admit it, it was still very much a problem to me.

Perhaps it would have been better if I had trusted those people enough to have shared it at the time, but I didn't and I couldn't. To me, it seemed as if admitting to this life-long desire would be the same as declaring that the Lord wasn't enough to meet all my needs. He had, after all, told me He loved me and the new friends I had made loved me too. In fact, although I could hardly understand it at times, it seemed as if I were surrounded by love all over the place.

This being the case, it should only be a question of time before my desire for one person who would love me in a special way disappeared. Indeed, I hoped very much that it would, for I was convinced that I had no right to think about a human companion now that I had the Lord to relate to. It was something I shouldn't even talk to Him about, I decided, and I didn't, for quite some time. But, trying to ignore the problem didn't make it disappear. Had I known then just how much of a problem it was to become, I might seriously have considered walking another way – but I didn't. Instead, I threw myself even more into my relationships with my new friends who, at times, bent over backwards to draw me in to what was happening.

Rick and Melanie put a lot of effort into making friends with me and often invited me out for coffee on Saturday mornings. At first, I had been reluctant to accept their invitations as I felt sure that three would be a crowd, but my fears were unfounded. Such was their ability to include me into their activities that I soon felt completely at ease with them (even if I *was* a little jealous of their obvious closeness).

At other times, it was Ken and Barbara that took me under their wing. Their children had grown up and married and the couple now devoted their time to running a small retail nursery garden, not far from Albert Avenue. When I wasn't out with Rick and Melanie, I would quite often drop in on them and talk for hours across the potting bench about anything and (almost) everything. After only a short while, we had become close friends. For this reason I was a little saddened to learn that they nursed a secret longing to become missionaries in South America (to whom, I wasn't quite sure, but they were very definite about the whole thing). They were now just waiting for the right time to go, but I had grown so fond of them that I secretly hoped such a time would never come.

Of all the Elders, Derek still remained my favourite. He was a sweet, fatherly man, in his early seventies, who had lost his wife to cancer several years ago. I watched him

121

closely for some trace of bitterness or resentment, but found none. My heart warmed to him greatly and he was to become a great friend and counsellor to me in future years.

Jim, on the other hand, was a different story altogether. If I was honest, he frightened me just a little and I was quite relieved to learn that he produced this reaction in most people who didn't know him well. He was a man of few words, but the words he did speak were weighty and powerful and always seemed to hit the target head on. By day, he was a self-employed accountant, working from home, with a particular emphasis on helping small businesses. When Ken and Barbara had found his name in a local directory as a possible keeper of their nursery accounts, it had been the start of a most significant and sovereignly-appointed relationship. Indeed, Jim and Ken spent a lot of time together, discussing the books – only the "books" usually turned out to be two well-worn Bibles, a Greek lexicon and a large Strong's Concordance.

Jim was a man whose strength and stability I coveted greatly, although I felt certain that he must have been through some severe storms in order to have gained such serenity. But, much as I would have liked to, it was unthinkable that I should ever pry into the inner dealings of this very private man. Time and circumstance were to confirm, soon enough, that my suspicions had been correct. In the light of the nervousness he often aroused in me, I would never have believed then just how close I would eventually become to him and his family. For the time being I treated him with careful respect and was always on my best behaviour whenever he was around.

Gradually, I watched myself open up to the Lord and this small group of people, like a tightly-closed bud, slowly unfolding in response to the sun's warm rays. Indeed, I would sometimes surprise myself at some of the things I shared, things which in times past, I would only have ever talked to Ben about. One instance opened up a very significant conversation that was to hold great relevance in years to come. It happened one day when I had gone to visit Ted in the nursing home where he lived.

Even though I had begun to make steady progress since the get-together at Jim's house, I still experienced down days quite often and it was then that Ted was a constant source of inspiration and strength to me. He wasn't an up-front, easily noticed person, with a colourful ministry and eloquent speaking abilities. In fact, he was so quiet it was easy to just walk past him without even noticing that he was there. I discovered, however, that underneath the fragile, deteriorating body that housed his spirit, there was a powerful man of God. His very presence was able to lift me out of my depression and point me to a bright hope, not dependent on circumstance and situation, but dependent only upon Him who had proved Himself faithful from time immemorial.

As I got to know Ted, I discovered that his physical ailments were far worse than I had at first imagined. He was compelled to live in the nursing home, almost totally dependent on those around him. Constant bouts of illness and frequent spells in hospital had prevented him from forming any lasting relationships. For this reason he had never married and had no other surviving relatives. With this in mind, I often wondered, whilst watching him in meetings and seeing his face literally light up with radiant joy, how he could possess such peace and freedom of spirit in the midst of such obvious suffering.

"If I were in your position," I declared candidly on the afternoon of my visit, "I think I would have become very bitter and angry at God for allowing me to suffer the way you have." It was a statement, but Ted, shrewd as ever, readily perceived the question it contained.

"Well," he said, smiling, "underneath this decaying shell, I'm a human being, the same as you, Lindsey, and I *was* bitter, for quite some time." Ted? Bitter? It seemed unthinkable.

"You were?" I asked incredulously. "How did you get over it?"

He leaned back in his chair until the sunlight streaming through the window caught the lenses of his thick, blue spectacles, making them sparkle like sapphires, and began to tell me the most touching story I had ever heard. As he spoke of years of bitter anguish and pleading with God to heal him, I began to recognise myself in the emotions he described. Of course, I had never shouted at God the way Ted said he had done, but I had been just as angry about things that had happened to me. Perhaps I had been able to hide from this fact because my way of coping with it had been to close in and become quiet and perhaps I had fooled myself into thinking that I had actually maintained a fairly balanced attitude about things. Now, however, as Ted continued his story and it became obvious that his own anger had been dealt with, I wondered if I had ever really given this emotion over to the Lord. After a while, Ted paused in his recital and I was eager to get at the key of his own deliverance.

"So what then?" I asked. "Did you just stop being angry?"

"Oh, no, Lindsey. There was a very important step I had to take before my attitude changed." I leaned forward, resting my chin in my hands and listened even more intently. Why it all seemed so important, I wasn't quite sure, but I felt almost as if I were storing up provisions to take with me on a long journey and that I would, in the future, need every ounce of encouragement that I could carry.

"What was that?" I asked eagerly.

"Acceptance, Lindsey. I made the deliberate decision to accept all that was happening to me from the Lord." I listened to his answer in stunned silence. Somehow it all seemed too obvious, too nice, too easy. Fleetingly I remembered my experience of salvation that Friday night in my room. In order to have a new beginning, all I had been required to do was to accept the Lord into my life. Could it be that this simple principle applied to any aspect of my life that still needed to be made "new"? But even as I pondered the question, I still wasn't totally convinced and decided to convey my feelings as tactfully as possible.

"And did it really make any difference?" I asked as unsuspiciously as I could. Ted's smile widened and that familiar glow spread over his face.

"Oh yes, it was like giving up after years of fighting. I realised then that I didn't have to protect myself any more. Of course, I didn't actually have any answers, and the situation didn't change – except for the worse later on. But *I* changed, Lindsey. Taking that simple step was like being set free from myself at last."

I felt my brow furrow in confusion as I listened to his unbelievable declaration, unable to accept all its implications. Even as I struggled to grasp them, I realised that here, indeed, was a "whole" man, one who was completely healed on the inside and who seemed invincible. As I listened to his story, I longed to possess the same qualities that he did, but was unsure whether I wanted to pay the necessary price to obtain them. The opportunity of finding out, however, was to present itself soon enough. The price required of me would not even scratch the surface of Ted's sufferings nor those of many of the other people I would come to know, but to me, it would seem like everything. For the time being, however, I allowed myself to be encouraged by this man's wonderful testimony, unconsciously storing it away for the time to come.

"Phew, I'm exhausted!" I puffed as we sat down at a small table by the window.

"At your age! You ought to be ashamed of yourself. Wait till you get to my age, then you can talk about being exhausted!"

I picked up the menu and laughed. "What are you having, Sally?"

"Salad," she replied, wrinkling her nose. "I'm on a diet – again!"

"What on earth for?" I asked in surprise. "You look great as you are."

"Try telling Jim that," she replied drily.

"He thinks you're overweight?" I gasped, hardly able to believe that this deeply spiritual man could be at all concerned about such trivial aspects of life. Sally smiled.

"No, he's very good really, but sometimes he wants to buy me something really nice to wear and it's tight in all the wrong places. It's my idea to lose weight, but he's in agreement with me."

"He's very strange," I said, studying the menu and then looked up at her quickly. "But nice as well."

"Yes," she smiled. "I wouldn't swap him for the world." She picked up her menu and shot me a mischievous grin over the top of it. "Mind you, those delicious Danish pastries might provide some reasonable competition." We both laughed as the waitress approached and set about ordering our lunch.

It was one of my many shopping trips with Sally who, although much older than me, was rapidly becoming a firm friend. Her easy-going, unaffected attitude had made it very easy for me to open up to her and as we had lunch together, I was excitedly telling her about my studies.

Since becoming a Christian, the fact that a change had taken place had become increasingly apparent at college. The girls often remarked on how well I looked and even Mrs McNeil seemed somewhat surprised by the marked improvement in my work. In the end, her curiosity had got the better of her and she decided to confront me about it one Friday morning.

We were just about to disperse for lunch when she called me over to her desk. In her hand were the papers I had just typed and my mind flashed back to the unfortunate incident that had taken place the previous year. I shuddered slightly as I made my way towards her and wondered if a possible re-play were in store. The other girls, obviously wondering the same thing, seemed to be hanging around much longer than usual and it was quite a few minutes before the last straggler had eventually departed. At last, we were alone and I wondered anxiously what stupid mistake in my work was about to be revealed. As I awaited the onslaught, I couldn't help noticing that Mrs McNeil, usually calm and collected, now seemed unusually awkward and fidgety. After a few moments of embarrassing silence, she removed her glasses and began to fold the arms in and out, like demented wind-screen wipers, until I felt sure they would very soon snap off in her hands. Eventually, the wipers slowed down and the question tumbled out of her lips.

"I've become a Christian," I replied simply, which had the effect of starting up the wipers again in an even more demented fashion than before. After an even longer time, they came to rest completely and she looked up at me with an admiring smile. Then, in a rather reverent tone for a college lecturer, she advised me that it was "wonderful" and had made such a difference to my work. I breathed a sigh of relief as we embarked upon a light and pleasant conversation during which I apologised for my rather unsavoury behaviour during the previous year. This was accepted most graciously and from that day forward, it seemed as if I couldn't have put a foot wrong, even if I had tried.

"The thing is," I informed Sally, "she's now being so nice to me, it's almost irritating."

"So things are looking up then?" she laughed.

I nodded. "Yes, but mind you, they'd got so bad the only direction they *could* have gone in was up!"

Sally's remark had been an understatement, to say the least. Not only had my work improved dramatically, but my former, ambitious streak had returned with an even greater vengeance than before. Life had, once again, taken on purpose and meaning and the idea of becoming a court reporter began to fill my vision once more. During those dark, depressing days, prior to my conversion, I had almost given up the idea and begun to believe that it was, after all, an unobtainable goal. Now, however, it seemed to be within grasping distance at last and I pursued my ambition with all the energy I possessed. My diligence had, in a very short space of time, been rewarded and I had been selected, along with only four of the other girls, to take my higher speed shorthand exam much earlier than the rest of the class.

"The average speed is between eighty and one hundred words per minute," I explained to Sally. "But you need to be able to write at one hundred and forty just to take the entrance exam for court reporting."

"So what's your speed now, then?"

"Well, I've just passed the hundred and thirty, so the next one's the really big one – the deciding factor if you like." Sally looked thoughtful as she picked unenthusiastically at her salad.

"When I've got this one out of the way, the five of us have got a special time-table and we're going to really home in on the other subjects because you need good passes in them as well," I continued, trying hard to regain her waning attention, but she didn't look up. "So it's really important to pass this one in a fortnight's time," I finished flatly upon realising that the salad had, after all, proved to be more enthralling. Sally finished crunching her way through a raw carrot stick and then looked up at me.

"So what happens if you don't pass?" she asked. I pursed my lips and thought for a moment. Since things had begun to change, I had never entertained the thought of failure, although, in the back of my mind, I had always known it was a possibility.

"Well," I replied cautiously. "I suppose I could take it again with the other girls, but they won't be up to it for another six months and I doubt they'd organise an exam just for me." Sally sipped her black, unsweetened coffee and let me continue without making any response. It was at times like this, I reflected, that she reminded me very much of Jim.

"Anyway, I'd want to get on with our special time-table for the other subjects, so I think I'd rather take it later anyway."

Sally looked dissatisfied. "No, what I really meant was, what if you don't pass it at all, not even in six months time?"

I cupped my hands round my coffee cup and looked down, wondering why she had to have such a negative attitude about the whole affair. "Well, I suppose . . . well, actually, I hadn't thought about not passing. There's no reason why I shouldn't, so . . . "

She smiled, just a little. "So you've really set your heart on being a shorthand court reporter?"

"Yes, I decided on it years ago, ever since I got a teenage crush on Perry Mason and watched every one of his courtroom dramas." To my great relief, she laughed.

"I'm more of a Columbo fan myself, but don't tell Jim." We both laughed for a moment and then became simultaneously serious.

"Actually, Sally," I said quietly, "it really means a lot to me. I've never been so sure about anything in my life before and I really *must* pass this exam – preferably first time."

"But there must be other things you can do if you

don't pass," she replied, with a definite note of concern in her voice. I wrinkled my nose at the prospect and tried to shrug her comment off.

"I'm sure there are, but I'm not really interested in anything else and I'm sure the Lord's going to help me through it." But in spite of my efforts to sound convincing, I was acutely aware that my definite attitude had failed to erase the look of concern from her face.

"Well, just be open, that's all," she said as we got up to go. "He may have something else lined up for you, Lindsey."

As we left the café with our laden bags, I felt uneasy. Sally had seemed definitely concerned about my choice of career and I half wondered if I ought to tackle her further about it. On the other hand, things had never looked so good. Mrs McNeil was bending over backwards to be nice to me, my work had improved beyond all recognition and I couldn't afford to spoil it all by thinking about failing now.

Sally was an expert at knowing when and how to subtly change the subject and did so with great skill as we strapped ourselves into her red Cortina. By the time she dropped me off in Albert Avenue, our earlier conversation was almost completely forgotten and we were in stitches over some tale she had recounted about Jessica's antics at school. I waved her off cheerily and we parted as good friends, but as I mounted the stairs to my room, my earlier feelings of uneasiness returned. On the surface, there was nothing detrimental about the course I had chosen. It was a respectable enough career and I felt sure I would never have attained such a high speed if it wasn't the Lord's will for my life. Everything I could see indicated that I must be on the right track, but this made me wonder all the more why it was that I felt less than total peace about the whole thing.

That evening, I sat for quite some time, aimlessly strumming my guitar. This was something I usually did whenever I was in a contemplative mood, but tonight, no words accompanied my music. Instead, my fingers strayed into minor chords and melancholic strains of songs recently replaced by the choruses we sang at our meetings. The latter were full of positive, lively hope and carried a message of life. The former were the sad and doleful songs I had listened to back at the farm and their message was of shattered dreams and broken relationships. As I continued to play, the hollow music struck at the minor chord still hidden in my otherwise melodious life. I had kept it so carefully concealed and blended skilfully into the cheerful, major chords that rung out on every side. But every so often, my circumstances were arranged in such a way that the discord became glaringly apparent.

Slowly and reluctantly, I admitted to myself the truth that I would never have admitted to Sally, or anyone else for that matter. To all intents and purposes, everything was going my way at last. My life-long ambition seemed to be materialising, I was feeling more confident about life than ever before, and I should have been completely happy – but I wasn't. Although it worried me to admit it, that familiar dull pain was still there. Underneath it all, I was still lonely, just as the sad singer had been. Of course, the Lord had, to some extent, relieved this problem, but there were certain limitations to my relationship with him. Sometimes, I wanted to actually *feel* a comforting arm around my shoulder, or to have a physical person to turn to, especially on the days when the Lord seemed so very far away. If I were honest, there were times when I wondered if this Supreme Being really was enough to meet my emotional and physical needs. Often I remembered that night at the farm when I had identified this feeling for the first time. I had been convinced then that the answer lay in finding a husband and I wasn't any less convinced of this now. Indeed, as I entered my twenties, the thought of getting married began to completely dominate my thinking. Throughout my teens, I had always managed to push it away, telling myself that I was still quite young and that there was plenty of time for it to happen. Also, since becoming a Christian, I had realised that a lot of inner

131

healing needed to take place before I was ready for such a responsible relationship. But, now that I was getting older, the thought of marriage became more persistent than ever before. The way I saw it, I had gained considerable ground in being able to take down defences and open myself up to others. In view of this, surely it was high time that the Lord sent Mr Right in my direction. But the more time went on, the more it seemed that, for me, Mr Right didn't exist.

As this realisation grew stronger, I became aware of yet another familiar emotion. It was one that I had only considered briefly since my conversion, during my conversation with Ted, and one that I was certain had disappeared – but it hadn't. Although I tried not to admit to this feeling either, it soon became obvious (if only to myself) that I was angry. Furthermore, I wasn't just slightly angry, or even moderately angry, I was blazing mad! God, I told myself, was just like Mum. She hadn't let me have a boyfriend, and now neither would He! In the first instance I had solved the problem by running away, but how, I wondered did one "run away" from a sovereign, omnipresent God? Realising that I was no better off in this respect than when I had lived at the farm, my first instinct was to pout and stamp my foot at God and tell Him it wasn't fair, just as I had wanted to tell Mum all those years ago. Why *couldn't* I have what I wanted? Why didn't He trust me the way He trusted Rick and Melanie and the other couples I knew? Why was He so determined to withhold from me the very relationship that might meet my deepest need? But one wasn't supposed to speak to God like that, I told myself. I had no right to feel the way I did, but I had to do *something*. I couldn't just sit around and become swallowed up in black depression like I used to. In the end, it was once again my studies and ambition that I turned to in order to hide from the problem. Every spare minute I had was spent in frantic study, practising those nonsensical squiggles until I almost saw them in the air as people spoke. But, try as I did to keep them at bay, my inner feelings still managed to push their way through all my activity whenever I slowed down the pace, even for a few moments. One Saturday afternoon, I became aware of how dangerously near the surface they actually were.

I was sitting in my room, practising shorthand as usual when a noise outside distracted my attention. Actually glad of an excuse to stop writing for a moment, I put down my pencil and walked over to the window to see what it was. As I drew back the curtain, I saw a small, speckled bird on the slate roof, standing with its head pointing upwards, chirping a shrill, bird-like song. I smiled faintly as it jerked its round little head from side to side and its small eyes sparkled like black beads in the sunlight. After a few moments, its performance was rewarded and a similar bird landed on the slate next to it. They regarded each other with some suspicion for a few moments and then, obviously convinced of each other's credibility, they took off together, both picking up the same shrill refrain.

I turned away and sat down again, feeling suddenly weary. Resting my head in my hands, I tried valiantly to come to terms with the mixed emotions that clamoured for my attention. Again I reminded myself of what the Lord had done for me. I had a whole new life, a Friend that was always there whenever I needed Him, and people who loved me more than I felt I should have been loved at times. But now it no longer seemed enough. For some reason, I felt my life would never really seem complete unless I had another person to share it with. I pushed back my hair and sighed as my thoughts returned to the little bird and its mate and then to the couples in the fellowship, finally alighting upon Rick and Melanie.

We still spent a considerable amount of time together, but now there was a difference. One Sunday evening, they had surprised us all by announcing that they had become engaged. I had tried my hardest to appear as happy as all the others, but the event had unpleasant implications for me. From that moment forward, it was as if some kind of invisible barrier had been erected between us. Although they still invited me to go out with them it seemed as if they could now think and speak of little other than their future life together as husband and wife. During our weekend trips into town, they would invariably gravitate towards estate agents' windows and furniture shops and begin animated discussions about their future dwelling. Fairly soon, it became obvious that I was not an important factor in these discussions and I often ended up wishing I had declined their offer of a morning out. At other times, they would join hands as we walked, whilst I pretended not to have noticed and became engrossed with the paving-slabs at our feet.

As I watched them and the other couples in the fellowship, the desire that I had tried so hard to conceal began to surface more intensely than ever before. Now, more than ever, I longed to find that person with whom I, too, could share my life in a deep and intimate way. Of course, this was possible to some extent with the people at the fellowship, but it did have its limitations. Hospitable though they were, I sometimes almost felt as if I were some kind of extra, something tagged on to the end of their own private, family lives. This seemed especially true whenever I would call round to see them, only to find that they had gone out together, just as a family, and I would return to my room feeling even more lonely and isolated than before.

On several occasions, I came close to sharing my feelings with one of the Elders who had been so much help to me in the past, but my growing conviction that a Christian had no right to feel lonely made me even more determined to keep it all to myself. In any case, if I did share it all with them, there was no telling what their reactions might be. Maybe they would want to back off, or perhaps doubt that I had a genuine relationship with the Lord. Worse still, they might start to pity me, just as I had always feared people would, and I wouldn't stand for that! Now, as the conversation with Sally returned to my mind, I could hide from the truth no longer. My ambition was all I had to hold on to. This, at least, was one thing to which the Lord seemed to be giving a nod of approval. At least I could have *something* that I really wanted and no one, not even the Lord, was going to take it away from me! Even if I *was* still lonely underneath it all, I could take comfort in the fact that I would one day be a glamorous shorthand court reporter. Then I would be certain to meet Mr Right at some point during my wonderful career.

As the days preceding my exam dropped away with alarming speed, the thought of passing it completely took over my mind. I spoke of little else and spent every spare minute revising. Sometimes I would even bring a shorthand book to the meetings and study the outlines before the singing began. I was vaguely aware that this was causing some concern to the people there, but assured myself that they were only worried that I shouldn't overdo things. Occasionally, however, some of them would voice their concern as nicely as possible.

"Remember the Lord *could* have something else lined up for you, Lindsey," they would comment.

"I know," I would always reply confidently. "I'm sure I could hear Him say it if He wanted to, but I'm also sure that this is what He wants me to do."

Sensing my stubborn determination, they usually let the matter drop, but I knew, deep down inside, that they hadn't been really convinced about my "open" attitude. Alarm bells were ringing all around me, but I deliberately refused to listen to any of them. And as for taking their advice actually to *pray* about the matter, it was unthinkable. I had plotted my course perfectly and I wasn't going to risk hearing anything from the Lord (or anyone else) that might change my direction now. Accepting Him as Lord of my life was one thing, but allowing Him to exercise His Lordship, when it cut across what I wanted to do, well, that was quite another!

The exam was scheduled for Monday morning and, the preceding Sunday evening, Jim concluded the meeting by calling me up to the front. I wondered nervously what was about to happen and was overjoyed, at least initially, by what he did.

"Well, I expect we're all aware that Lindsey's taking an important exam tomorrow," he announced, with just a hint of humour in his voice. Sniggers rose from all sides of the room. I had made such a song and dance about the event that it would have been impossible for *anyone* not to know about it. When the laughter had subsided, Jim laid a hand on my shoulder.

"We want to pray for you, Lindsey, that the Lord will have His way with your life." As he spoke, my heart sank just a little. That kind of prayer seemed a little too noncommittal. Couldn't we pray for me to pass the exam? That would make more sense! But, much as I would have liked to voice my opinion I realised that this would probably not be the best thing to do. Instead, I nodded graciously, assuring myself that at least *some* prayer was better than no prayer at all.

Jim was joined by the whole congregation in praying that I would allow God's will to be done in my life. I added my Amen rather cautiously and then shrugged the whole thing off and continued to contemplate the wonderful career that I had already decided would soon be mine.

— 12 —

The following morning, my sleep was rudely interrupted by the jangling ring of my alarm clock going off an hour earlier than it should have done. I shook my head, wondering what could have caused such an unwelcome disruption of my unvaried routine when suddenly I remembered. It was "the day" and, in my eagerness to make sure nothing went wrong at the last minute, I had re-set the alarm the night before. This sudden realisation was enough to propel me out of bed, in and out of the shower and into my clothes in record time. After dragging a comb quickly through my dripping hair, I searched hurriedly in the cupboard for a tin of ham. Not that I felt hungry. I was already so wound up that the thought of eating was quite abhorrent. Nevertheless, I knew I would feel hungry by lunchtime and sensibly decided to arm myself with suitable provisions.

Having found the required tin, I broke off the key attached to the underside and tried to push it under the small, metal flap. It had been some time since I had bought this type of meat, because it was such an effort to get inside the tin. This was difficult enough at the best of times, but this morning, it seemed to be even more than usually unco-operative. Only after three attempts was I able to lift the flap and thread it through the key's minute eye. Heaving a sigh of relief, I began to unwind the slim, metal strip. At the same time, I glanced furtively round the room, making sure everything was in order and that all my books were ready to be gathered up as soon as I wanted to leave.

Just as everything was going according to plan, the key suddenly refused to move. I had been winding the metal

137

strip around it helter-skelter fashion and it was now immoveably lodged. Extremely annoyed, I fumbled clumsily with the offending article but seemed to have acquired too many fingers and not enough thumbs and eventually I lost my grip completely. The rebellious little tin performed a perfect backward somersault, inflicting a deep gash upon my right thumb before bouncing to the floor in defiance. I gasped in horror as blood began to seep out from the cut and the impending exam surged into my mind. A moment later, as I held my thumb under the tap, the familiar words sprang to my mind.

"He may have something else lined up for you, Lindsey."

The minutes ticked away far too quickly as I ran the tap and tried to take in what was happening. Anger and self-pity spun round inside me until I could contain my feelings no longer.

"Why, Lord?" I demanded angrily. "Why did this have to happen now?"

Without waiting for Him to answer, or for my thumb to stop bleeding properly, I dried it quickly and applied generous amounts of sticking plaster. My earlier self-pity was rapidly replaced by defiance and determination. I hadn't come so far and worked so hard, only to be turned back at the last minute. I was going to take the exam that morning, if it was the last thing I did! I quickly finished making my sandwiches, ignoring the bright red stain slowly spreading under the plaster I had just applied and dashed out of the room, just in time to catch my usual bus. As I sat down and glanced at my watch, I realised that I had gained nothing by setting the alarm early and by the time I reached college, I felt as if I hadn't slept for a week. This feeling was obviously reflected in my appearance, judging by the comment I received upon entering the classroom.

"Couldn't sleep last night then?" asked Jane as I pushed through the door. I managed a tired smile as I slapped my books on my desk, but winced suddenly as they squashed my thumb. Jane became a little more concerned.

"Hey, what's up, Lindsey?" she asked anxiously. "Are you okay?"

"Oh . . . er . . . yeah, I'm okay, it's only . . . " Suddenly she noticed my plaster and gasped in surprise.

"What have you done to your thumb?"

"Oh, it's okay really," I answered as casually as I could. "I just cut it a bit, that's all." Just then, Mrs McNeil entered the room and I hurriedly hid my hand under my desk.

"Well, girls, are we all ready then?" she asked brightly. A general murmur of confidence went up from the five pioneers of the one hundred and forty exam as the others looked on with mixed expressions of jealousy and relief that they weren't in our position.

"Right, in that case," continued Mrs McNeil, "let's start with a little speed test at one hundred and forty."

I flipped open my pad and precariously balanced my pencil in the least painful position that I could find. But as I began to take down the passage, it was impossible to ignore the stinging pain in my thumb. Mrs McNeil had gone "walkabout", as was her wont when she dictated passages, and had come to rest just in front of my desk. I turned alternately hot and cold as her voice wavered just slightly and I realised that she was watching me with considerable concern. Gradually, my well-practised outlines turned into nonsensical gibberish until I finally ground to a halt and put down my pencil. Mrs McNeil's voice slowly trailed off and I looked up at her in defeat.

"Lindsey, what *have* you done to yourself?" she gasped. I sucked in my cheeks and drew a deep breath as the awful truth dawned on me.

"I . . . I cut my thumb this morning," I replied in a carefully controlled voice. "I don't think I'll be able to . . . " She looked as upset as I felt and was so sympathetic that I wondered why I had ever disliked her.

"I'm so sorry for you, Lindsey," she began, "but look, don't worry too much about it, dear. You can take it next time." I drew another deep breath and nodded slowly.

139

"Why don't you go and have a cup of coffee and think about it," she continued. "Maybe we can arrange something later on." I quietly gathered up my books, doing my best to remain composed.

"Okay, I think I'll do that," I replied, as steadily as I could. "I don't think I'm going to get much writing done, so I might as well." She nodded and smiled sympathetically.

"Very good, dear. Come back and see me at three o'clock and we'll talk about it then." I nodded and made my way towards the door, turning briefly to look at the other four girls.

"Good luck," I said, as sincerely as I could, and then pushed through the door and found myself alone in the corridor.

Numb with disappointment, I made my way slowly across the forecourt to the refectory, wondering why it had all had to go so wrong, just when things had begun to look up so dramatically. Once again, the frequent admonishment of those around me returned to my mind and I wondered if they had been right after all. Maybe the Lord had allowed me to cut my thumb because He really did have something else lined up for me. But I didn't care, I thought angrily, and I didn't want to know about it, even if He did!

Totally engulfed in self-pity, I sat down at a table by the window and absent-mindedly stirred my coffee. In contrast to my inner turmoil, the world outside looked calm and peaceful. The green, grass verges, backed by the clear, blue sky, reminded me a little of my life at the farm and I sighed wistfully. Life had somehow been so uncomplicated then. Shut up in my own little world, with my music and dear old Ben, I had hardly had to think for myself at all. But now it seemed that with age had come responsibility and life had become an ever-changing kaleidoscope of activity and decision. Just when it seemed the pieces had settled into some pleasant semblance of order, the slightest touch of some Sovereign hand would knock them all out of line again and leave me reeling in confusion.

140

Sipping my coffee, I mulled over the possible solutions to my present dilemma. It would probably not be considered a good idea to set up an exam just for me as one had already been set for the other girls at a later date. In any case, even if it could be done, I had been very much looking forward to the new time-table that had been set up for the five of us. If I did try to take the exam earlier, it would mean . . .

"Anyone sitting here?" an unfamiliar voice interrupted my thoughts. I looked up to see a tall young man, smiling down at me and indicating the chair opposite mine. I studied it for a few seconds and then smiled back.

"I don't think so," I replied humorously. The stranger laughed and put down his files.

"In that case, mind if I join you?" I certainly didn't as he seemed very amiable and had a rather interesting twang to his voice.

"American," he replied when I questioned him about it.

"Really? Which part?"

"Texas," he smiled. "Ever been?" I shook my head.

"No, but it always looks good on these TV westerns," I laughed, quite forgetting my predicament.

"Well, maybe you should go some day. But your accent isn't local either, is it?"

I had, by this time, become quite an expert at handling this most familiar of questions and had formulated a well-rehearsed, stereotyped answer. It supplied just enough information to dispense with the need for any further questions without being dismissive. This time, however, my carefully-constructed speech flew out of the window and I felt quite flattered that he should show such interest in a total stranger. Before I knew it, I was eagerly telling him of the little town on the south coast where I was born and he listened so intently that I suddenly became embarrassed and stopped speaking. To my great relief, he short-circuited the awkward silence and stepped gallantly into the breach.

"See you don't have your books today," he drawled. I frowned slightly, sensing that the comment was supposed to hold some significance, but I couldn't, for the life of me, think what it was.

"Books?" I replied helplessly.

"Yes," he smiled. "Last time I spoke to you, you seemed to be very attached to them." Suddenly, the penny dropped and I recognised him as the young man who had spoken to me in the corridor during my days of dismal depression. I laughed, mainly with embarrassment, as I recalled the incident.

"Oh yes, I remember you now," I smiled. "You'll be glad to know that I'm not quite so attached to them any more." We both laughed and then he became a little more serious.

"Made many friends since you moved up here?" he asked as he stirred his coffee.

"Yes, I've got quite a few at the church I go to." He looked up, quite obviously surprised, and then smiled.

"Like some more coffee?" he asked pleasantly. I nodded eagerly and stole a sideways glance at him as he joined the queue at the counter, thinking what a nice person he was. A few minutes later, he returned with two cups of steaming coffee and resumed his seat.

"So what's your name?" he asked, stirring his coffee once again.

"Lindsey."

"I'm Hal," he smiled and proceeded to tell me about the course he was taking. Immediately, I was struck by how easily he talked and also by how relaxed I felt with him. I found myself smiling and laughing as he described some humorous incidents that had recently occurred during his lectures and completely forgot my earlier predicament. After some time, he glanced at his watch and looked a little surprised.

"Hey, I got so carried away there," he smiled. "I'm almost late for my next lecture." He quickly picked up his files and stood up.

"Well, so long, Lindsey. See you again some time."

"Yes," I replied sincerely. "And thanks for the coffee."

"It was a pleasure," he smiled and then swung out of the doors, leaving me floating on a sweet, fluffy cloud.

At three o'clock, I sat opposite Mrs McNeil in a deserted classroom, kicking around vague ideas of how to plot my next course of action.

"We could set up an exam just for you," she advised. "But it would be a lot easier if you don't mind waiting to take it with the other girls." I pursed my lips and thought hard. I still wanted to concentrate on the other subjects with the other four girls, aware of my need of a slight undertone of friendly competition to spur me on to obtaining good results. Also, we had already begun our special time-table and I knew I would feel badly about not being there at the same time as them.

"Well, I think I'd be happy to wait and take it at the end of the course with the others," I replied at length.

"That's fine, Lindsey," she smiled. "I'll put you in for it in about six months' time then."

That evening, I sat on the bus home, trying to make sense of how I felt. I should have been depressed. Indeed, I *had* been, and quite angry too. But I didn't feel like that now. Instead, I felt happy and somehow certain that everything was going to work out all right. At first, I thought I must have taken a massive leap in faith and that my joy was a product of trusting the Lord, but the longer I thought about it, the more it became apparent where my sense of well-being had come from. It had started as I was talking to the charming American in the college refectory. For just a little while, he had made me forget my disappointment and I had felt good ever since. As my mind drifted back to our brief and pleasant encounter, I found myself very much hoping that I would see him again.

On Thursday evening, I arrived at the youth club with my inner joy still very much apparent.

"So you think you've passed then?" asked Melanie, basing her assumption on my radiant smile, but, much to her surprise, I shook my head.

"No, I didn't even get as far as the exam room." Her eyes widened and a look of deep confusion crossed her face.

"You didn't? So why are you so happy about it?" I shrugged my shoulders, still smiling.

"Well, I can take it later on. Mrs McNeil has put me down for the next one in six months' time." She still seemed rather astonished at my ready acceptance of what should have been a devastating disappointment, but managed to make a suitable reply.

"Oh, I see," she smiled. "Well, that's okay then." For a moment I wondered if I should tell her about my chance encounter with Hal, but decided that there was nothing to tell anyway and began to help with stacking up the chairs. Once this task was completed, I slipped out and waited in the back of Ken's car whilst he and Barbara did a final check round and locked the main door. As I waited for them to arrive, I peered through the side window and noticed the familiar outline of Rick and Melanie, walking hand in hand down the long, tree-lined driveway. Usually, I felt quite jealous of this touching scene, but tonight, for some reason, it didn't seem to matter.

Over the weeks that followed, my wish came true and I did see the out-going American again. Sometimes we had lunch together, or just happened to meet up in the canteen during free lectures and would sit laughing and chatting over steaming cups of abysmal college coffee. Whenever this happened, I couldn't help noticing how happy I felt, but there was only one problem. The more I saw him, the more I wanted to see him, and no matter how much time we spent together, it never seemed quite long enough. Hal, I concluded, was another person who stirred up in me conflicting emotions, but not quite in the same way that Uncle Tom, or even Jesus had. Whenever I was with him, I felt like the happiest girl in the world, but when he wasn't there, I felt gloomy and, for some reason, quite sad. Since meeting him, it seemed as if all my emotions had been tipped out of their tightly-sealed container and then been quickly bundled back in completely the wrong order. Wherever I went, he was always on my mind and eventually, I became convinced that he was the special "someone" I had wanted for so long.

Actually, it was quite obvious, I told myself one day. This must be the "something else" that everyone seemed so certain the Lord had lined up for me. He must have allowed me to cut my thumb just so that I could meet Hal in the refectory. The more I thought about it, the more I convinced myself that this very charming young man must be the Lord's answer to the secret desire I had shared only with Ben, so long ago. Having assured myself that the whole thing must be "of the Lord", I made no attempt to stop myself thinking about him, or believing that it was all going to work out just as I had hoped. But then, when I stopped to examine the situation more closely, I was suddenly grounded. Hal hadn't actually asked me out yet, I reminded myself. There was no guarantee that he wanted anything more than a platonic friendship and, even if he did, there was one thing about him that was a point of major concern – he wasn't a Christian. Neither did it seem, from our conversations so far, that he had any interest in becoming one.

Had it been anyone else, I would, by now, have told them all about my spiritual convictions, but for some reason, I

145

just couldn't tell him. I reflected that it had been easier, by far, to confront an out and out Hell's Angel with the gospel, than to tell this very charming and extremely personable individual that he was a sinner in need of salvation. But, underneath it all, my concern was not primarily for him, it was much more for myself. Although he wasn't actually "mine", I had already made up my mind that he soon would be. So far, he was the only thing that looked anywhere near like an answer to my deepest longing. As Rick and Melanie continued to plan excitedly for their wedding, the desire to have someone of my own became even more intense and that special someone, I had firmly decided, was going to be Hal. But then, I could remember so well his obvious surprise when I had confessed to the innocent crime of going to church. How on earth would he react if he knew the full story? I decided that, if he discovered just how much of a church-goer I actually was it would completely ruin my chances of a deeper relationship with him, so I kept the truth carefully concealed.

Had I stopped long enough to study the situation more closely, I might have given up my fanciful expectations there and then. Already, the whole thing was proving to be a negative influence and I was steadily losing my appetite for all things spiritual. Before meeting Hal, I had spent my spare time reading my Bible or praying. At other times, I would be at meetings, or visiting some of the folks from the fellowship. Now, all I wanted to do was be with him. Eventually, I stopped thinking about the Lord altogether and, in any case, He had recently seemed so far away that it was much easier to think about Hal – real, live Hal! After only a short while, I was totally convinced I was in love with him. Each time we met up, I found myself more and more captivated by him, but how, I wondered, did he feel about me?

There was no doubt that he liked me, perhaps even that he liked me a lot. He was definitely interested in me and listened with rapt attention to everything I had to say. But love? Did he love me, I wondered? And what if he didn't? I loved him – at least I genuinely believed I did, and I desperately wanted to tell him as much, but I couldn't, not until I knew whether or not the feeling was mutual. When I was with him, the suspense was just about bearable, but when he wasn't around, I found it very difficult to cope. This was especially true when other people made the most irritating comments.

"Where's your boyfriend today then?" asked Jane one lunchtime as I sat alone in the refectory. She had caught me on a bad day and I was feeling a little less than civil.

"He's not my boyfriend," I snapped. "We're just friends." But, try as I did to convince people that I was quite content with the relationship the way it was, inside, it was quite a different story. I didn't want us to be "just friends", I wanted more than that. It was no longer enough to be with him, I wanted to belong to him in the same way that all those women in the Fashions and Millinery department had belonged to their husbands. Furthermore, despite my childhood hatred of being touched, I now wished, more than anything, that he would touch me. I wanted to feel his arm around my shoulder and his hand in mine, but I couldn't let him know that. It was vital that I didn't let anyone know. The girls at college should only believe that we were friends and I had, so far, managed to keep him a closely-guarded secret from the folks at the fellowship. However, the day came, all too quickly, when I could keep my secret no longer. One Wednesday morning, we were just packing up for lunch when Jane and Tracy sidled over to my desk.

"Hey Lindsey," began Jane, with exaggerated casualness. "Are you ... er ... doing anything on Saturday night?" I shrugged as I stapled my papers together.

"Don't know yet," I replied vaguely.

"Fancy coming over to Rosie's then?" I stopped for a moment and then shook my head. Rosie's was a popular haunt for many of the college students and was considered one of the more romantic places to go. Knowing this made me feel quite certain that it was the one place I definitely didn't want to go.

147

"Don't think so," I said casually. There was a slight pause before she spoke again.

"Hal's going to be there," she volunteered eventually. I looked up at her quickly, wondering what I was supposed to deduce from this astounding statement.

"So?" I replied as innocently as I could.

"So you could ... er ... see him," she stammered awkwardly. Suddenly I realised that there was more to her innocent invitation than met the eye.

"Wait a minute," I said, with half a smile. "What is this, a set-up or something?" They both grinned mischievously and Jane shrugged her shoulders.

"Well, I suppose you could say that." I pursed my lips and tried to think quickly.

Over the past few days, my hopes of romantic involvement with Hal had begun to grow a little dim. Perhaps this was because he hadn't been at college for a week, but there was also that uncomfortable niggle, deep down inside, that I had been trying hard to ignore ever since our first meeting. Over the past week, I had found myself with quite a lot of time for reflection and, although I hated to admit it, the whole thing seemed to be doing me no good whatsoever. My relationship with the Lord had all but evaporated into thin air and, if I was honest, apart from the bubbly excitement I felt when I was with Hal, underneath it all, I was actually quite unhappy. By the time Tracy made her tempting invitation, I had very nearly decided to let the whole thing die a graceful death and to try and regain my spiritual appetite. Now it seemed as if it was all being stirred up again and I wasn't at all sure how to respond to this unexpected twist in the game.

"Well?" asked Tracy after some time. I looked up at her, feeling more uncertain than ever, and wondered just how this proposed set-up had been conceived. Were they setting Hal up, I wondered? They had watched our friendship with considerable interest and it would be just like them to drop him into something like this. Or, could it possibly be that Hal himself had engineered the whole thing and was at

148

last about to reveal what his own feelings were about our friendship? They were not questions I felt inclined to ask. The point was, I was being given the chance of meeting up with Hal at one of the most romantic venues in town – and there was no telling where things could go from there! I should have been excited – I had been at first – but all of a sudden, I wasn't so excited any more. I was irritated and confused and, I had to admit, quite angry. The truth was, I knew, and perhaps had always known, that the relationship I so much wanted could never be. I could never be Hal's girlfriend, even if he wanted me to be – unless, of course, he became a Christian. In my more honest moments, I had to admit that this prospect seemed highly unlikely. Aware that they were still waiting for my response, I started to gather up my books and made an attempt to appear quite laid back about the whole thing.

"Don't know, I'll have to think about it," I said casually. "I don't want him to think . . . "

"To think what?" asked Jane. I stopped for a moment and looked up at her.

"Oh, nothing," I said quickly. "I'll think about it."

That evening, I tried in vain to come to a definite decision about the event planned for Saturday night. One minute I had almost decided to put a stop to things before they actually got started, the next minute, I couldn't bear the thought of all my hopes and dreams slipping irretrievably away. After all, this could be the beginning of the one relationship I had wanted for so long, and I couldn't let it slip through my fingers, just like that! By Thursday afternoon, I had made up and changed my mind so many times that I couldn't stand the pressure any longer. When my lectures for the day were over, I took a short detour on the way home and called in at Jim and Sally's.

Why I should have chosen Jim, of all people, to share such a delicate situation with, I wasn't at all sure. Since my first visit to his house, some time ago, I had got to know him fairly well and Sally often invited me round for meals. But, even so, I still found it very difficult to talk to him about myself. Today was no exception and, as I pushed open the front gate, aware of the terrible confession I was about to make, I felt like calling the whole thing off. In spite of it all, however, I desperately wanted some answers. Jim was the most candid person I knew and was wont to lay his cards on the table, even though this sometimes cost him dearly in terms of acclaim and popularity. This, I decided, was the reason I so often did talk to him, in spite of how nervous I usually felt, and if anyone was going to give me a straight answer, it would be him.

After exchanging a few pleasantries with Sally, I found myself in the familiar black leather chair in Jim's study. For a few minutes, we discussed some trivial things that had been on my mind, but I was certain he could sense that I hadn't quite said it all.

"Well," he asked slowly, "does that answer it then?" I thought for a moment and ran my hands over the arms of my chair. They had once been decorated with large, black buttons that gathered in the folds of leather at the front, but during one conversation, I had become so intense about what I was saying, I had absent-mindedly pulled them off one after the other. Jim had seemed quite amused, but I had nearly died with embarrassment. As I remembered the incident, I stopped in mid-action and slipped my hands into my pockets for fear of doing more serious damage to the innocent chair.

"Well?" he enquired after a few moments. I drew a long, slow breath and looked up at him, unsure how to begin.

"Well, I suppose there is something else," I began cautiously.

"Oh yes?"

"But . . . well, I'm just not sure if I can say it all." Jim smiled, just slightly.

"Well, if it's bothering you that much, it's worth a try, isn't it?" he asked. All at once, my carefully controlled emotions rose to the surface and suddenly escaped before I could stop them.

"Jim, there's someone at college I think I'm in love with," I stammered in a strange, choking voice and then looked at the floor, awaiting his disapproving response. But Jim, as always, remained unruffled.

"What's wrong with that?" he asked calmly. "It's quite natural to fall in love, isn't it?" I looked up at him in surprise.

"Well, I suppose so but . . . he isn't a Christian."

Still, he remained unperturbed and waited for me to continue. Taking another deep breath, I told him of the plan for Saturday night and he listened without showing any emotion.

"Anyway," I said eventually. "I can't go . . . can I, Jim?"

As I realised the truth contained in my own words, tears suddenly came to my eyes, but I somehow managed to hold them back. Jim stared at me in silence for a few moments. This was something he frequently did when I talked to him and I often wondered what went on behind those piercing eyes during that tense, unnerving silence, though I had never felt inclined to ask.

"And would that be a question, Lindsey? Or a statement?" he asked quietly. I pursed my lips and shifted my gaze to the window, feeling suddenly angry. Now he was being deliberately evasive and not saying what I wanted him to. Why, I wondered, couldn't he find some nice, encouraging scriptures about God's ability to save even the most rebellious of characters, which, of course, would include Hal?

"I don't know," I said moodily. "Probably a bit of both I suppose." There was an even longer and more disconcerting silence before he spoke again.

"So what are you going to do about Saturday?" he asked.

"Oh, I don't know," I muttered miserably. "I just haven't got it all sorted out in my mind yet." He smiled again, even more slightly than before and then stood up.

"And therein lies a redeeming factor," he said quietly.

"I don't understand," I replied, quite truthfully.

151

"You haven't made up your mind, which, in this instance, isn't entirely a bad thing." With that, he swiftly changed the subject by inviting me to stay for tea and the conversation was over before I felt it had really begun.

On my way home that evening, I mulled over my predicament once again. Why did things always have to be so complicated for me, I wondered? Why couldn't they be easy and straight-forward, the way they were for everyone else? As I walked, I looked down at the pavement, watching the pink and grey slabs pass under my feet. I had taken it into my mind to avoid stepping on the lines in between them, just as I had as a child, hurrying along to church beside Mum. But occasionally, my step was ill-timed and they were impossible to avoid. The exercise echoed so perfectly how I felt about this most recent struggle. So far, I had managed to weave and dodge over the criss-cross lines that were so definitely drawn around me. But these were lines not manufactured by man like the ones at my feet. They were lines drawn by the Lord Himself. The perfect, symmetrical lines of the cross that He had now brought into my formerly self-governed life, and the thought of actually picking it up and following Him was becoming more and more difficult to accept.

There was, however, no escaping from that deep, inner voice that spoke with such irritating clarity as I thought the situation through that evening. If I was honest, I knew already that the relationship I wanted couldn't possibly work. Hal wasn't about to become a Christian, much as I had tried so hard to believe the opposite. But, even now, I couldn't bear to give up, just like that. I had at least to give it a try, after all, anything was possible, the Bible itself said as much! In the end, after two hours of intense, inner conflict, I decided what I was going to do. I would go along on Saturday and tell Hal everything, and if he didn't like it . . . but he *had* to like it, he just *had* to!

On Saturday evening, I sat at a small table in the corner of Rosie's romantic dance-hall with Tracy and her boyfriend, Phil, who was "in" on the set-up. I had already advised myself several times on the way there that the whole thing was quite ludicrous and that I really ought to go home. Now, as I sat in the semi-darkness, feeling slightly sick, I was more convinced than ever that I had made the wrong decision, but as I turned to tell Tracy she grabbed Phil's hand and stood up.

"We're going over to the bar, Lindsey," she said urgently. "Be back in a . . . oh, hi, Hal, want a seat?" As the familiar figure materialised in the darkness next to me, I froze. What on earth was I supposed to do now?

"Yeah, thanks," said Hal to Tracy, and I wasn't sure that Phil hadn't winked at him. Hal sat down and smiled warmly.

"Hi, Lindsey," he said brightly. "Would you like something to drink?"

"Um . . . yes, that would be nice," I said as convincingly as I could. As he disappeared into the darkness, I contemplated the daunting task that lay before me. In one short evening, I had to not only tell Hal where I stood as a Christian, but also persuade him that he needed to make a similar commitment to the Lord. If it hadn't all been so serious, I might well have laughed at the ridiculousness of the situation – but I didn't.

After a few minutes, Hal returned with two tall glasses and sat down. I thanked him and then we said nothing for several moments, just as if we were total strangers, meeting each other for the first time. Then, to my great relief, he tried his hand at breaking the ice.

"Like the music?" he asked. I thought for a moment. It was vaguely reminiscent of the music I would have played years ago at the farm and, although I hadn't listened to it since becoming a Christian, it did still have a certain amount of appeal.

"Yes, it's quite nice," I replied eventually. "But I couldn't listen to it all the time."

My comment prompted him to ask what I did like doing with my time. What, for instance, did I do in the evenings? Where did I like to go? Theatre perhaps?

Or cinema? Or just out for a walk? I managed, with some difficulty, to come up with a few reasonable possibilities, but noticed, in spite of my mission that evening, that I had carefully avoided any mention of what I actually *did* do in my spare time.

After a while, the cheerful, bouncy music was replaced by a slow, smoochy number and more couples got up and joined those already on the dance-floor. I watched with slight embarrassment as they drew their arms around each other, obviously succumbing to the romantic atmosphere for which Rosie's was so renowned. Then I realised that Hal, too, was watching the proceedings with rapt attention. Suddenly he looked at me and smiled.

"C'mon Lindsey," he said, "want to dance?" Suddenly my heart skipped a beat as I glanced at the entwined, swaying couples and realised the significance of his request. It should have been the happiest moment of my life. At last, I would be able to feel his arms around me, just as I had always wanted to and something inside me wanted immediately to respond. But I couldn't. No matter how much I wanted to, I didn't need Jim, or anyone else, to tell me it would be wrong. I knew myself, deep down inside. I simply couldn't do it, just the same as I couldn't have a boyfriend at school. Mum hadn't let me then and now God wouldn't let me! I looked up at him quickly, and then clutched at the only straw I could find.

"I . . . I think I ought to finish this first," I said, holding up my half-empty glass. He looked ever so slightly crestfallen, but managed to smile again.

"Okay," he said softly. "Maybe the next one." I lifted my glass without comment and sipped my drink as slowly as I could. A few minutes later, the record changed again, and I almost choked in horror as that unmistakeable voice echoed in the darkness all around us. The sad singer had come back, like a sinister ghost, to haunt me from the bitter past and as I listened to those forgotten words, those powerful emotions from so long ago swept over me again. Hal, oblivious to what was happening inside

154

me, noticed that my glass was empty and smiled at me again.

"Dance this one, Lindsey?" he asked softly. Suddenly, I could continue with the charade no longer and quickly looked away from the romantic couples.

"Um . . . Hal," I said shakily. "I . . . I think I ought to go home." Carefully avoiding his eyes, I bent down and picked up my bag, but his surprise was only too evident.

"Right now?" he asked. "Don't you want to stay and . . . ?"

"I really want to go home," I said quickly, before he could continue. I got up, fully intending to catch the bus home, but he insisted on taking me himself.

Feeling numb with disappointment as we drove silently through the darkened streets, I wondered why I hadn't listened to that inner voice after all. Hal, obviously still a little puzzled by my strange behaviour, did his best to appear unaffected.

"Didn't realise you had such an aversion to dancing," he said light-heartedly as we stopped at the lights. I looked down at my fingers, feeling completely condemned for making such an awful mess of things.

"I haven't," I said quietly. "I won a prize for dancing once." He glanced at me quickly before pulling away.

"In that case, you ought to take it up again," he said as we rounded the corner into Albert Avenue. I said nothing as he pulled up outside my house and switched off the engine. For a few moments I wondered if I should just apologise for my unusual behaviour and then forget the whole thing had ever happened, but before I had fully decided what to do, I realised Hal was speaking.

"Well, thanks for coming," he said a little awkwardly. "I suppose I could see you again if . . . " I looked up at him quickly before he could continue and decided it was now or never.

"Hal," I began cautiously. "Do you remember me telling you I went to church?" He shrugged his shoulders.

"Yeah, I sort of remember you mentioning it a while back," he replied casually. "But surely that doesn't mean you can't go out and have a good time, does it?"

"No, of course not, as long as . . . "

"As long as you don't dance with anyone?" he asked drily.

"No, it's not that," I replied, trying to keep my voice steady. "Of course I can dance but . . . but there are other things I can't do." He raised his eyebrows.

"Other things?"

I drew a slow breath, wondering how to continue without sounding like some kind of religious fanatic.

"I mean . . . well, for instance, I could never get involved with someone who didn't share the same convictions as I did," I volunteered eventually.

"Why not?" he asked after a short silence.

"Because it just wouldn't work. We'd always be pulling in opposite directions and making each other miserable." I paused for a moment, wondering why I didn't just tell him how I felt about him and that I couldn't care less about my "convictions". In a few weeks' time he, too, would be taking his final exams and then we would both be leaving college. If we didn't begin a relationship now, there would be no reason to see each other again. I looked up at him, hoping desperately that he was going to say something that might encourage me to continue, but I was disappointed.

"Hmm," he murmured as his brow furrowed again. "Sounds like a pretty restrictive life-style to me, not sure I could handle it."

As he spoke, my heart finally sank and any inclination I might have had to say more instantly vanished. Why, oh why hadn't I faced up to the truth before and saved myself all this heart-ache and embarrassment? It was obvious that we were worlds apart, just as Mum and Dad had been and I only wished I had admitted it sooner. After a few moments silence, Hal looked up, obviously expecting me to say more. I met his eyes for just a moment and then began to gather up my bag and coat.

"It isn't, Hal," I said quietly. "It isn't like that at all. But anyway, thanks for the lift and . . . and I'm really sorry about tonight."

He accepted my apology graciously, although I knew he would never know just how sorry I was.

"It's okay," he said quietly. "Forget it." I nodded, but said nothing. It was going to take me a long time to forget this evening.

A few minutes later, as he started up the engine, I suddenly reverted from the valiant Crusader for the truth, back to the lonely young girl, watching the embodiment of all her fondest dreams about to disappear into the darkness. All at once, I wanted to grab his arm and call him back, to tell him that I wasn't serious and that I wanted him more than anything else in the world – and even beyond it. But it was no use, and I had only made things harder for myself by not admitting it sooner.

As his car pulled away, I stood with my back against the stone pillars, watching it disappear down the road, until all I could see through my blurred vision were two tiny pinpoints of red light that suddenly turned a corner and were gone.

— 14 —

Over the next few weeks it seemed that nothing could alleviate my crippling, all-consuming loneliness. If I had felt lonely before, it was nothing compared to how I felt now. Suddenly, the world had become an empty place. Not that there were fewer people in it, but simply because none of them was the person I really wanted. I began to live in a kind of strange dream, seeing those smiling, blue eyes everywhere, and at times, almost hearing that slow, Texas drawl. But it all suddenly vanished, like a burst bubble, whenever I reached out to touch its fragile beauty. Again and again, I told myself that time would heal, but, far from becoming easier to cope with, that heavy, black mantle settled upon me more powerfully than ever before.

Of course, I knew that most people had, at some time or other, experienced the same situation, but I was convinced that no one really understood how I felt. Most of the time, I just wanted to curl up somewhere in tears, but as this feeling could come upon me at college, or in meetings, or some other similarly inconvenient place, I couldn't give in to it. Instead, I swallowed down the lump in my throat and held back the tears until I felt as if an entire ocean had accumulated behind my eyes. From somewhere way back in the past, the determination to conceal my feelings was resurrected and I hid them behind a reasonably cheerful exterior. But underneath it all, I knew only too well how many jagged emotions hovered dangerously close to the surface.

One day I walked past a poster in town, advertising a circus, and was arrested by the red-nosed, pseudo-smiling clown that leered out at me. All at once, I wanted to scratch it to shreds with my nails, for it reminded me too vividly of what a "damn good actress" I had indeed become. At the time, I just managed to control my anger, but at other times, it often got the better of me. Sometimes I would lash out and snap at people, for no reason at all, and then I would turn it inwards, telling myself what an ungrateful and useless Christian I was. And always, when I was with the couples at the fellowship, I would turn my anger towards God. After all, it was *His* fault, *He'd* done all this on purpose, and I was blazing mad at Him for doing it! But, difficult as they were, things were made infinitely worse one day as I stared at a glossy magazine in the newsagents.

Ever since walking off the stage during that live performance, the sad singer seemed to have disappeared from the present scene. There was no news of him anywhere, and any songs of his that might have been played by various DJs were his "golden oldies" from years ago. Now, as I stared at the magazine, my eyes widened in disbelief. There, staring back at me, was the man himself, although hardly recognisable as such. Throughout his career, he had always presented a very serious image to the world and a picture of him smiling was a rare possession. But the person I now studied was beaming broadly, displaying even rows of dazzling white teeth. His eyes shone brightly with some inner joy and it seemed as if he had grown ten years younger during his self-imposed exile. One didn't have to look too far, either, to see what had brought about such an amazing transformation.

There, standing beside him, was the "person in his life" that he had been searching for for so long and they were very obviously in love. I flipped open the magazine and read the article quickly, but couldn't bring myself to buy it. It was too upsetting, I thought, as I walked wearily home. Of course, I was glad that he was no longer lonely. Indeed, loneliness was something I would not have wished on my worst enemy. But that didn't help *me*. I was still lonely – more lonely than I had ever been in my life. The way I saw it, I advised the Lord that evening, was that I needed natural, human love, just as the singer had. It had completely transformed him and I was totally convinced that it would do the same for me. But the Lord, it seemed, did not share my opinion!

Eventually, in a desperate attempt to distract my mind, I once again buried myself in my studies. The final exam was only a few weeks away now and this time, it really would be final. If I failed it now, there would be no second chance. I was determined to give it all I had, in spite of everything that was going on inside. But, try as I did to hide my feelings from those around me, they were all very conscious of the struggle that I was going through. All of them were so kind and did everything they could to draw me into their lives, but this only seemed to make things worse. After all, I thought bitterly, they could be so generous and out-going because they were all married (or about to be). They wouldn't be able to do it if they were single. They would be miserable and fed up, the same as I was. And in any case, why *should* they know about it all. It was nothing to do with them. It was *my* problem and they wouldn't understand even if I did tell them about it!

So it was that I once again began to build up those invisible walls. Other people – especially married people – I decided should be held at arm's length. Of course, I would still talk to them, but only about superficial things that didn't really matter. None of them must be allowed to penetrate any deeper than the very surface of my life, but, in spite of my valiant efforts to keep them out, there was one that did. It was Derek. Why he was able to do this, I wasn't quite sure. Maybe it was because of his gentle, unobtrusive manner that continued to remind me so much of Uncle Tom. But perhaps it was also because he was, in a sense, alone himself – although I hastened to remind myself that at least he had been married once! As my lectures began to drop off one by one towards the end of the course, I found myself with several free afternoons. Many of these,

I chose to spend having afternoon tea with Derek in his small bungalow on the outskirts of town. One particular day, I had turned up feeling more than usually down and at my wit's end to know how to cope with it all.

"There we are," said Derek. "I'll pour yours first because you drink it like milky water." I managed a faint smile and hung up my coat. Then, as I brushed past the sideboard, I picked up a small picture in a silver frame.

"Is this Peggy?" I asked.

"Yes," replied Derek. "Lovely girl, isn't she?"

"Beautiful," I said, carefully replacing the delicate frame. "It must have been very difficult when . . . " My voice trailed off as I was unsure whether or not it would be right to continue.

"Yes," said Derek quietly, "it was – *very* difficult." I sat down on the sofa opposite him and gazed into my tea-cup. If anyone would understand, surely Derek would, I told myself. But still, I was unsure whether to open my heart to this sweet, fatherly man, who seemed to love me as if I was his own daughter. After a few minutes, he left the room in search of some firewood and I continued to wrestle with the thought. Apart from Jim and Sally and Rick and Melanie, I had told no one else at the fellowship about Hal. The four that did know had been sworn to secrecy because, for some strange reason, I had felt very ashamed about the whole thing. But even if I didn't let Derek in on the secret, surely I could share some of the problem with him.

Eventually, Derek returned with his arms full of small logs and began to pile them into the grate. I watched him for a moment, then suddenly decided that I simply couldn't bear the burden alone any longer. As he knelt down and stirred the glowing embers, I drew a deep breath and decided to give it a try.

"Derek?" I began cautiously.

"Yes, love?" he said, without looking up.

"Can I tell you something?"

"Of course you can," he replied warmly and returned to his seat. I folded and unfolded my hands, unsure of how to begin.

"It's just that ... that ... " Somehow, the words just wouldn't come. Derek pulled out his handkerchief and began to polish his watch, which was a habit he seemed to employ whenever he sensed that there was something I wanted to say, but was having difficulty saying it. Suddenly, I couldn't keep it to myself any longer and looked up at him in despair.

"Derek, I'm lonely," I blurted out before I could stop myself.

"Are you, love?" he asked softly.

"Yes ... I am, desperately lonely and ... and I just don't know how to cope with it." I buried my head in my hands as tears rolled steadily down my face. Before I knew it, he was sitting on the sofa next to me, with one big arm around my shoulders and the handkerchief extended in his other hand. He held on to me without saying a word and let me cry until my tears subsided.

"Well, shall we talk about it?" he asked eventually. I dried my eyes for the hundredth time and nodded. Derek was a good listener and let me pour out my tale of woe until he was certain I had said it all. Then he spoke himself.

"Well, you were right, Lindsey, it wasn't at all easy when Peggy died. I suppose I felt much the same way as you do now, completely alone – and lonely. I felt there was no one I could turn to (at least, no one that would *really* understand)." He stood up and resumed his seat whilst I curled my legs up on the sofa and settled down to listen.

"I suppose I should have been prepared for it really, because we both knew she was dying. It's funny, though," he said, with a slight laugh, "it seems that no matter how much someone prepares for something, the actual event always seems to take them by surprise." I nodded in agreement as he leaned back in his chair. Then, resting his neck against the top ridge and fixing his eyes at some point on the mantelpiece, he continued.

"She had been ill for such a long time that we had both learned to live with it in a way. Then the day came when she was committed to hospital and we both knew that she could go at any time."

"That must have been terrible," I said sincerely. Derek nodded.

"Yes, it was. But actually, it wasn't quite as bad as you might imagine. There were constant trips to the hospital, twice a day. Then, when I got home, there would be the cooking and cleaning and washing to do. By the end of the day, I was so tired I just flopped into bed and was asleep in minutes. It was quite a good thing really because it could have been the other way and I could have been awake all night worrying." He stopped for a moment and drained his tea-cup.

"It was very strange, really," he continued. "Just living one day at a time, knowing that any day could be the last. I suppose it made me grateful for even the smallest amount of time we could spend together, and some of that mentality is still with me today. You know, Lindsey," he said, with a sad shake of his head, "people spend so much time disagreeing and arguing over some trivial matter or other, when life is so short. They could just as easily spend it getting on with each other and forgiving each other. Anyway, I thought I was handling it quite well and would be all right when 'it' happened. But the day it did could not have found me more unprepared.

"I received a phonecall from the hospital, asking me to go in as soon as possible. It wasn't normal visiting hours, and so I was a bit suspicious. When I got there, the nurses all seemed more than usually solemn. Then, one by one, they left the room until we were alone, just Peggy and me. I had helped her with a drink of water and was just sitting holding her hand. We didn't even say anything, there was something special about those few moments and it seemed as if words were irrelevant. Then she squeezed my hand, just a little harder and lay back on her pillows." Derek dropped his gaze from the mantelpiece to the floor and

163

paused. Suddenly, I felt guilty, knowing that it was on my account that he was re-living such painful memories.

"Derek," I said quietly, "you really don't have to tell me the rest if . . . " He looked up and smiled, a typical, "Derek" smile.

"Don't worry about it, love. You see, there's nothing wrong with feeling sad sometimes. Goodness knows, Jesus did! But it's what you *do* with your sadness that's the important thing. Some people turn inwards and are swallowed up in self-pity. I hope neither of us ever does that, Lindsey," he said earnestly, as I tried not to flinch. "Self-pity is a deadly poison and will eat you up from the inside out. On the other hand, some people take the sorrow that they feel and allow it to make them sensitive to the hurts and griefs of those around them. Those people have never lost out and even the most painful situations have turned out to be a blessing in disguise. Did you ever talk to Ted by any chance?" I nodded as the point hit home and Derek continued.

"Well, then she took a deep breath and her grip on my hand loosened. Her head sank deeper into her pillows and I noticed that her face then was more beautiful than it had ever been since the cancer was discovered. The corners of her mouth were slightly up-turned and the peaceful expression on her face erased all the lines of pain that had been so evident over the past months. At last, the moment had come, and I didn't know what to do except hold on to her hand in silence for a while. Then I kissed her for the last time.

"I can't really describe to you how I felt then, Lindsey, except to say that it was as if I had been enjoying a pleasant walk down a pretty country lane, expecting to arrive at some beautiful destination, but suddenly bumping into a solid, brick wall, with no way round. It was the end, there was nowhere else to go, the journey was over." I bit my lip, remembering how I had felt as I had watched Hal's car suddenly turn the corner and had known that all my hopes and dreams would never be.

164

"That night, Lindsey," continued Derek, "I returned to a house that seemed more empty than it had ever been and, somehow, I knew that it would never really seem 'lived in' again. As I shut the door behind me, I felt as if someone had pulled every bone out of my body, reducing me to a quivering heap of useless flesh. I missed her so much, and felt as if a huge chasm had opened up inside me that could never be filled – but that was just the beginning.

"The weeks and months that followed were almost unbearable. I saw her face everywhere – her smiling face. Even during those last, painful months, when it was all she could do to lift a spoon to her mouth, she always managed a smile for 'her Derek'. It was things like that that I missed the most, all the little things; having someone to hold in my arms. Someone to ask me 'how it went today'. Or even just to sit quietly in a corner of the room, without saying a word, but just being there. The more time went on, the more I realised that nothing had prepared me for this.

"During those months, my life became a kind of jumbled nightmare. I hardly ate or slept and became quite ill myself, but I didn't care. Looking back, you know, I think I actually wanted to die. My life seemed to have somehow lost its purpose and meaning."

"But what about the Lord? Were you a Christian at the time?" It was a question I had wanted so much to ask and one that had bothered me ever since that Saturday night. I wondered if it were right for a Christian to feel that their life had no meaning and had concluded that there must be something terribly wrong with my relationship with the Lord if I could feel that way myself.

"Oh, yes," Derek nodded. "But sometimes, Lindsey, we focus so much on our problems and what's going wrong and then we tell ourselves that knowing the Lord doesn't help and that we're no better off with Him than we were without Him. The truth is, we haven't even given Him a chance to prove Himself, we just run around like chickens with our heads cut off and declare that He let us down, just when we needed Him most." He stopped and looked up at me for a moment. "It's taken time, Lindsey," he continued quietly. "But I've proved His faithfulness again and again. No matter how low I've felt at times, when I hit rock-bottom, He was still there. But it didn't feel like it at the time, I can assure you.

"When the initial pain had slackened off a bit, I progressed into that barren land called Bitterness. I hope you never go there, Lindsey, it's the most devastating place a person can ever find themselves in." I nodded gravely. I was extremely angry at God, it was true, but I felt sure I hadn't actually given in to bitterness.

"I remember so many lonely days, rolling endlessly into one another, when I would throw my head back and shout at God, asking Him why He had allowed such a thing to happen to me. We had saved up all our lives so that we could spend a happy retirement together, but it had all been so cruelly cut short. In the end, I ran out of every word except one: 'Why?' It was all I could say, over and over again."

My mind flashed back to the accident on the morning of my exam, as I had held my wounded thumb under the running tap and asked the same question. At the time, it had been eclipsed by my meeting with Hal. Now, I wondered if I had ever received an answer and was eager to discover if Derek had.

"Did you get any answer?" I asked at length. Derek looked at me and smiled again, in his own, inimitable way.

"Yes," he said quietly. "It took me quite by surprise at the time because, by then, I had just about given up on God and had all but thrown my spiritual life out of the window. I wasn't praying, or going to church, or doing any of the things that all good Christians are supposed to do in times of great distress. I was actually sitting at home, feeling more than acceptably sorry for myself, when a passage from Philippians came to my mind. Well, I was in no mood for reading scripture, but it persisted and persisted until, with very bad grace, I got the good book out and found the appropriate passage. I must admit, I only skimmed over the words quite hurriedly, until I came to that very familiar verse: 'In everything give thanks, for this is the will of God in Christ Jesus concerning you.'

"I had read it time and time again, but it was the word 'everything' that leapt out at me like never before. And I must admit, it confused me for a while. I went back and re-read it to make sure it didn't say in some things, or even in most things, but actually, it really did say in everything. It posed a dreadful question, Lindsey. I wondered what kind of a God would require me to give thanks in *everything*, even the death of the one that had been closest to me for much of my life. Surely I wasn't supposed to be thankful for *that*! I struggled with it all evening, telling myself how ridiculous it was, how unthinkable, how pointless it would be. But the thought just wouldn't let me alone.

"Now you have to understand, Lindsey," he said, leaning forward and throwing a finger in my direction, "that I'm not one of these people that easily 'gives up to God', but it was so persistent that there was nothing else I could do. I leaned back in my chair and just said the words: 'Thank you Lord'. Of course, I was very reluctant to say them at first, but, having said them once, I found I wanted to say them again and again. In fact, I kept on saying them, over and over, out loud. You know why? It had a strange, healing effect on me. Three simple words, but their significance was so profound.

"You see," he continued, enthusiastically, "just by doing what He wanted me to do, I was yielding my mind and my voice and my whole being, even though for just a few seconds, back to Him. After months of focusing all my attention on myself and my hurt and pain, I was, just for a moment, looking again at Him. Then, I was actually thanking *Him*; admitting and acknowledging that the whole situation had come from *His* hand. By thanking Him, I was, in effect, saying, 'Okay, Lord, *You've* allowed this to happen, but I'm still going to trust you and believe that what You're doing is for my good.' I remembered the words of Job, the man that lost everything

167

but his life and yet was able to declare: 'Though He *slay* me, yet will I trust Him.'

"Finally, in some strange, inexplicable way, Lindsey, it brought the Lord back into the picture. I had somehow made contact with the Lord again. Up until then, I had been trying to struggle through it all without Him, but by thanking Him, I was again acknowledging His presence, His authority, His wisdom and, yes, even His love." He paused for a moment and when he spoke again, his voice was slow and deliberate.

"Lindsey," he almost whispered. "Be thankful . . . it will *deliver* you." I thought over his words for a few seconds and then looked up at him doubtfully.

"Well," I sighed, "I suppose it's worth a try, after all, it worked for you."

"And it'll work for you too," he replied cheerfully.

"You think so?"

"I *know* so, but . . . " here he paused again, stroking his beard and I knew what would follow, " . . . it may take time." It was a favourite expression of his that alternately encouraged or irritated me, depending on the situation. In almost every case, however, I found it vaguely amusing and felt sure he adopted it whenever he wanted to get himself off the hook. It slightly amused me now and I laughed reluctantly.

"That's just a cop-out," I said accusingly.

"So it might be," he grinned. "But it also happens to be true. Here, have another cup of milky water."

168

— 15 —

It was funny, I reflected, how words that seemed so meaningful at the time of being spoken, somehow managed to lose their significance when placed against the ordinary and mundane routine of life. Sitting in Derek's cosy living-room, so vulnerable and ready to listen, I had been completely captivated by his story. At the time, my heart had made an immediate response, but I had, very soon afterwards, been drawn down some obscure rabbit trail. Two days later, I had quite forgotten the powerful key he had placed into my hands. The distraction was, of course, my final exam, now only three days away. But it also came in the form of an irritating pain in the third finger of my right hand.

"It's pure imagination," said Jane when I mentioned it in passing. I shrugged my shoulders helplessly.

"That's what I keep telling myself," I said sincerely. "But it's much worse now than when I got up this morning." I looked the finger up and down and bent it in every conceivable direction. "Can't be broken," I continued, "or I wouldn't be able to move it so easily." Jane rolled her eyes heavenward and set about drawing margins down one side of her shorthand pad. I sighed, took a final look at the finger and began to follow her example. I had probably "slept funny" on it, I assured myself and, in any case, it wasn't one of the main fingers I used for shorthand, so it shouldn't pose any great problem. By the end of the day, however, not only was the throbbing pain much worse, but when I held the finger up against the corresponding finger of my left hand, there was no denying the fact that it was twice the size. I frowned in confusion. There was nothing apparently wrong with it; no cuts, no bruises, I could move it quite easily, and even write perfectly well by keeping it curled up with my little finger. But there was definitely something not quite right. A quick glance at my watch informed me that I would just catch the college doctor if I went straight away.

I reached his office only five minutes before he was due to finish for the day, and it was painfully obvious that he was not overjoyed to see me. I hesitated in the doorway for a moment, wondering if I should forget the whole thing and go home, but it was too late.

"Yes, yes? Come in, come in," he said, with barely suppressed irritation. "What's the problem?" Suddenly feeling as if I were there under false pretences, I sheepishly held up my hand and shrugged.

"I'm . . . er . . . not quite sure but . . . my finger hurts." He looked at me over the top of his glasses for a moment before echoing my pathetic statement.

"Your finger hurts?" He drew a deep breath. "Let me have a look then."

"It's twice the size of the other one," I volunteered helpfully as he pulled and pushed the swollen finger in every direction, just as I had done earlier.

"Yes, I can see that," he said, again fixing me over his glasses. I decided to keep any further helpful comments to myself and eventually he pushed my hand back over the desk with an air of dismissal.

"I expect you've bruised it," he muttered. "Just run it under cold water for a bit and the swelling should go down."

Slightly offended by his dismissive manner, I was more relieved that he had treated the whole matter so lightly and convinced myself that he was right. When I arrived home, I followed his instructions and held the finger under the cold tap until it seemed as if frost-bite might be a distinct possibility. Then, I went to bed, convinced that it would be back to normal in the morning.

The next day, I woke up early, wondering why I was lying in such an awkward position, with my right hand stretched out over my pillow. I soon discovered that this was because a sharp, stabbing pain shot down my arm whenever I tried to move it. Realising the implications, I was instantly wide awake.

"Oh, no," I groaned. "What now?" Far from having returned to its normal size, the finger had swollen up even more, making it look almost the size of two fingers put together. In addition to this, it was bent over and flattened against the palm of my hand in a most unnatural position. I frantically dug out a note-book and pencil and tensely scribbled a few outlines, but the pain was unbearable and I soon put it down in defeat. A torrent of anger rose inside me once again. The first time had been bad enough, then Hal, now this!

"Why?" I hurled the word into the air, just as Derek must have done. "Why do you do these things, God? Can't I have *anything* that I really want?" It seemed just as if He had set Himself up against me, like some arch-enemy, bent upon repaying me for some distant misdemeanour that I must have committed. Well, I wasn't going to let Him do it, I told myself. He had asked enough of me already, and I wasn't going to let Him win this time! I dressed fairly quickly, considering my latest handicap and set off immediately for the outpatients' department of the local hospital. Perhaps they could get it sorted out before tomorrow and everything would still be all right. Even if the finger wasn't completely back to normal, I felt certain I would still be able to write fairly well with it curled up.

Some time later, I was once again seated in a doctor's office and, if I had thought the college doctor had been surly enough, this one made him look like Florence Nightingale.

"Why didn't you come before?" he asked curtly after glancing quickly at the finger. By now, my idea of having "slept funny" had disappeared and I wondered if there might be something seriously wrong.

"Well, I went to see the college doctor yesterday and he seemed to think it was just bruised so . . . " But my explanation was cut short by him rising from his seat and giving mumbled instructions to a nurse who had been working quietly in the opposite corner of the room. She nodded knowingly and began pulling open drawers and assembling some kind of syringe. Without a word, she rolled up my sleeve and pushed the needle into my arm to ensure that I didn't go down with a dose of tetanus and then walked out of the room, leaving me with the irascible doctor. He was scribbling something completely illegible on a prescription form and giving me instructions, although I wouldn't have known they were addressed to me, as his eyes never left his paper the whole time. By then, I had decided that I had taken just about enough and was going to find out exactly what was going on. After all, it was *my* hand, and I had a right to know!

"You've got a poisoned finger," he informed me, rather ungraciously, upon being questioned. "Furthermore, the poison is spreading at some considerable rate and has to be checked immediately." I looked down at my hand as he spoke and was horrified to see that the swelling had already spread half way across the back of my hand. The dips between my knuckles were no longer evident and the whole hand looked as if it were filling up with water.

"It was very foolish of you to continue using your hand as you did yesterday," continued this most unpleasant man, "which has only served to spread the poison more quickly and to make our job harder to carry out." I was beginning to dislike him more and more with every passing moment and was fairly certain that he was more concerned about his personal inconvenience than he was about my hand. Boiling with rage, my mind switched from his monotonous voice to the awful truth that was gradually sinking in. So He did, after all, have "something else" lined up for me. But whatever it was, I didn't want to know, and it was probably going to be something terrible anyway!

172

All I could think about was how unfair it all was and wished I could dissolve in tears there and then, but the doctor, obviously oblivious to the fact that my life's plans were being smashed to pieces yet again, had begun the second stage of carrying out his job. He curled all my fingers over into a tight fist and then began to calmly and systematically wind a white bandage around my whole hand until I looked as if I were wearing a white boxing-glove. My eyes grew wide with horror as I realised what was happening. Secretly, I was still determined to sneak into the exam room, hoping that nobody would notice my over-sized finger, and take the exam regardless. But now it was completely out of the question.

When the ceremony was over, he looked up in a satisfied manner and informed me that I was not to attend college for two weeks and to keep the hand completely still. He then re-inforced his instructions by placing my arm in a sling and tying it tightly at the back of my neck. I was furious.

"Can't I take it off for a little while?" I asked, as civilly as I could. "I'll need both hands for some things."

"Such as?" he asked, with the air of a man whose patience had already been severely tried. By this time, my own had been pushed to the brink.

"Well, such as a wash, for a start!" I replied, as *un*civilly as I could. "And dressing and . . . "

"Get someone to help you with it, you must not remove the bandage for any reason. Come back and see me in a week's time."

"But that's impossible," I replied helplessly. "There's no one that . . . " But he wasn't in the mood for talking.

A few minutes later, I pushed through the revolving doors with my good hand and marched down the long driveway with the bad one held across my chest, Horatio Nelson style. As I walked methodically along the road to the bus-stop, hardly noticing where my feet were taking me, I made a promise. I was conscious that I wanted to break down uncontrollably in tears, but I decided then that I had cried once too often. I promised myself (and God too, if He was listening!) that I would never cry again – not even for Him. He had shattered my dreams once too often, once too often He had snatched from my grasp the very thing I had most wanted and *this* time, I had had enough. My life might have been a mess before I met Him, and I didn't mind admitting it, but at least I could do as I pleased with it. At least I had had some sort of plan, some goal and purpose, but now I had to drift along mindlessly, wherever He chose to lead me. Well, I wasn't going to do it! I could manage my life quite well without Him, or anyone else for that matter. I would live life *my* way – just let Him see if I couldn't!

Twenty minutes later, I got off the bus and strode purposefully into my classroom, to the horror of all therein assembled.

"Lindsey!" gasped Mrs McNeil. "What on earth have you done now?" Having pondered my fate from all angles on the bus, I had arrived at college feeling as if every emotion once contained in my soul had died.

"I've got a poisoned hand, Mrs McNeil," I replied, with cold indifference. "I won't be taking the exam tomorrow afternoon." Her mouth dropped open and silence descended upon the whole group, broken only by the systematic ticking of the large, yellow-faced wall-clock.

"Oh, Lindsey, I'm so sorry, dear," she began at length. "But you could always do evening classes, or perhaps come back and . . . " Of course, she could have been right, but perhaps she ought to tell God about her wonderful ideas, I thought furiously!

"It's quite all right, Mrs McNeil," I replied dispassionately. "I'm sure I'll think of something else. I've been advised to have two weeks off college, but as that brings me almost to the end of term, I won't be coming back." I turned to the sea of horrified faces. "Goodbye," I said simply, "and good luck."

Without another word, I turned and walked out of the classroom for the last time, down the corridor, through the large glass doors and into the car-park. Then, as if the shattering of my career prospects wasn't enough, I just happened to notice Hal's car, parked in its usual place, and the memory of that ill-fated Saturday night came flooding back to my mind.

If ever I wanted him, I wanted him then. But I couldn't have him, and I couldn't have my career. In fact, I couldn't have *anything* I really wanted, because *God* wouldn't let me!

By the time I got home, I was boiling over with anger and self-pity, asking myself again and again how God could allow such things to happen, and wondering why I had ever decided to follow Him in the first place. Eventually, I flung open the front door, unable to contain my feelings any longer.

"IT JUST ISN'T FAIR!!" I said loudly as I slammed it shut behind me.

"No, dear, I don't expect it is, but really, there's no need to take it *quite* so badly." Caught completely off my guard, I traced the muffled voice back to its source, which amounted to Miss Peters' feet and posterior, protruding from the cupboard under the stairs, and almost died with embarrassment.

"Oh, I'm sorry, Miss Peters," I muttered sheepishly. "What did you say?"

"You were telling me that it wasn't fair, and I was agreeing with you, only . . . " She sat back on her heels with a flushed face and a tendril of wiry grey hair falling over her forehead. But then she noticed my new "war veteran" look and immediately changed her tack.

"Lindsey, dear, what on *earth* have you done to yourself?"

"Well, I'm not exactly sure, Miss Peters. The doctor says it's poisoned and . . . "

"Oh, you poor dear, and with your exam and everything." I flinched as she mentioned the poignant word and wondered why I had to be reminded, yet again, of how badly things had turned out.

"Are you going to be all right?" she asked anxiously.

"I think so, only . . . " I felt myself turning red with embarrassment and wished I didn't have to continue, but there was no choice. "Miss Peters, I wonder if you would be able to do me a favour."

"Of course, dear, I'd be glad to help."

"It's just that I'm not supposed to take this bandage off for a whole week. In fact, I'm supposed to move the hand as little as possible to avoid spreading the stuff up my arm. Thing is, I won't be able to do a few things and I wondered if . . . if you could help me get washed and dressed in the mornings – if it's not too much trouble." It was obvious that she had been thrown into her element and I could sense her latent nursing tendencies rising as she spoke.

"It would be a pleasure, dear," she replied, as enthusiastically as if I had invited her out to dinner. "I'm used to doing that sort of thing, you know. What time shall I come up?"

"Well, whatever time's most convenient for you. I won't have to get up as early as usual because I've left college now."

"Shall we say seven-thirty then?"

"Yes, that would be fine for me," I said, with an attempt at smiling, but as I turned to go, a thought occurred to me and I turned around again.

"I'll be able to do most things, of course," I said, looking down at the carpet. "It's just, well, you know, the things you need two hands for." She smiled sympathetically.

"Of course, dear, I understand. Now, why don't you come in for a nice cup of tea?"

"Well, thanks all the same, Miss Peters, but I have quite a head-ache at the moment. I think I'll just go and lie down for a bit. It's very kind of you though."

"Not at all, dear, you get off to bed and don't hesitate to call me if you need help." I thanked her again and began the weary climb to the fourth floor. As I entered my room, my white-hot rage had cooled to a blank apathy. I just wanted to be alone but, in some infuriating and exasperating way, I knew I wasn't. Just as I had known on the night of my conversion that the Lord was with me, I knew now that He was still there, waiting patiently for me to speak to Him and to share with Him the innermost feelings of my heart. But I wasn't going to do it! If I had broken down and cried, as I usually did, it might have been better, but I was determined not to. Instead, I allowed a cold hardness to settle upon me and spent the rest of the day planning yet another "new life" – this time, a new life without Him!

The week that followed was by far the worst since I had become a Christian. Having lost interest in almost everything, and immensely restricted by my handicap, I spent the time sitting in my room, just as I had done during my early days in the north of England. Several times, I was aware of that calm presence, gently pleading with me to turn around and let Him in. It was almost like a continual knocking at a heavily barred door. But each time it came, I would refuse to answer it until, after only a short time, I began to believe that He really had gone.

"It doesn't matter," I told myself. "This is how I want it to be. I don't want Him any more, I want to live life my way."

My Bible remained unopened for the entire seven days and I didn't speak to Him once. Indeed, I was convinced that, in time, I would be able to forget about Him completely, and maybe I would have done, had it not been for my faithful friends.

Since my visit to the hospital, I had not made any attempt to contact any of them, or to let them know what had happened. To all intents and purposes, I could have vanished from the face of the earth, but they were far too concerned about me to leave it at that. Sometimes, as I sat staring out of my window, I would see a familiar form, making its way towards the house. A few moments later, my bell would ring, but I wouldn't rush down to let them in and watched nervously from my window until I saw them walking away again. Some got the message the first time, but others were more persistent. One day, one of them even had the audacity to climb the four flights of stairs and knock on my door. I had tensed every muscle, hardly daring to breathe and hoped desperately that they wouldn't open the door, just to make sure I really wasn't there. I had no idea what I would have done if they had, but fortunately, I didn't have to find out. A short while later, I rushed to the window and saw the receding form of Derek, sweet, fatherly Derek, walking slowly down the road.

"I hope you never go there, Lindsey," his words echoed through my mind. "It's the most devastating place a person can find themselves in." The Land of Bitterness, that I had been certain I would never visit, but there I was, eaten up from the inside, just as he had said. But it didn't matter, I reminded myself, I didn't need them any more. I could live quite happily without them, and Him, and I was about to prove it too!

For the entire seven days, I patiently endured Miss Peters' polite chatter as she attended to my needs with expert skill. I was, of course, grateful for her much-needed help, but inside, I was disgusted by the humiliation of it all and the final day arrived none too soon.

Steeling myself for another unpleasant encounter with the surly doctor, I was surprised and relieved to see a complete stranger sitting behind his desk. He was a good deal younger than the previous man had been and commanded a much nicer bedside manner. As he motioned for me to sit down, he informed me that the doctor I had seen before was off sick.

"Right then," he smiled, "let's see the damage." Slowly, he began to unwrap layer after layer of the gauze bandage that I had faithfully kept in place for the whole week. When the final layer was removed, I was horrified by what was revealed. My fingers were wrinkled and clammy and looked strangely bleached and the whole hand looked floppy and useless.

"Is it okay?" I asked as casually as I could.

"Well, we'll see, shall we?" he said, still smiling. I thought later what a good thing it was that he had been so nice, or I might not have so easily forgiven him for what he did next. Laying my hand on the desk, palm upwards, he slowly bent back the good fingers until they touched the desk-top. I noticed, with mixed feelings of apprehension and relief, that he had not attempted to move the damaged finger.

"All seems A-Okay at the moment," he said brightly, but then he got down to business. Touching the tip of the faulty finger, which was still almost flattened against my palm, he gently pulled it back, just a little. I tensed every muscle as a sharp, stabbing pain shot through my hand, but just managed to smile when he looked up at me.

"Okay?" he asked.

"Y . . . yes, I think so. I suppose it'll take a while before I can completely straighten it and . . . " But he wasn't really listening and, in one short, sharp movement, he pulled the finger right back until it touched the desk-top as well as the others. I winced and bit my lip as hot, searing pain shot up my arm and just managed to keep myself from squealing. (The fact that tears had sprung into my eyes was *not* an indication that I had broken my promise not to cry, I told myself, but simply a perfectly natural reaction to what was happening.)

"I'm sorry if that hurt you," he said, quite sincerely. "It really is the best way you know. Here, drink this." He handed me a glass of water, which I drank out of politeness rather than necessity. My finger had sprung back to its original position, but he seemed quite content to leave it there, at least for the moment.

"How does it look?" I asked, as steadily as I could.

"Well, the real danger period is over and the poison appears to have dissipated, but it may take some time to regain full use of the finger. What we have to do now is provide you with some gentle exercise to bring it back to where it should be. Have you got a rolling-pin?" There was something about the way he said it that made me laugh, something I hadn't done for so long. He laughed

179

too, which put me much more at ease as we discussed several possibilities for gentle exercise.

"So you've got a portable typewriter then? Well, that's great. I want you to just push up and down on the keys for, say, five minutes a day, nothing more. Anything else you do that uses all your fingers?" I thought for a moment and then hit on a bright idea.

"Well, I play a guitar – but not very brilliantly."

"Great, that's ideal too. Can you pluck?"

"Yes."

"Well, do a bit of plucking, perhaps ten minutes a day, that should loosen it up quite considerably."

"And the rolling-pin?" I asked, completely mystified as to what significant role this mundane object could possibly play in my rehabilitation.

"Oh, yes, best of all. Just roll it away from you with both hands, as if you were rolling out pastry. Pull your fingers right back until they're stretched right out, but don't worry if the bad one doesn't straighten out right away." I looked at the withered finger and wondered if it would ever straighten out, let alone "right away".

"You can start immediately," he continued, "and come back and see me in a week's time." Still speaking, he rose from his seat and walked over to a bench by the window. "I want you to wear this," he said, fiddling with something I couldn't quite see.

"It'll be a bit uncomfortable at first, but you'll soon get used to it." He held up something that resembled a metal ruler, minus the numbers, which was bent over at one end. Laying my hand on it, palm downwards, he carefully positioned the third finger on the slim strip of metal. "It's supposed to eventually lie flat against this splint," he explained.

"How long do you think it will take?" I asked doubtfully.

"Oh, no way of telling really, but there's no need to rush – unless you're in for exams or anything like that, are you?" I flinched slightly as he mentioned that poignant word and remembered, yet again, how much this event had cost me.

"No," I said quietly. "I won't be taking any more exams now."

"That's okay then." He had been winding a new bandage around my wrist and round the bent finger to secure it to the splint, at the same time as giving me some new instructions.

"You can take this off at night, and for exercise, but keep it on at all other times," he advised pleasantly. "Each time you replace it, try to push your finger down a little more." I listened attentively, although, in the back of my mind, there was one point even more pressing than the state of my hand.

"Someone's been helping me get dressed," I said, with slight embarrassment. "Would it be all right to . . . "

"Oh, yes, you can do all that yourself now," he said, smiling. It was the best news I had heard for a long time and I arrived home feeling overjoyed that I would no longer have to endure Miss Peters' bedside prattle, not to mention the humiliating purification ceremony.

The next week was spent in much the same way as the first; continuing with my plans for my next "new life". At the same time, I tried to accept the fact that I would have to bury my life-long ambition and search for a job as an ordinary secretary, or something similar. But this task was proving to be extremely difficult. The only cheering aspect of the whole time was that the gentle exercise began to yield good results. Indeed, I was more than happy with my progress as was the doctor when I went back to see him at the end of the week.

"Looks a lot better, doesn't it?" he asked encouragingly. I wrinkled my nose and tried to wiggle the finger a little.

"Well, it moves a bit more easily now, and it's not such a ghastly colour. But it's still very bent. Do you think . . . " I decided to voice the fears that had been lurking in the back of my mind. Most of the pain had now gone but, try as I might, I could not keep the finger straight for more than a second or two.

"Do you think it'll ever straighten out completely?" I asked quickly. He winked at me and smiled.

"Of course it will, but these things take time, you know."

"How long will I have to wear this splint then?"

"Well, I couldn't set a date on it, but I'd say probably about four weeks."

I gasped in horror. "Four weeks!"

"Well, it won't seem that long really. Are you planning on starting a job yet?"

"Not immediately. I didn't really want to have any interviews like this," I said, holding up my hand. "Anyway, I've got all the holidays to think about job-hunting, so I suppose it won't matter too much."

"Great, in that case, you can consider yourself discharged – you can keep the splint with our compliments." He got up to open the door for me. "All the best for the future."

"Thanks," I said, and managed to smile, even though I was now faced with a future that I considered would be anything but the best.

On the way home, I wondered what to do next. I was glad that my finger was getting better, but inside, I still felt as bitter and angry towards the Lord as I had been when the whole thing had begun. As far as I was concerned, I had walked out on Him, and He had let me go. *That* proved how much He cared anyway, and if He didn't care, neither did I! I spent endless hours alone in my room, contemplating a future for which I had made no provision whatsoever, and lacking the incentive to even go out and see what might be available in the way of employment. I didn't want to do anything, except sit and mope and might well have continued in this state of self-induced hibernation for quite some time, had it not been for the need to do some shopping in town.

Armed with my small shopping list and a wire basket, I browsed unenthusiastically along the laden shelves. Then, quite suddenly, I caught sight of a familiar face at the end of the row and immediately realised that he had seen me too. Panic-stricken, I turned and dived down another row. My heart was beating much faster than usual as I headed for the nearest check-out, feeling like a hunted animal. My only thought was to leave the shop as quickly as possible and as I stood in the long, slow-moving queue, my impatience with the cashier and the customers in front of me mounted.

"Hurry up, please hurry up!" I screamed inside, but this only seemed to make the cashier more clumsy, and she rang for the supervisor to help her out of yet another predicament. At last, it was my turn to pay and I heaved a deep sigh as I stood on the pavement outside, but my relief was short-lived as, a moment later, someone placed his hand on my shoulder. If it had been the store detective, about to arrest me for robbery, I would have felt ecstatically happy. But it wasn't, and I didn't. Whirling round in anger, I met those familiar, unflinching eyes.

"Jim, why are you following me?" I hissed, keeping my voice as low as possible. "Can't you all see I want to be by myself?"

"No, you don't," he said quietly.

"For goodness sake, leave me alone!" I snapped, shrugging off his hand. "I don't want anything to do with you, or anyone." Jim remained unmoved by my childish outburst and continued to stare at me calmly.

"Lindsey, what's all this about, love?" he asked at length. I looked away, for there was something in the tone of his voice and his earnest expression that made me feel slightly deflated. I continued in a calmer voice, still determined not to give in.

"I've thrown it all in. I wish I'd never heard of God, or salvation, or anything. Ever since I got involved with it all, everything's gone wrong. I don't understand any of it. I don't even understand God any more. One minute I'm told how much He loves me, and the next minute He dashes my life to pieces. Can't He make up His mind?" Jim continued to stare at me, without saying a word, which only made me angrier.

"Anyway, now He's gone off somewhere," I muttered, but there was just the slightest waver in my voice which Jim immediately picked up.

"And you really wish He'd come back, don't you?" he said softly. I looked up at him with blazing eyes. How dare he accuse me of such emotional weakness? Didn't he think I was capable of looking after myself without always having to run to some Big Daddy in the sky to hold my hand?

"No, I don't! I couldn't care less if I never hear about Him again!" I spat out fiercely and realised then just how angry I was. At one time, I would have displayed no emotion in public whatsoever, but now I wasn't in the least bit bothered that we were standing on a very busy street corner. I was going to let him have it, both barrels loaded. And in any case, people would probably just think we were a father and daughter, arguing over some insignificant trifle. Jim, however, still remained unmoved.

"But He cares about you, Lindsey," he said quietly.

"Well, it's too late to tell me that now," I replied vehemently. "He should have thought about that last week and . . . and before that."

"Well, I'm sorry you feel like this, Lindsey," he said, after a short silence. "But what you feel about Him doesn't change what He feels about you." He paused for a moment and the faintest of smiles played over his lips. "He loved you first, remember?" I quickly looked down again, feeling furious with myself for not just walking away, but for some reason, I couldn't.

"Anyway," he continued, in a slightly lighter tone, "I can see you want to be off now. If you need anything – anything at all – you know where we are. Okay?" I didn't know if I was sad or mad, but one thing was for sure, I wasn't about to give in to the usual urge to burst into tears – I had promised! I looked up and met his eyes for just a moment. Then, without a word, I marched off down the road without looking round once.

As I walked, I told myself to forget the whole incident with Jim and to continue with my steely resolve to live without God. I promised myself over and over again that I could make a better job of running my life than He ever could and again assured myself that, in time, I would forget all about Him. The only thing was, I couldn't. In the most irritating and infuriating way, He would return to my mind, no matter where I was, or what I was doing. Sometimes I would remember snatches of a conversation with Derek or Ted. At other times, scriptures would flash into my mind, or lines of songs I had sung at the meetings and, although I tried desperately to turn my mind to other things, it would automatically bounce back, like a ball attached to a bat with a piece of elastic. One afternoon, the recent conversation with Derek came back to me very vividly.

" . . . we declare that He let us down, just when we needed Him most, when the truth is, we never even gave Him a chance to prove Himself."

It lodged immoveably in my mind, in spite of my efforts to think about something else and there was no escaping from the truth it contained. Gradually it dawned on me that I was guilty of this very thing. As soon as things had gone wrong, I had flared up in anger and turned away from the Lord. Now I began to wonder what would have happened if I had done the opposite and turned the whole thing over to Him. The thought persisted and I became more and more curious to discover just what He *did* have in mind for me. Irritated though I was, by this apparent chink in my armour, my curiosity was aroused. I simply had to discover what He would have said if only I had given Him a chance. But, as my curiosity mounted and I decided I really must get in touch with Him again, a major problem presented itself. I had walked away from Him and declared that I didn't want to hear about Him ever again. In view of this, I was now convinced that He wouldn't ever want to speak to me again, even though I really did want Him to. It was quite a terrifying thought and, much as I hated to admit it, Jim had been right. Underneath the hard, self-sufficient exterior, I was still very much a confused young child, wishing desperately that someone would tell me where Dad had gone.

As hours that seemed like years dragged slowly by, the thought that He really didn't want to hear from me began to take over my mind. In desperation, I did everything I could think of to try and regain His acceptance. I prayed and read my Bible, or just sat quietly and tried to listen, but it all seemed utterly futile and I only became more tormented by the thought that He really had turned His back on me and never wanted me to speak to Him again. Turning my back on Him was one thing, but the thought that He might have turned His back on me was quite another!

In the end, I could endure it all no longer. All my efforts obviously weren't enough for Him, I told myself, He must be expecting something more. Just as I was wondering what more I could possibly do, I remembered how we had all got together one day and fasted on behalf of a sick man at the fellowship. Not long afterwards, he had been completely healed, but I had quite forgotten the incident until now. Of course, I realised that there was nothing magical about fasting itself, but the attitude contained in it had seemed to hold some kind of sway with the Lord.

Had I not been so emotionally unstable at the time, I might have realised that going to such extremes was not really necessary and that He was actually more ready to speak to me than I was to listen. But I wasn't really thinking rationally at the time, my mind was so full of doubts and fears that it seemed the only thing left to do. Without giving any thought to the possible risks to my health, I decided to begin my fast the following day.

Rising early, with my resolve still fresh in my mind, I poured myself a drink of water and knelt by my bed. Of course, I hadn't *actually* expected the heavens to open and angelic beings to descend, offering words of encouragement, but neither had I expected things to seem *quite* so dead. But I shouldn't be surprised, I assured myself, after all, I hadn't prayed for some considerable time, or read my Bible, or tried to make any sort of contact with the

Lord, or His people. Little wonder, then, that when I had decided to get back in touch, He seemed to be a million miles away. I wasn't even sure what I was supposed to say to Him and ended up spending most of the morning on my knees, thinking about nothing in particular, but occasionally remembering why I was there. By lunchtime, I had almost given up the ridiculous idea and was so hungry that I almost gave in to my baser instincts. But something stopped me, and the afternoon passed much as the morning had, except that I began to feel very tired. By eight-thirty, I was curled up in bed and fast asleep not much later.

When I woke up the following morning, I had completely forgotten my plan and couldn't understand why I felt so hungry. It wasn't long, however, before I remembered and decided that the sooner I got some answers, the sooner I would be able to eat again. So began an exact replay of what had happened the day before, in all but one respect.

The day before I might well have been accused of daring Him to speak to me, so that when He didn't I could, in a way, say: "I told You so, You *didn't* really care!" But now there was just the hint of a change in my attitude and I really did want Him to say something to me. I spent the first couple of hours listening intently for any word from that still, small voice that was usually apparent, even when I wished it weren't, but, for the first time since my conversion, it seemed to have left me completely alone. This, in itself, was quite terrifying. Feeling alone before I was a Christian was one thing, but, having experienced some measure of relationship with the Lord, the thought that He really was no longer there frightened me more than anything I had ever experienced. My sense of desolation threatened to overwhelm me, and still I seemed alone in that small, stifling room.

After quite some time, I noticed how dry my throat felt and decided to have a cup of coffee. Drinking, I assured myself, was quite permissible whilst fasting, and might go some way to relieving my physical discomfort, if nothing else. As I wearily spooned some coffee into my cup, a single word flashed into my mind: "Sing". I stopped suddenly, wondering where it had come from. Maybe I had seen it written on my songbook, I thought, and it had become imprinted on my mind. But there was no incriminating literature lying around. By this time the kettle had boiled and I poured the steaming water into my cup. As I sat down and lifted it to my lips, it came again: "Sing". By the third time, I got the message.

God? Telling me to sing? Now? I was furious, more furious than I had been with the doctor who had sealed up my hand and my future. How *could* He? How *dare* He tell me to sing? I was desperate, at my wit's end, I needed answers, not a sing-song! Eventually, I decided that I couldn't do it. Furthermore, I *wouldn't* do it. Sing, indeed! Didn't He have anything better to say? Angry thoughts spun round in my mind, like a whirlwind gathering speed until I could stand it no longer. I picked up the Bible on my bedside table and hurled it across the room with all the might that my left hand could muster. With tremendous satisfaction, I watched as it slid down the opposite wall and flapped to the ground with a papery thud.

"Good!!" I thought. "*That'll* show Him. Sing? I WON'T DO IT!" For a few moments I stared at the fallen book in silent fury. For the first time since early childhood I had thrown a tantrum, albeit a sophisticated, grown-up type of tantrum, but a tantrum nevertheless. After a while, a calm, resigned quietness came over me and I went and picked up the Bible. It hung limply in my hands, like a wounded bird with a broken spine and, as I patted the pages back into place, my resolve broke and I began to cry.

Strangely enough, I wasn't angry with myself for crying, I was glad. I wanted to cry. At last, that vast ocean of tears that I had bottled up over the past few weeks began to flow, cascading over my hands, soaking my gauze bandage and trickling off the edges of my battered Bible. But I didn't care. For some reason, it didn't matter. In fact, nothing mattered any more. I didn't care then if I never got what I wanted, all that really mattered was that I got back in

188

touch with Him. I had lived without Him for just a few weeks. For just a few weeks, I had caught a glimpse of a life without Him, and I couldn't stand it any more. I had tried to pretend that I was glad about being able to do just what I wanted. That it was great not to have to pray and ask Him about every decision that I made. But it wasn't, it wasn't like that at all. For the first time in my life, I didn't care any more what happened, or didn't happen to me, I just had to renew my relationship with Him, whatever the cost might be. If He wanted me to sing, then I would just have to get on and . . . sing!

— 16 —

I gingerly approached the front door, feeling as if everyone in the neighbourhood was watching as I pressed the bell and waited. In a matter of seconds, it was opened by Sally.

"Lindsey, how nice to see you," she smiled. "Come on in." Feeling every inch the Prodigal Son, I was a little overwhelmed by such an obvious display of acceptance, but nevertheless, stepped into the hallway. A moment later, Jessica, who had been leaning over the banisters, bounded up to me in her usual, enthusiastic manner, her face flushed with surprise and excitement.

"Lindsey, Lindsey!" she squealed. "You haven't been for ages. Have you come back from a holiday?" I glanced quickly at Sally as my face began to burn with embarrassment.

"Well, not exactly, Jessica." Before I could say more, another small face had appeared on the stairs.

"Georgie, Georgie," shouted Jessica. "It's Lindsey. She's not exactly back from her holiday yet, but she's come to see us. Come on, hurry up!" Georgie appeared, looking slightly mystified, but soon brightened up when he realised I was actually there in the flesh. A moment later, he threw both arms around my waist, making me flinch involuntarily as my bad hand hit my side.

"Hey, George, be careful," said Sally reproachfully. "Lindsey's had a bad hand." George looked crestfallen as he made his apology.

"Oh, sorry – hey, what's that?" He pointed to the slim metal strip attached to my hand.

"It's a splint, George," I explained. "It helps keep my finger straight."

190

"Do you have to keep it on for ever an' ever?" asked Jessica, her eyes wide with horror.

"No, Jessica, just till the finger's better."

"Now, come on, you two," interrupted Sally. "Lindsey didn't come here to be interrogated by you, and I'm sure those rooms aren't tidy yet, are they? Go on, off you go." The two youngsters obediently bounded up the stairs and from the top landing, Jessica's voice was still audible.

" 'magine that, Georgie, she has to keep it on for ever an' ever!"

Sally shrugged helplessly. "People say I was just like her when I was a child, but I can't believe I was *that* bad." We both laughed and chatted for a few minutes before I got round to the reason for my visit.

"Is Jim around, Sally?" I asked a little cautiously. "I . . . er . . . just wondered if I might have a quick word with him."

"Course you can, he's in the study."

"Is he very busy?" I asked doubtfully. "I could come back another time."

"Oh, no, just the usual." I knew immediately what she meant. Not only was Jim a devoted husband and father, he was an equally devoted Christian and spent much time in prayer and Bible study. Knowing this made me feel a little unsure whether I should interrupt him or not.

"He won't mind at all," smiled Sally reassuringly.

"Okay, thanks." She rushed upstairs to check on the children, as I approached the study, feeling for all the world like a naughty schoolgirl reporting to the Head. I stood outside for a few moments, wondering what kind of reception awaited me.

"Come in," came a voice in response to my knock and I hesitantly obeyed. Jim was at his desk by the window, sitting with his back to me. He didn't turn around as I closed the door. Taking a deep breath I steeled myself for rejection before speaking.

"Jim?" He spun round on his swivel chair.

191

"Lindsey!" His eyes met mine with a look of joyful surprise. "It's good to see you again." I dropped my gaze for a moment, unsure of how to begin.

"Jim, I . . . I really came to say sorry about . . . "

"There's no need, Lindsey," he smiled. "It's just good to see you again." I looked up quickly, feeling that perhaps I hadn't made my apology sincere enough.

"I mean I really am, Jim. I shouldn't have taken it all out on you, and right in the middle of . . . " He continued to smile and shook his head slowly.

"Lindsey, I told you, there's no need to apologise . . . okay?" I tried to smile myself, and nodded as convincingly as I could. Then I looked at the floor again, wondering if I should continue.

"Well?" he inquired, with his head on one side. "What are you thinking now?" All at once, I felt choked with emotion and a little embarrassed, but I didn't care, I was going to say it anyway, even if it did make me feel small and stupid.

"Nothing much really," I said, ignoring the lump in my throat. "Except . . . I wish you'd been my dad while I was growing up." Whether he realised the full significance of my statement, I wasn't quite sure, but I was overjoyed by his response.

"Well," he began softly. "That's about the best compliment anyone could give a dad." There was a moment's silence before he continued in a slightly lighter tone.

"But anyway, you haven't quite finished growing up yet." He smiled. "So maybe you could adopt me."

"It's a deal!" I replied with conviction. Jim laughed and ruffled my hair, in the same way that Ted and many of the older folks in the fellowship were so fond of doing. It didn't annoy or irritate me, despite my childhood dislike of being touched. In a funny kind of way, I liked it.

"Well," said Jim, motioning for me to sit in the familiar black chair opposite his. "I never had any doubt that the Lord would bring you through it, Lindsey. But I have to admit, I'd be interested to know how He did. Fancy telling me?" I leaned back against the softly padded leather and swivelled round slightly so that I could look out of the window.

"Well, it's a bit of a long story, and it's not all exactly . . . er . . . edifying," I grinned.

"I *love* long stories," he said with a slight laugh. "And the end result looks pretty edifying to me, so why don't you go ahead?" I swivelled back to my original position and began to recount my desperate search for God, including the incident with the Bible. To my utter amazement, he seemed to find it quite amusing.

"I'll never do it again," I said earnestly.

"Don't count on it, Lindsey," he laughed. "You may well have to hurl a few more Bibles at a few more walls before God's through with you."

"Really?"

"Really. But go on, I'm riveted."

I continued with my story while Jim listened with a wry expression on his face. As I spoke, the experience of those amazing seven days became real again.

"Not only did I not *feel* like singing, I didn't know what to sing either," I told him. "In the end, I remembered that we'd sung a lot of Psalms at the meetings that I really liked. There's something about the Book of Psalms that always manages to sum up just how I feel."

Jim nodded. "That's because it's such a candid expression of how someone *did* feel."

"Well, I'm glad he took the trouble to write it all down. Anyway, I opened up my Bible, then got my guitar out and just began to sing them one after another, not even in any particular order." I giggled slightly as I remembered how silly I had felt at the time. "It must have sounded *terrible*," I confided to Jim. "And I felt sure that the whole house must have been listening to my abysmal performance. Anyway, I carried on because I knew it was what He wanted me to do and I think it must have been the first time that I didn't care how I 'felt' about it. I knew He had said it, so I just did it."

As I continued speaking, I remembered how stupid I had felt and how ridiculous it had seemed to be singing when it was the last thing I had felt like doing. And yet, as I continued with this seemingly ludicrous exercise, I began to experience a great sense of release, deep down inside.

"It was as if I was letting go of something I had been holding on to for years," I told Jim. "I spent three days, just singing. I didn't even pray, I just sang and each day, I felt as if I'd let go a bit more."

"So then you stopped fasting?" he asked.

"No, I kept at it for seven days in all, but maybe it took the three days of singing to get me to the place where I could listen." Jim nodded and I carried on with my story, recounting the two things that had really struck me during those significant seven days.

"The first thing," I told him, "was that I realised how childish I'd been. I'd always believed that as I grew older physically, I would mature in all the other areas too and that I would kind of 'grow out' of all my problems and hang-ups. But I think I realised for the first time, that it just doesn't happen that way and that even though I've got older physically, I've still been a child inside. When I realised that, I suddenly didn't want to be a child any more, I wanted to grow up – if you know what I mean." Jim nodded again, which encouraged me to continue.

"I'm not sure what relevance it has at the moment, but I think maybe I've been treating God in much the same way as I treated Mum. I always felt she was holding out on me and every time the Lord's stepped in lately to stop me doing what I want to, I suppose I've reacted in the same childish way as I used to at home." Jim listened attentively, frequently nodding in agreement.

"The other thing happened when I was singing. It was just a release at first, but gradually I became aware that there was more to me than just my physical body and emotions. I think I realised I had a spiritual side to me as well. I've always known that really, but it had never been quite so graphic before."

As I spoke, I remembered how clear this point had become, especially in relation to my struggle with loneliness. In some ways, I had been convinced that the answers were physical, like having a comforting arm around my shoulders, or someone to talk to when I felt down. In other ways, the answers seemed to be in the emotional fulfilment of having another person to make me feel loved and worthwhile. But, as I had fasted, I realised, more clearly than ever before, that I was not just a physical and emotional being. I was also a spiritual being and that part of me required fulfilment just as much as the others did. I had started with the wrong end of the problem, trying to solve it from the outside, but doing this would have supplied only a temporary solution. For a fleeting moment, I had realised that something needed to happen inside me if the problem was ever going to really be solved. Exactly what the something might be, I wasn't entirely sure, but it seemed to hinge on the acceptance that there really was more to me than what I could feel and see.

"I suppose I'm not actually that much better off than when I started fasting," I advised Jim. "But maybe the difference is that I'm beginning to see things a bit more clearly. Maybe I'm just beginning to give the Lord a chance to show me some real answers." Jim smiled.

"Yes," he agreed, "and as we've said before, it may not happen overnight. But it sounds like you've been through a good experience, Lindsey."

I laughed drily. "I promise you, Jim, it didn't feel good at the beginning. In fact, I think it's the most awful experience I've ever been through. I felt as if I was being completely broken up inside and having to let go of all that I've been working towards for so long."

"How you felt about it doesn't make it any less good," he smiled.

"Well, I suppose not, but I still wonder what the purpose of some of it was. I mean, wouldn't it have been so much easier if the Lord had spoken to me at the beginning, instead of me having to get as angry as I did and all the rest of it?"

"Maybe," he replied calmly. "But I doubt very much if you would have been able to listen at the beginning."

I thought for a moment.

"Yes, I suppose you're right."

"But, with regard to purpose," he continued, leaning back in his chair and gazing out of the window, "when you walk with the Lord, everything has a purpose – even those things that seem insignificant, or 'wrong'. But he doesn't always reveal the 'why' of His dealings straight away. Most of the situations we go through are preparation for something He intends to do with us, usually at a much later date. Do you realise, Lindsey, that God can sometimes spend a lifetime preparing a person in order that they can perform just one, significant act?" I gasped in amazement.

"Isn't that a terrific waste of a person's life?"

"No, not once the deed has been performed. It could change the course of history."

"All that's been happening to me, Jim, I know it's only small compared to what some people go through, but do you think it really does have some purpose, somewhere? For instance, why is it so important to the Lord that I don't become a shorthand court reporter?" Jim turned to face me again.

"The answer to the second half of your question, Lindsey, is undoubtedly, that nobody knows – at least, not at this point. But with regard to purpose, there's no doubt about it, and He's going to reveal that purpose to you."

"You think so?"

"Most definitely, but . . . " He adopted a typical "Derek" pose, stroking an imaginary beard. " . . . it may take time." We both laughed as I realised I wasn't the only one amused by Derek's favourite expression. After a few moments, we both fell silent and I continued a little cautiously.

"You seem to know a lot about it, Jim. Did you read a good book on the subject or something?" It was a loaded question and I hoped he would bite the bait. Secretly, I had always been intrigued by the depth of this man's wisdom and understanding and, indeed, knew that it wasn't all the product of reading a "good book". Jim pursed his lips and stared out of the window.

"No, Lindsey," he said quietly, "I didn't read any books on the subject, but there have been 'dealings' in my life too." I waited for a moment, wondering if it would be right to ask him about it all, but he supplied the answer himself.

"But that's another story, and I'm sure you don't want to hear it now. Needless to say, though, there have been times when I, too, felt that God was a million miles away. One particular time, I was convinced He had gone off somewhere and had no intention of ever coming back."

I laughed in surprise.

"I can't imagine you ever feeling like that, Jim."

He nodded and laughed too.

"You'd be surprised how I feel sometimes, Lindsey, and I suppose I was about as desperate as you were at the time. I'd tried everything, but He just didn't seem to want to be disturbed and I just about gave up – which, incidentally, is not a bad place to come to. It's usually when we give up that He gets a chance to start moving in our situations. This particular time, He used a visiting minister at our church to speak to me." He turned and gazed out of the window again, as if casting his mind a long way back.

"He was a strange chap really, and the first thing that struck me about him was how 'ordinary' he looked. He wasn't even wearing a dog-collar, but a roll-neck jumper underneath a dark jacket and trousers that didn't quite match any of the rest of his outfit.

"I had watched carefully as he walked across the platform to the pulpit and was certain he had something in his hand, and I was right. It was a ginger biscuit."

I laughed incredulously.

"A ginger biscuit?"

Jim nodded. "Yes, a ginger biscuit. He stood on the platform, brandishing it in the air, while I sat there wondering

197

what possible significance this object might have to the service. Actually, the first significant thing it did was to secure the undivided attention of all present; young, old ... and rebellious," he said, pointing a finger at himself as he mentioned the final category.

"There he stood, in complete silence, studying the biscuit from all angles, as if there was no one in the room except him and it. Then, all at once, he turned and pretended to notice us. Of course, by this time we were riveted. He looked from us to the biscuit and to us again. Then, with a shrug of his shoulders, he just said: 'Ginger biscuit' and put it down on the chair, behind him. Now that he had our full attention, he went on to preach one of the most meaningful sermons I had ever heard."

"What was it about?" I asked eagerly.

"Jacob," replied Jim. "Remember him?"

"Well, sort of."

"His very name means 'Supplanter' and 'Schemer'. He was a wriggler, able to squiggle and squirm his way out of any situation that didn't quite suit him – and quite successfully too. But it all caught up with him in the end. God loved that man too much to allow him to run away for ever and there finally came a point in Jacob's life when his supplanting and scheming came to an end."

I knew the story very well myself, but there was something about the down-to-earth way in which Jim recounted scripture that always brought it right up to date and made it seem so significant. It was like that now, listening to his slow, matter-of-fact voice and I began to see myself reflected in the character he was talking about.

"It was the final show-down for Jacob, Lindsey, confrontation with a badly offended brother. Jacob knows his brother's not too sold on the idea of meeting him again and so he resorts to his old, scheming ways and tries to soften him up a bit. He gets to the ford of the Jabbok and sends over such presents as would make a king feel over-indulged in order to pave the way for this painful meeting. But he doesn't just stop at possessions. We then find him sending over, not only his servants, but his wives and his sons. Finally we are told: ' . . . Jacob was left alone'." He paused for a moment and his next words hit home all the more for the silence that had preceded them.

"Lindsey, where Jacob was at that moment was the best place he had ever been in. He had nothing else to trust in, nothing to lean on and nothing to blame, all he had left was himself. God had pursued him all his life and now, at last, he finally had him, just where he wanted him.

"I'm sure you know the story and how he wrestles with the angel and has his leg put out of joint. But that wasn't all that happened, Lindsey. His name was changed. No longer was he a 'Schemer' and a 'Supplanter', but a Prince with God, as his new name 'Israel' means. Something so profound happened to that man, on that cold, lonely night, when he finally came face to face with himself and God and the two of them fought it out together. Isn't that just how it feels? You want so desperately to let go of what you are and take hold of what He is. It can be a very painful experience, but when it's all over, something will have been done in you, that could have been done in no other way. You will be changed, even though you had to be broken in order to get there. That man was never able to walk the same way again, he was changed for ever – and so will you be, Lindsey. You will one day come to realise that what you lost in that struggle was nothing compared to what you gained of Him."

Jim's words touched something deep inside me, they summed up so perfectly the struggle I had been through. I felt as if no more words should ever be spoken in case they detracted from the truth I had just received. But, after a few moments, a thought occurred to me.

"Jim," I asked quietly, "what significance *did* the ginger biscuit have?" He flexed back in his chair and smiled.

"Well, when he had finished speaking, and it was so quiet you could have heard a pin drop, he picked it up and broke it in half with both hands. It was fresh and crisp and took a little pressure before it finally broke.

'There,' he said. 'That's what God had to do to Jacob. It wasn't easy because he was a hard nut to crack.' There was a bit of a snigger from the congregation at this point but then he pressed the two halves together and put the whole biscuit down on the pulpit. 'Now,' he said, 'if I ever want to break that biscuit up again, all I have to do is touch it gently with the tip of my finger.' He did just that and the biscuit again split in half.

"I don't think anyone missed the point, because it applied to all of us. We never believe how strong our resistance to God is, until He challenges us about something, however insignificant. Then we *really* find out just how much we're willing to yield to Him. Sometimes it can take quite a lot before we finally break and give up to Him. But once someone has been truly broken by God, it takes only the slightest nudge for that person to yield to Him again." Jim looked at me and smiled. "Take courage, Lindsey. However harsh His dealings have seemed to you, you will, most definitely, find a greater ability to yield to Him as time goes by, and find your relationship with Him becoming deeper and more satisfying than you ever imagined possible."

His voice became very serious as he continued. "Most of us cringe from these 'breaking' experiences, but remember this, Lindsey, it's not on the dizzy summer days of God's apparent blessing that the deepest work is done in you. The greater part of it is done during those cold, dark nights, spent alone with God on the banks of Jabbok."

As he finished speaking, I felt as I had done a few times before, after speaking to Ted and Derek, or hearing things said at meetings. Those were the times when I knew that important keys, keys to the Kingdom, had been placed in my hands. Before I had thrown them on one side and pursued my own plans for my life. Now, for the first time, I heard of a Christianity that was much deeper than anything I had ever imagined. It spoke to me of having my own will turned around and allowing His will to be done in my life instead. It challenged me with the choice of following

Him, even if it meant through trial and trouble and all kinds of need. But it promised also that, if I did, I would be transformed, that He wouldn't leave me as I was, but that He would make me a new person, changed beyond recognition and, one day, made just like Him. I wanted so much to share with Jim how I felt, but knew I would never be able to find adequate words and was quite relieved when, just then, Sally popped her head round the door.

"Lindsey, George and Jessica are already arguing about which one of them you're going to sit next to at lunch. Would you make their day by staying?" I gladly agreed, feeling very humbled by their warm display of acceptance.

"Jessica, will you give thanks?" asked Jim when we were seated round the large family dining-table.

"It's Georgie's turn," protested the little girl.

"No it isn't, I did it this morning," returned George.

"Jessica," said Jim firmly. "Give thanks, please." I smothered a smile as she solemnly clasped her hands and closed her eyes.

"Dear Lord, please bring Lindsey completely back from her holiday, and please don't let her have to wear that nasty squint for ever an' ever and . . . "

"Thank Him for the food, Jessica," whispered Sally.

" . . . and thank you for this yummy food. Yours sincerely, Jessica." She looked up at Jim with bright eyes, like a young puppy, waiting for a pat of approval, but Jim slowly shook his head.

"No, Jessica, we went through this yesterday. 'Yours sincerely' is for when you've finished a letter. When you've finished praying, you should say 'Amen' – 'so be it'." He added the latter by way of explanation, but Jessica, true to type, caught the wrong end of the stick. With a deep sigh, she closed her eyes again.

"Amen, so be it," she said, mimicking Jim's tone to perfection. With stifled giggles, we all added our "amens" and started on the "yummy food".

Simple though it was, it was a meal I would always remember. I truly felt like the Prodigal Son, come home after years of wandering in a far country and, as I sat at the dining-table with those four precious people, I knew that I would come to see them as my family. Happily, I joined in with the conversation, which was, at times, quite hysterical, due to Jessica's capacity for getting the wrong end of the stick. But, at the same time, I was mulling over all that had happened since I had left the little farmhouse in the country to begin a new life of my own.

On the surface, nothing had worked out as I had hoped, and even expected it should. Dad hadn't come back after all, my desire for that special someone of my own was still unfulfilled and my glamorous career prospects had been hopelessly shattered. To all intents and purposes, everything had gone wrong. In the light of this, I wondered why it was, then, that deep down inside, I was certain that everything was all right and that none of it had been a mistake. It was a question I wouldn't be able to answer for some time. For the moment, I consoled myself with the knowledge that the light which had, only recently, been a faint flicker of hope, was now burning just a little more brightly than before.

— 17 —

Jim and Sally laughed uproariously as I sat on the edge of their large armchair, tweaking imaginary braces and adopting that grave tone of voice peculiar to Commissioners for Oaths.

"Then what happened?" asked Sally, when the laughter subsided.

"Well, then he suddenly jumped up, spun round on one foot and suggested that we 'say yes' to each other. It was really amazing, because I'd seen some of the other applicants in the waiting-room. They were all much older than me and must have had quite a lot of experience, but he seemed to like me instantly."

"So you accepted the job?" asked Jim.

"Yes. Working for a solicitor's not *quite* the same as being a court reporter, but at least there are vague similarities."

"So when do you start?"

"A week on Monday. I know I've had a lot of time off already, but I couldn't really do anything with it because of my hand and everything. So I thought I'd have a proper holiday next week."

"Are you going to go away?" asked Sally. I paused for a moment and became a little more serious.

"Yes," I said quietly. "I'm going home." They both nodded and smiled understandingly.

"Good girl," said Sally softly. I smiled as convincingly as I could, even though I felt less than confident about the whole thing.

Since becoming a Christian, I had kept up quite regular correspondence with Mum and Uncle Tom and they had frequently invited me to spend my holidays with them, but I had never felt able to take up their offers. With such great distance between us, it was fairly easy to be warm and sociable in my letters, but how, I wondered, would I cope with face to face confrontation. Maybe I wouldn't be able to follow through on the friendliness I conveyed on paper and would revert to the moody, sullen child I used to be. And what about Mum? What if she wanted to touch me and kiss me and do all those things I had never let her do? Had I *really* been healed enough inside to take down *those* barriers as well?

Had it not been for my week of fasting, a lot more time might have passed before such questions were answered, but as that enlightening week came to an end, I had been left with the deep conviction that the first step towards growing up lay in putting things right with Mum. I could see how much of my attitude towards the Lord was a throw-back to my attitude towards her and I realised that if I was ever going to take a step forward, it was time to bury the past.

After lengthy consideration, I had written, asking if they could have me to stay for a week at the farm. Mum had sent a reply in which her obvious joy was barely disguised and this made me feel all the more nervous. So she really was expecting a dramatic change. But what if I did clam up at the last minute and behave like my old self? It was no use wondering though. I knew most definitely that, just as they had been at the Pool of Bethesda, the waters now were troubled and it was time to step in.

Some days later, as I watched the world flash past my window, I pondered the fact that I had never re-gained my affection for train journeys. To me, they always seemed to culminate in some terrible happening or dismal destination and I felt as nervous now as I had been on that journey home from the beach so long ago. As the train clattered noisily down the track, I wondered how to make my grand entrance. Maybe I should be loud and boisterous, completely the opposite of what I had been at home. Or perhaps I should take a softer approach and be the perfect, demure young lady that would plant a gentle kiss on Mum's cheek and sedately shake Uncle Tom's hand. Or maybe it would be better if . . . But before I had invented many more possibilities, the warmth of the carriage and the train's regular motion had sent me off into a much needed sleep. I had spent most of the previous three nights awake, worrying about this very journey, but now, at least for a short while, it could fade into welcome oblivion.

Much later the train drew slowly to a halt at a vaguely familiar country station. The basic outlay was the same as I remembered, although the ageing structure that we had discussed on the morning of my departure was slightly different. In some places, the crumbling woodwork had been replaced by modern panels and everything had been painted a bilious shade of green. Gathering up my coat and small case, I stepped on to the platform and made my way towards the ticket barrier, but before I reached it, a man's voice behind me spoke my name.

"Uncle Tom!" I exclaimed in surprise. "I . . . I hardly recognise you!" Although his basic structure was also the same, there had been a certain degree of change in him too. Those tell-tale streaks of black had disappeared from his hair and it was now completely white, but the most noticeable difference was in his size. Although still a large-framed person, he had lost a terrific amount of weight. His eyes, deep-set anyway, now seemed much further sunken and his face looked gaunt and bony. Such was the transformation, I was worried for his health.

"Are . . . are you doing okay?" I asked hesitantly. He smiled warmly and I noticed that the one thing that hadn't changed was the merry sparkle in his dark eyes.

"Yes, I'm fine. Just a little problem with my heart, that's all. Had to lose weight, you see."

I nodded. "Yes, of course." I put down my case and looked round quickly. "Where's Mum?" I asked brightly.

"Oh, she's back home. Said she wanted to get the meal ready so I left her to it." He paused for a moment and then added, almost as an afterthought. "She's really looking forward to seeing you." I nodded quickly and picked up my case again.

"There's been a few changes at the farm," he said as we pulled out into the road. "Can't do as much as I used to any more." I nodded, only half listening, as we wove down the familiar country lanes that held all my childhood memories and was suddenly engulfed in a wave of nostalgia.

"I can't wait to see it again," I said dreamily.

Eventually, we turned into the familiar driveway and pulled up outside the house. As I stepped out on to the gravel, I thought how much smaller the place looked than when I had seen it last.

"Here we are then," smiled Uncle Tom. "Go straight in, love. I expect Mum's in the kitchen." I stepped into the hallway, feeling more nervous than ever. Uncle Tom followed, pushing the door shut behind him and indicated for me to go in. A few moments later, I stood in the kitchen doorway. Mum was bent over, examining something through the glass oven door, quite unaware that I had entered the room. I drew a deep breath, completely at a loss as to how to begin this significant meeting.

"Hello, Mum," I managed eventually and noticed how thin and strained my voice sounded. She turned quickly and it was immediately obvious that she, too, had undergone a change, though not so dramatic as Uncle Tom's. Her hair, usually worn fairly long, had been cut to a classic short style, much more in keeping with her age, but there was something in her expression that puzzled me. Whatever it was, it counterbalanced the ageing hairstyle, making her look younger than when I had seen her last. She studied me in silence for a few moments, searching my face, as if trying to make sure it really was me, and seemed as unsure as I was about how to proceed.

"Hello, Lindsey," she said at last. "Come . . . come in. Take your coat off." I did so noticing that she kept her distance and didn't try to embrace me, much as I sensed she would have liked to.

"We got your old room ready," said Uncle Tom from behind me. "We thought you'd like to be up there again. Here, I'll take your bag up." I smiled awkwardly and handed him my small case.

"Thanks, Uncle Tom." He headed towards the door and then turned briefly.

"I'll put this upstairs and then I'll just pop over and check on Harry." Mum nodded.

"Okay, Tom." I looked at her enquiringly.

"Harry?"

"He's a new neighbour," Mum informed me. "Tom's got quite friendly with him and they often go fishing together. He's got some kind of flu at the moment though, so Tom's offered to pop in every so often. He's a widower, you see."

I nodded. "Oh, right." There were a few moments of uneasy silence and then Mum turned her attention to the oven and began to bustle round the kitchen.

"I suppose you'll be working now," she began awkwardly as she pulled out a tray of roast potatoes. "It's quite a different world when . . . " Her voice trailed off as our eyes met and she put the tray down. I shifted nervously, wishing I could break the silence with some insignificant comment, but it was no use, I knew very clearly why the Lord had sent me home. Uncle Tom seemed to know too and had deliberately left us alone.

"Mum," I began cautiously, "I really want to say I'm sorry – I mean about the way I was for all those years." She said nothing as she slowly removed her oven-gloves and leaned back against the draining-board.

"I didn't mean to be the way I was," I continued quietly. "But I couldn't help myself . . . I really couldn't." She looked up and smiled.

"I know, Lindsey," she said at last. "It wasn't easy for any of us." Once again, I remembered the days leading up to my departure and wondered, just as I had then, if I really could undo in five minutes what I had built up over so many years. Back then, it would have been impossible, for it was something I could never have done on my own. But there was a difference now. Ever since that life-changing encounter with the Lord, and even through my most recent struggles, I had always known, deep down inside, that I was no longer alone.

I slowly returned her smile. It was a small gesture, something people did every day and perhaps something that had become commonplace enough to lose some of its significance – but not for Mum. It was the first time in almost twenty years that I had smiled at her and I knew it held tremendous significance. To her it would seem as if I had at last pushed open a heavily-barred door, allowing her to step in for the first time in so many years.

"I'm glad you came home," she said softly. "I've missed you."

Her words brought a lump to my throat and tears to my eyes. So she really hadn't felt any bitterness towards me, in spite of my unresponsive attitude and something inside me melted as I realised that she had actually missed my dismal company. Once again, I was aware of how much I was loved and, just as on that Friday night, years ago, I couldn't help but respond.

I drew a deep breath and walked slowly towards her. As I did, I noticed that she didn't move, as if still wary of coming too close. A moment later, I stood in front of her and placed my hands on her shoulders. Feeling my heart beating wildly, I leaned forward and kissed her gently on the cheek. Still she stood her ground, watching me with a mixed expression of wonder and joy. Then, quite suddenly, she threw her arms around me and held me close. It was something else that hadn't happened for almost twenty years and, as I responded at last, the effect it had was dramatic. All at once, I had found her again. Over the years, she had become lost in the swirling mists of resentment and confusion, but now, in that fleeting moment, she had become my mother again. As I felt the joy and relief that swept over her, I realised that yet another new beginning had taken place.

By the time Uncle Tom returned, the atmosphere had completely changed and we had one of the happiest meals I could ever remember having at the farm. We talked excitedly until late into the evening, catching up on all the news and not even noticing when dusk fell and we sat in semi-darkness.

"Well," said Mum eventually. "I suppose we ought to wash up, or it'll still be sitting there tomorrow morning." We all laughed and began to clear the table. Then, when we had finished I was keen to get on with another important reunion.

"I'd like to go for a quick walk round, if it's not too late," I said, looking at Uncle Tom. "I can't wait to see Ben again." He glanced at Mum and I sensed that something was wrong.

"Lindsey, love," he said gently, "Ben died not long after you left." His words were like a crowbar on the back of my neck and I could only stare at him in stunned silence.

"He . . . he was never quite the same dog after you left," he continued huskily. "I suppose he got used to having you around and . . . well, he was getting on anyway and . . . " I nodded slowly and tried to smile.

"Yeah, I suppose he had to go sometime." I looked up quickly, with an attempt at light-heartedness. "Anyway, I think I'll still have a quick stroll round, get some fresh air and all that."

"Of course, love, you go ahead, we'll see you later." I grabbed my coat and let myself out of the front door.

It was a clear night and those familiar hills stood out as black mounds against the navy-blue sky. I strolled slowly round the small farm that had once been my home, occasionally stopping to look up at the stars or to listen to the night owl's ghostly, haunting call. At the five-bar gate, I stopped and placed one foot on the bottom rung, just as I had as a young girl, and remembered how exciting the world once promised to be. Finally, I made my way round to the back yard where Ben used to sleep and sat down on the concrete step. I noticed immediately how vast the empty space on my right seemed to be. All of a sudden, I could see the bouncy young puppy, bounding round the corner with his small, silky ears flapping as he ran. Then I remembered the huge, heavy-footed dog he had become over the years that followed our first hand-shake. And, at last, I could see him lying beside me in his favourite position, his head laid gently on his outstretched paws and his round, black nose poking out from his fur. How clearly I could remember the endless hours I had spent there, with my arm draped over his shaggy shoulders dreaming my childish dreams.

"Well, Ben," I whispered softly, "I kept my promise after all, but I guess I was just a little too late." I drew my knees up into my arms and surveyed that vast, empty space once more.

"Goodbye, old boy," I whispered and then laid my head on my arms and cried.

Sneaking in through the back door and up to my room was a trick I had learned years ago. If I had ever been crying and wanted to get in without having to meet Mum or Tom, it was the ideal solution and one that I had often used. I resorted to it now, but for quite different reasons. The reunion had been going so well that I didn't want to ruin it now by showing how sad I was. Having successfully entered the house without being noticed, I quietly tip-toed up to my old bedroom, not even pausing to look at it properly and fished out a towel and small purse from my case. A few minutes later, I was in the bathroom, splashing my face with cold water. Once dry, I applied a light dusting of grey eye-shadow to my red, puffy lids and finished off my disguise with a thin line of black kohl on the lower rims. My task completed, I studied the slightly blotchy face that stared back at me and sighed.

"Well, it might work," I thought to myself and then began my descent. Mum and Tom were sitting in the lounge and I entered as confidently as I could.

"Hello, Lindsey," smiled Mum. "We were just about to send out a search party." I laughed quite convincingly and sat down.

"I was just going to make some coffee," volunteered Uncle Tom. "Like some?" I nodded eagerly, for my throat was still quite dry from crying.

"Can I help you make it?" I asked.

"Okay, that would be nice." I followed him into the kitchen, amazed that I could still remember where everything was and tried desperately to think of something to say. Obviously, my distress was still apparent and he sensed it immediately.

"I felt like that too, Lindsey," he said quietly. "But you really will get over it." I looked up and smiled. Sad though I was, I realised that Ben's death had been perfectly timed. He had met my need at the time, but now I was able to open myself up to others of my own kind, was re-united with Mum, and I no longer needed to turn to an animal for affection.

"Yes, I know," I said quietly. "And I suppose I had to let him go some time."

The following day was warm and sunny and we had lunch in the open air. By now we had talked about everything there was to talk about – or at least, so I had thought. As the meal drew to an end, Mum looked up at me.

"You know, Lindsey," she said, with a faraway smile, "I've almost lost track of time. You must be twenty . . . "

"Twenty and a bit more," I laughed.

"Sarah!" exclaimed Uncle Tom. "It's very bad manners to ask a lady her age!" We all laughed and then Mum continued.

"Have you got any plans for . . . well, a boyfriend . . . or anything?" I cringed inwardly as she touched the sore spot that still remained inside, but managed to appear casual and light-hearted about the question.

"No, not yet. I'm going to start work when I get home, so I'd like to get settled into my job before I think about that kind of thing." Mum and Tom had never known about Hal, or indeed, about my struggle with loneliness and I was determined that they never should. Furthermore, I was determined that no one else ever should either. Now that I was taking steps forward, I hoped that I would be able to overcome the problem without actually having to admit to it any more than I had.

"Very sensible," said Tom with a wink.

"And in any case," I said, with a reproachful glance at Mum, "I thought you were dead against me having a boyfriend." It was said without malice and confirmed to me all the more that my former bitterness really had gone. To my surprise, it was Uncle Tom that spoke.

"When it comes to romance, Lindsey," he said, with a grin, "you'll find your mother has had a dramatic change of mind." I looked at Mum, who had turned a definite shade of scarlet.

"Mum?" I queried. She looked down and fiddled nervously with her fingers and I noticed for the first time that she wore a ring on her left hand.

"You're engaged!" I exclaimed in joyful surprise.

"Yes," she said, unable to keep from smiling. "He's someone I met at Tom's church." All at once, I realised what that strange light in her eyes was, and felt more convinced than ever of how much younger it made her look, despite her older features.

"We got friendly over a period of time," she continued quietly, "and . . . well, we're going to get married in the new year." I smiled, mainly in surprise, but also out of sheer joy. At last, she had found someone to love her and make up for her the years that had been so sadly lost.

"Can I meet him?" I asked eagerly. Her eyes lit up still further.

"Of course you can. Actually, I've invited him over tomorrow, especially to meet you, but I wasn't sure how you'd feel about it."

I smiled again. "I can't wait," I said sincerely. "I really can't."

That night, I tried in vain to get to sleep, but as this

proved to be impossible, I eventually got up and drew back the curtain. Leaning one shoulder against the window-frame, I looked up at the silver stars and the large moon, shrouded in a pale, glowing mist. As I surveyed that vast expanse of shifting clouds, I suddenly felt too small to contain all the mixed emotions that washed over me. Of course, I was overjoyed by Mum's news, but at the same time, it had struck a deep chord inside me. Although I had often prayed about my feelings of isolation and loneliness, I had never actually asked the Lord for a husband outright. It had always seemed as if He were as dead against the idea as Mum had been and so I had only ever told Him as much as I would have told Derek or Jim. But now, as I beheld Mum's unconcealable joy, I could hold back the question no longer. I wanted a husband too, someone to love me and care for me, just like Mum.

"Lord," I prayed, "you've done such a wonderful thing for Mum," and then, as if I were asking the most unthink-able thing in the world, I added hesitantly, "would you do the same for me . . . please?"

From that day forward, it was a request that I would often make, and just as often seem to receive no answer.

18

The rest of my stay at the farm went without a hitch and I had taken instantly to my future stepfather.

"Now don't forget, Lindsey," he said warmly on the day of my departure, "we want you to come and stay with us next year."

"I'd love to," I replied sincerely.

"And don't go forgetting your old Uncle Tom either," said Tom as he drew his arm around my shoulder.

"As if I could." I smiled.

Later that day, as I travelled home, my mind turned to my new job, now only twenty-four hours away. In spite of myself, I was quite looking forward to starting work as personal secretary to this quaint old solicitor, who looked and behaved as if he had just stepped out of a Dickensian novel. After seeing the job advertised in the local paper, I had gone along to the interview with very mixed feelings, but had been captivated by the sight of the building alone.

It was constructed of some ancient-looking grey stone and dated back to 1888, which date was deeply inscribed in the wall, just above the front door. A large, brass wall plaque, badly in need of a polish, informed me that these were the offices of Messrs Bradbury, Parker and Johnson, Solicitors and Commissioners for Oaths.

Stepping uncertainly into the dingy hallway, which made the one at Albert Avenue look like the entrance to Buckingham Palace, I was transported back in time to the age of Victoria the Good. The wide curving staircase in front of me, winding its weary way to the next floor, was made of bare stone blocks. No holes or markings were apparent to suggest that a carpet to cover its stark austerity had ever even been thought of. Gazing round the walls, I noticed that the original gas lamps, although redundant as such (or at least, so I hoped!) still hung from their ancient holders. Later, as I was given a conducted tour by my future boss, I was intrigued by the mountains of books and original parchments, still bearing their red wax seals, that lay almost concealed beneath cobwebs and years of dust. The final stop on our tour had been the forbidding strong-room, solidly built out of plain red brick and housing hundreds of wills, divorce papers and goodness knew what else. It all conveyed such an air of mystery and suspense that I was quite mesmerised as we proceeded at last to his inner sanctuary – the ancient office of none other than Mr Parker himself.

He conducted the interview leaning back in a round wooden chair and had punctuated his sentences with the occasional tweak of his out-dated braces. With extreme effort, I managed to remain composed as he described in ostentatious detail the grand position that was to be mine if I accepted his offer of employment.

"And so you see, Miss Fairweather," he had said, rising from his seat and walking slowly across the room, "by accepting this post, you have taken on the mantle of my personal and . . . " he turned to face me and dropped his voice to almost a whisper, " . . . *confidential* secretary." He had bent forward as he spoke the last two words and seemed to freeze on the spot for a good few moments until he was sure that his words had made their full impact. Then, he stood up slowly, obviously waiting for a fitting response. Somehow, I knew it would have been fatal for me to speak and so I had, instead, managed a polite smile and nodded silently.

"Very good, very good," he said briskly, obviously under the impression that I was so overcome by the wonderful offer that I was completely lost for words.

"We shall look forward to Monday then. A pleasure, Miss Fairweather, a pleasure." I shook his outstretched hand once more and forced myself not to giggle until I was safely on the pavement outside the firmly-closed door of this strange time-machine.

"I'll be the only secretary," I told Jim and Sally after the interview. "With a junior working under me."

"Sounds quite demanding," murmured Sally.

"Yes, I suppose so, and I haven't got any experience yet, but you know, if I'm honest, I'm quite looking forward to it."

"Well, it's obviously where the Lord wants you at the moment," said Jim. "And I'm sure you're going to really enjoy it."

It seemed, at first, as if Jim was right and I took to my job like the proverbial duck to water. The novelty of starting work at the offices of Bradbury, Parker and Johnson temporarily erased from my mind the struggles I had recently been through. By now, I had fully accepted that my career as a court reporter would never be. This enabled me to give myself completely to the "something else" that the Lord did, after all, have lined up for me – at least as far as employment was concerned. But when the novelty of my new vocation had worn off, my desire to get married began to take on interesting proportions.

Although I had taken some significant steps forward, there were still a number of hurdles to be negotiated before complete victory over this life-long ambition could be mine. Little did I imagine what an uphill struggle lay ahead of me. But neither would I have imagined what it would be like when, at last, the summit had been reached. From that new vantage point, I would be able to see the whole picture from a completely different perspective. Suddenly, when seen from that high place, all the dark shadows and painfully narrow pathways would, at last, make sense and I would realise how bland a picture my life would have been without them. But first, there was the valley.

During those first few months at work, I found myself in a completely different world. The ones I had known so far had been thoroughly woman-dominated. In the Fashions department, I had worked with and served women. All the residents at Albert Avenue were women and the secretarial course I had taken was all-female too. Now, for the first time, it seemed that I was thrust head-long into a world wherein existed Men. I met them by the dozen, every day; other solicitors, accountants, estate agents, even old Fred, who came to fix the typewriters when they were "on the blink", as he put it. They were all very pleasant, and all seemed to find it necessary to ask me two questions of vital importance. Firstly: "How did I like working for ol' Parker then?" and secondly: "Did I have a boyfriend?" I usually replied very positively to the first, and equally negatively to the second. Upon discovering that I was unattached, several would then make amorous advances and I was asked out quite a few times during the early days of my employment.

Some of them were quite genuine and even quite nice, and I was, of course, flattered by such attention. But in every case, I declined their offers as graciously as I could. If I had learned anything from my experience at college, it was simply that a believer could not be unequally yoked with a non-believer. It was a difficult fact to face, but I knew, deep down inside that the consequences of pursuing such a relationship would, ultimately, prove more difficult to handle than it was to accept the truth of God's word.

As the first year of my new employment drew to a close, it seemed as if the Lord had turned a deaf ear to the earnest prayer I had prayed that night at the farm and almost every day since. Whenever I talked to Him about getting married, as I often did now, I was greeted with eloquent silence, yet at the same time, He supplied even the most trivial of my other needs with amazing accuracy and speed. Without variation, however, when I broached the subject of marriage, He seemed to have shut up shop and gone on holiday.

As time went on, I began to feel more and more isolated and, much as I hated to admit it, that dark, heavy cloak which settled upon me first as a very young child, was still there. Like it or not, I couldn't deny the fact that I was a lonely person. But now I was not lonely because there was no one to talk to, or because I was the odd one out at school, or even because I lived physically alone. I was lonely because my emotions and feelings and all the minute, most meaningful things in my life were not shared with another person. Suddenly, I was a single person, in what appeared to be a married persons' world, and wherever I went, I was reminded that to be single was to be odd. A table for two, for instance, posed no problem whatsoever, but the table for one always seemed to be situated at the back of the restaurant, right in front of the kitchen, from whence the humble kitchen porter would flash the occasional, sympathetic smile as he scrubbed his pots and pans. I never tried any of the competitions on the back of jars, partly because they were of little interest, but mainly because the prize always seemed to be a weekend break for two, or tickets to some London opera house – for two, and any number of weird and wonderful rewards – but always for two!

As I struggled to find my feet in this new, adult world, I constantly bumped my nose against the harsh lines of demarcation that separated me, a single person, from what was deemed to be acceptable and "normal". Everything around me seemed to be geared towards married people and their families and I began to feel a complete mis-fit wherever I went. Once again, that familiar sense of not belonging came upon me. I wasn't "special" to anyone, and, for some infuriating reason, it mattered – tremendously.

Nor were my feelings of isolation restricted to the pressures of the media and outside world. Gradually they seeped into my church life too. I was now more conscious than ever of being surrounded by families, particular units, linked together in a special way, and that I was a solitary person, alone, in the middle of them all. Being together with them posed a completely different set of problems from the ones I had experienced at the beginning. Back then, I had been afraid to open myself up and allow others into my life. Now I felt I had opened myself up too much and had become too dependent upon them. Of course, I realised that, in one sense, we were all one big, happy family. But, on the other hand, they had natural families too. They belonged – but I didn't.

Secretly, I hoped I might be going through a passing phase that would somehow just go away, but on the contrary, it seemed to grow steadily worse as time went on. Why, I often wondered, did I have to live in a world where natural, human love was not permissible? Of course, I knew that the Lord loved me, and that other people loved me too, but why couldn't I be loved in a special way, by one, particular person, just like everyone around me? The more I thought about it, the more it mattered that no one ever put their arm around me and told me they loved me, the way Rick told Melanie. Nor was there ever a shoulder that I could spontaneously cry on when I felt down, the way there was for Sally and Barbara and others, and having all those happy, well-meaning people around me only seemed to make things worse. At the end of the day, they would return to their families, and I would return to my empty room, alone, isolated and without a companion of my own.

The problem itself was difficult enough to cope with, but it was complicated by my growing sense of shame for having such feelings in the first place. I was a Christian and Christians, of all people, shouldn't feel lonely and unloved. But the point was, I did! And the more lonely I became, the more ashamed I felt about it, and the more ashamed I felt, the more I wanted to keep the whole thing a closely guarded secret. I could never tell anyone about it, I decided. If they once discovered how I felt, they might begin to treat me differently. Maybe Melanie would become suspicious of my friendly relationship with Rick, who I often laughed and joked with after meetings. And what about the wives? Maybe Sally and Barbara would become suspicious of my constant counselling with their husbands and jump to the wrong conclusions. Maybe even Derek, who had taken me under his wing, and often invited me round to his small bungalow, would begin to back off and think I was in some way dangerous. I imagined they would all begin to look upon me as some kind of scarlet woman, desperate to catch a man at the earliest opportunity, when I knew that all I wanted was a perfectly proper and wholesome relationship with someone I could call my husband.

No, I told myself, it would never do for anyone to find out how I felt about being single. I would just have to arm myself with a dazzling smile and pretend I felt mightily called of God to live the celibate life. Most of the time, I managed to pull off this pathetic charade, but underneath it was quite a different story. Never before could I so fully identify with that pseudo-smiling face of the clown on the circus poster in town. I *should* have scratched it to pieces there and then, I told myself, I really should have! As my feelings became more and more difficult to cope with, I began to feel unnoticed, unattractive, and unnecessary, and as the next two years progressed my attitude began to show in my physical appearance.

Deep down inside, I was angry at God for having made me a woman in the first place, with all the emotions and feelings that went with it. If He really didn't intend me to marry, what had He done it for? My Bible constantly informed me that "marriage was honourable", that the "younger women *should* marry" and that "he that found a wife, found a good thing". Genesis laid out the truth that God Himself had seen Adam's need for a human companion and had set about supplying it in the creation of Eve. This, of course, fuelled my argument that He was, indeed, holding out on me and requiring me to live in a way that was, if not impossible, at least exceptionally difficult. Maybe Mum had been guilty of almost the same thing, but at least she had had some motive for doing so. She had, after all, only tried to protect me from being hurt and I had been able to forgive her for the restrictions she had placed upon me. But what was God's motive for holding out on me? What was He trying to prove by requiring me to be single? The answer, I concluded, was nothing

– nothing at all! He was just doing it because He felt like it, and I couldn't forgive Him for that!

As time went on, and almost without realising it, I found my own way of getting back at Him for being so unfair. If He didn't want me to be treated as a woman, I wasn't going to live like one! In the past, I had always wanted to be bright and pretty and, above all, feminine. I had never been able to understand girls who spent all their lives trying to look and act like boys. But now, I couldn't care less. God, it seemed, wasn't a bit concerned about how feminine and womanly I might be. He expected me to live like some kind of gender-less being, as if I had no emotions and feelings, and if that was what He wanted, that was what He would get! Gradually, I lost interest in myself completely. After all, if no one else was interested in me as a person, why should I be? My physical appearance went rapidly downhill and when, one morning, it was a great struggle to do up the button on my skirt, I could evade the truth no longer – I had put on weight. Of course, I had been aware of my clothes getting tighter for some time, but I had tried not to notice. My ostrich philosophy was, however, not shared by onlookers. One day, I met an old friend from college and my head was rudely extracted from its granular hiding-place.

"Hello, Lindsey," she began, cheerfully enough. "Put on weight then? Must be contented living." I started a little in surprise, for as my frame had become larger, so had my clothes and I had tried to conceal my ever-increasing proportions beneath layers of loose, baggy attire. Somehow, I managed to rally my hurt feelings, and responded as jovially as I could.

"Didn't think anyone would notice underneath all this," I said, grabbing handfuls of my large, shapeless jumper with an attempt at smiling.

"Well, why not?" she laughed. "You only live once, so you might as well enjoy it!" I nodded in agreement and tried to laugh too, for I knew she hadn't intended it to be a hurtful jibe. But hurt it had.

When I got home that evening, I had vague aspirations to solve the problem, but then I wondered why I should. Who cared, after all, if I was slim or fat? No one was going to take much notice either way. And in any case, it was *my* body, and I could do as I pleased with it!

As cooking with my limited facilities had become quite a tedious chore, doing as I pleased meant swapping a healthy, balanced diet for junk food, high in calories, but low in just about everything else. Sometimes, I would skip meals altogether and find myself snacking on chocolate and crisps and similar unnutritious substances, and, actually, I quite enjoyed doing it. Before long, eating had become a means of coping with the depression I had, yet again, sunk into. Not that I ever ate a lot, but what I did eat was so completely lacking in any real goodness that the effects soon showed up in my health. Life at the farm had given me an insatiable appetite for the great outdoors. Even on the coldest of days, my face had been tinged with a vibrant, rosy glow as Ben and I had tramped across those windswept hills. But now I quite often caught coughs and colds and didn't want to do anything except curl up in front of my gas fire, feeling thoroughly miserable.

My sedentary occupation did nothing to help the situation and by the time I met my friend in town, I weighed roughly two stone more than all the good books informed me I should. When they mentioned it, people invariably assured me that I wasn't "fat", just "rounded" or "well-covered", but in truth I was considerably overweight, whatever they said, or didn't say. But I didn't care – or at least, I convinced myself that I didn't.

When the clothes I had worn as a young college student became too small, I built up a new wardrobe of the most unattractive clothes I could find. The jumpers were large and baggy, and designed to hide any curves (most of which, by that time, were in the wrong place anyway), and the skirts were all of some muddy looking shade, made of tweedy material and hung four inches below my knees. The new look was perfected by a pair of completely flat, lace-up shoes and the drastic decision to have my hair cut. In a moment of rashness, I decided I didn't want long hair any more. It was too silky, too soft, too feminine – and I didn't want to be feminine any more. And in any case, who cared if I was?

It had been a terrible mistake. I knew I would always remember sitting in front of the mirror in that rather down-market hairdressing salon. While I focused all my attention on the glossy magazine in my lap, the scissor-happy hairdresser eagerly carried out my instructions for a "short, layered cut". I tried not to listen as the long, dark locks fell softly to the ground, forming a silky carpet around the legs of my chair. When it was all over, I raced out of the shop as quickly as possible, trying to erase from my mind the sight of my crowning glory lying in a glossy heap on the salon floor.

As I walked home, I couldn't help catching sight of myself in shop windows, an almost unrecognisable, pathetic creature that stared back at me for a few, fleeting moments, before turning hurriedly away. To make matters worse, when I got home I realised that it was Thursday and that we would be having a meeting in a few hours' time. My first impulse was not to go that evening, maybe not even until I had been able to get a wig, or fancy hat, or head-covering of some sort. In the end, however, I convinced myself that nobody would notice and went along regardless. Unfortunately, I couldn't have been more wrong.

As I walked through the door, Jessica grabbed Sally's skirt and hid behind her, as if I had been a total stranger and there were a few veiled comments of "liked it better before". The only slightly encouraging comment came from Barbara, who informed me that it quite suited me, before adding, reassuringly, that "in any case, it would soon grow".

I swallowed hard as I sat down and tried to participate in the meeting, but it was a hopeless task. I hardly took in a word that was said, being thoroughly distracted by a strange, draughty feeling around my neck and shoulders

223

and the realisation that I could no longer tip my head forward and hide behind a silky screen of brunette hair. It didn't matter, I kept telling myself, no one was really that interested anyway. Whenever the wide-eyed, astonished faces that had greeted my arrival that evening came to mind, I assured myself that they were only pretending to be interested. If they really had been, they would have told me how nice it looked when it was long!

So it was that the attractive young college student had disappeared – and so had the amorous admirers. No one ever asked me if I had a boyfriend any more, which was hardly surprising. No one in their right mind would have wanted to be seen with the drab person I had become. But I still told myself that it didn't matter and that now I could at least get on with my work without interruptions. In any case, my new image rather suited the staid and stuffy offices of my current employer. So gradual had been the change that I hadn't fully realised what I had become until one eventful Friday at the offices of Messrs Bradbury, Parker and Johnson.

I had been sitting at my desk that morning, reading through a lease I had just typed when the metal eyelids on my antiquated, black telephone began to blink up and down, informing me that "Sir" required my assistance. I picked up the receiver and awaited instructions.

"I'd like a file please, Miss Fairweather," came Mr Parker's voice. I waited for a moment, hoping he would elucidate, but he didn't.

"Yes?" I queried.

"Yes!" came his curt reply. I sighed as quietly as possible.

"I mean 'yes', Mr Parker, *which* file did you want?"

"Hmm? Oh ... er, yes ... let me see. Yes, that's it, 'Morgan', Lily Morgan' ... er ... 'Deceased'." I scribbled the name down on my pad.

"Do you want to see anything in particular?"

"Mmm . . .er, yes, death certificate, please."

"What about . . . ?" My sentence was cut short by a loud click on the other end of the line. I pursed my lips and stared into the silent mouthpiece for a moment before replacing it with controlled accuracy – it was going to be one of those days.

I spun round on my swivel chair and propelled myself in the general direction of the filing cabinet. A few moments later the required folder was in my hands and I searched through the contents for the death certificate. Once located, I scanned it quickly, taking in the relevant details: Name: Morgan Lily. Cause of Death: Carcinoma of the lung. Marital Status: Spinster. As the final word slapped into my mind, I felt as if I had walked into a cold-shower. The poor soul had failed to find lasting love in this life and had gone to her grave, branded a "spinster". I wondered if anyone had mourned her death, or even been with her at the time, and felt it more likely that she had died, just as she had lived – alone.

And what of myself, now in my mid-twenties, I suddenly wondered? Most girls of my age would be married by now, and even have children of their own, but I was a "spinster", just as Lily Morgan had been. I sat on the edge of my desk, wondering if I, too, would bear the same epitaph when my time came when that infernal blinking began again. Grabbing the file, I pushed through the door into Mr Parker's office. He didn't look up as I made my entrance, but continued writing in his scrawly, illegible hand, that caused me endless problems.

"Your file, Mr Parker," I said quietly.

"Hmm? Oh, yes, very good. Now then, just hand me the copy will, if you please." I searched through the contents and handed it to him, holding the death certificate in readiness. After a few moments, he handed me back the copy will and resumed his writing.

"Very good, thank you, Miss Fairweather. You can put the file away now."

"But Mr Parker, what about . . . ?" He looked up impatiently.

"Miss Fairweather, I am uncommonly busy today." That was probably true, I thought. " . . . And I should be uncommonly grateful . . . " and that was *definitely* true! " . . . if you would do as you are asked." I drew a slow, controlled breath and nodded slightly before pushing through the door to my own office. Slapping the death certificate on top of the metal cabinet, I pulled open the drawer and, just as Lily Morgan was once more laid to rest, the door flew open and Sue burst in looking flushed and bright-eyed. Sue was the office junior who worked under me. With her bright eyes and blonde, curly hair, she was every inch the giggly young teenager; unruly, with a touch of good-natured rebellion, and I liked her. As she threw her bag on the desk, we simultaneously glanced at the clock.

"Sue, where on earth have you been?" I asked in amazement. "It's nearly ten-thirty!" An unconcerned smile spread over her pretty young face.

"I know, but I met Tony in town and we went and had an egg muffin in McDonalds," she replied breathlessly.

"Well, you'd better watch it, it's not going to be long before he suspects you're doing more than just 'deliveries' in the mornings." Sue laughed, obviously unperturbed.

"But he's so dishy, Lindsey. Honestly, you've got to meet him sometime." Her constant prattle about her latest heart-throb was just about bearable on the good days, but today, I found it more than a little irritating.

"Well, I hope you can get him to sparkle his baby-blue eyes at Mr Parker when he hands you your notice. I'm not sure he's going to find Tony quite so 'dishy' as you do." She laughed again and hung her coat untidily on a hanger.

"What kind of mood's he in today anyway?" she asked with a grin.

"Oh, just the usual: 'Miss Fairweather do this, Miss Fairweather do that, Miss Fairweather do the other.' Only when Miss Fairweather does this, that or the other, she pretty soon finds out she didn't ought to have done this or that, let alone the other in the first place."

"Oh, I see," she said, still grinning. "Like that, is it?" She turned to face the heavy, supposedly sound-proof door that separated us from Mr Parker's inner sanctuary. "Your wish is my command, oh Great Master," she chanted, bending over to touch her toes in a bow of mock obeisance. Just then, the door shot open to reveal a rather irate Mr Parker.

"Miss Levi!" he growled. Sue sprang into an upright position and I spun round quickly and buried my head in my lease, hoping desperately that I wasn't going to giggle out loud.

"Might I suggest," he said, placing his hands on his hips, "that deliveries to the locality need only take half an hour." He glanced at the clock. "Not *one* and a half? Might I further suggest that coffee is served *promptly* at ten o'clock." Again he glanced at the clock. "It is now ten thirty-five – and a half! And, might I also suggest," he continued, whipping off his glasses, "that morning exercise is taken in the privacy of one's own home, *before* one arrives at one's place of employ – and not afterwards!" I bit my lip and screwed my eyes shut tight in a desperate attempt to remain composed.

"Miss Fairweather," came Mr Parker's voice in my direction, "I have some urgent letters to dictate." I grabbed my pad and pencil and stood up.

"I'll have coffee in Mr Parker's room please, Sue," I said, carefully avoiding her eyes in case I cracked up completely. Satisfied that I had understood his instructions, Mr Parker disappeared through the door, letting it swing softly shut behind him. I glanced round at Sue, whose efforts to keep a straight face had turned her a most peculiar colour.

"I'll have mine black, with two sugars," I said with a grin.

"But you don't take . . . "

"And you can lace his with the washing-up liquid as far as I'm concerned!" She laughed and threw me a mock salute before disappearing out of the door with a tray of cups and a carton of milk.

I pushed through the door to Mr Parker's office, wishing I could make it shut with a loud slam. Obviously, previous secretaries had felt the same way, as someone had taken it into their heads to line the entire frame with green felt. The result was that it brushed shut with a soft thud, something similar to an amplified heart-beat.

For the next couple of hours, Mr Parker dictated letters at a speed that made me very grateful I had put so much into my shorthand at college, and I sensed that it was going to be a typical Friday. This meant that Sue and Mr Parker would leave the office at a reasonably civilised hour, and I would stay behind to ensure that all the day's letters got into the post. As I continued to scribble page after page of those modern hieroglyphics I wondered why it was that everything I pushed under his nose on a Monday as being urgent, never surfaced until Friday, by which time it was desperate and simply *had* to get off that evening. In truth, I didn't really mind. I was, in fact, quite enjoying my employment, particularly probate work, which Mr Parker was gradually letting me deal with independently. As for the man himself, despite his officious manner, he was, underneath it all, a kindly old gentleman who would not have deliberately done anyone harm. However, I often had to remind myself of this fact when he was in a less than amiable frame of mind.

After lunch, I passed on the local searches and other standard work to Sue and concentrated on typing up my shorthand notes. Then, just as predicted, Sue departed at roughly five o'clock and Mr Parker a few minutes later, advising me on his way out to "have a good weekend". I returned his remark and continued with the last few letters still to be transcribed into legible English. Half an hour later, everything was "signed in his absence" and duly stamped, so I decided to call it a day.

As I picked up my bag and grabbed my coat, I glanced round the room, ensuring that everything was in good order, and noticed a document lying on top of the filing cabinet. Having become quite a perfectionist, at least when it came to work, I couldn't bear the thought of it lying around until Monday morning. I snatched it from the cabinet, and stopped suddenly, realising that it was the death certificate of the unfortunate Lily Morgan. My eyes fixed on the taunting word once again: "Spinster". Lily Morgan was a "spinster" – and so was I!

As I walked home that evening the word haunted me as never before. As if to magnify its significance, the town seemed particularly full of couples travelling home together after a hard day's work. My self-pity mounted with every step, blowing the situation up out of all proportion until I was almost not thinking rationally. Although only in my mid-twenties, I was convinced that I had been left on the shelf and was destined to be a spinster for the rest of my life. Not for a moment did I stop to think how exaggerated my thoughts would seem if heard by an onlooker, for I was completely swallowed up in my feelings. Even the Lord seemed irrelevant at that point and I chose not to remember what a very real friend He had been to me as a young Christian. Right then, all I wanted was a real, human companion, just like everybody else and I wondered why He wouldn't let me have one.

When I got in I flung down my bag and hung up my coat. I felt cold and damp and miserable and decided that a hot shower would at least remedy my physical discomfort, if nothing else. Grabbing a towel, I headed for the bathroom, hoping to find it vacant, and I did. Heaving a deep sigh, I bolted the door and was about to pull off my jumper when I caught sight of myself in the full-length mirror attached to the opposite wall. As I stood, immobilised, staring at my own reflection, all doubt was then erased from my mind. I had, indeed, turned into a spinster, in every sense of the word. My short haircut had added at least ten years to my age and my drab, shapeless clothes hung limply around my well-covered form like over-sized curtains. Although only in my mid-twenties, I would have passed easily as an "old" thirty-five.

I turned quickly away, trying to push the depressing picture from my mind and continued with my shower. This proved to be far less therapeutic than I had hoped and I returned to my room feeling worse than before. Closing the door behind me, I stood with my back against it for several moments, running my fingers through my wet hair, shocked at how quickly they slid through the ends. What would Mum and Uncle Tom say if they could see me now.

I might have stood there for some considerable time, indulging my sense of miserable failure, had I not begun to shiver with cold. Reluctantly, I decided to swap my towelling bath-robe for something a little more substantial and I pulled open a drawer in search of some underwear. As I did, I was reminded, yet again, of how little self-esteem I possessed. All sight of frills and lace had disappeared long ago and the underwear I now owned would have been better placed in the armoury of a medieval jousting knight, than the bedroom of a young woman. Frills and lace were nonsense, I had decided. Foundation garments should be practical and do the job they were designed to do. And in any case, no one was going to see them anyway!

Gradually, I sank deeper and deeper into my miserable despondency, which was made worse by the anticipation of a long-awaited event. Only a couple of months away was the wedding of Rick and Melanie. We had all been very much involved in the preparations, and I tried to appear as excited as everyone else about it. I had been quite involved in the behind the scenes work and had put in a lot of time helping with the reception arrangements. But, although genuinely happy for both of them, underneath it all, I was dreading the moment the ceremony took place. When it did eventually arrive, it was every bit as distressing as I had imagined. I slipped into the back row, as inconspicuously as possible and watched as Melanie walked slowly and serenely down the aisle. She looked so beautiful and Rick was equally stunning in his smart grey suit, that I couldn't help wishing it was my big day instead. The service was fairly short, but very touching and, although I had sung and smiled in all the right places, deep inside I was terribly upset.

After the wedding things seemed to go from bad to worse and my loneliness became almost unbearable. I tried to maintain an out-going, gregarious attitude, but was unable to keep it up for very long. Whenever we were together as a group, my feelings invariably got the better of me and I felt even more isolated than when I was physically alone. One incident, in particular, lived on in my mind for a good while after it had happened.

One Saturday afternoon, we had all decided to go for a hike through the woods behind Albert Avenue and to end up at Jim's for a barbecue. It was something we had often done and an activity I particularly enjoyed when I first joined the fellowship. Now, however, these corporate outings were becoming an increasing problem. If ever that uncomfortable feeling of being tagged on arose, it was then. I usually found some convincing reason for not joining in, but on this occasion, I had failed to come up with a reasonable excuse. Despite my misgivings, I went along anyway and it proved to be just as awful as I had anticipated.

As soon as we reached the woods, the couples got together, hand in hand and began a romantic ramble through the undergrowth. The children ran off to play hide-and-seek and I was left alone, watching the love-struck wanderers disappear into the distance. Normally I would have turned to Derek, but this time, he had stayed at home with a cold. As the last couple moved out of sight, my feelings rose to the surface yet again. It wasn't fair, I told myself, as angry tears trickled down my face. How could God do this to me? Didn't He care how I felt, watching others enjoying the relationship I had so much wanted myself? What was He trying to prove? What had I done that was so wrong he had to punish me for it like this? I decided I couldn't take any more. Quite certain that no one was watching, I doubled back the way we had come, not looking round once until I at last found myself alone, in my room. Weeping bitter tears of frustration, I promised myself that I would never go on another fellowship hike. I would come up with some excuse – any excuse, but I would never, ever be caught in that awful position again. Of course, I still went to meetings, and was still quite friendly with the folks there, but I stopped relating to them quite as openly as I had before. But they didn't seem to have noticed, I thought to myself. They were probably glad that I wasn't on their doorstep every five minutes, like I used to be. In only a short space of time, I became convinced that, actually, I had been quite a nuisance and only got in the way of their own private, family lives if I did call round.

This, in reality could not have been further from the truth. My latest struggle had caused considerable concern amongst the others. But I wasn't ready yet to let them in and share it all. I was still very worried about what they might think if ever they discovered how I really felt. But, if the truth were known, it was even more because I was too proud to admit to the problems that were still apparent in my life. If I ever did pluck up the courage to call round and see them, I would always arm myself with a tape that I was returning, or a book I had promised to drop round, or anything else I could think of that would enable me to make a quick get-away if it was obvious I had called in the middle of a family time. If this did turn out to be the case, I wouldn't even stop for a quick cup of coffee, but would return, instead, to my most recent pastime of wandering aimlessly through the vast woodlands at the back of Albert Avenue. This was what happened one day, when I had decided to call on Jim and Sally.

Even before I reached the gate, I realised from the absence of Jim's car outside the house that they had gone out. I sighed miserably as my plans for a morning in their good company disintegrated and wondered how I could best spend the time now.

It was a bright Saturday morning, promising that yet another glorious spring was just around the corner and so, with nothing more pressing on my mind, I decided to go for a walk through the local woods. As I set off in the familiar direction, I remembered the hundreds of tiny green shoots, pushing up through the leaf-mould floor that I had noticed the week before and was actually quite eager to see how much they had grown. Making my way through the endless corridors of trees, I arrived at my favourite spot. There, like a giant corpse, lay a large, ivy-covered tree. Obviously uprooted years ago by some fierce gale, it had fallen, never to rise again. From its gnarled trunk, one large branch reached up towards the sky, forming an excellent seat against which to rest my back. The water table in that part of the woods was quite high and a natural reservoir had formed, not many yards away. From the centre of this rose the smooth, barren limbs of another dead tree. Completely devoid of any life of its own, it had become the home of another life that had established itself as part of the landscape – a solitary wood pigeon.

Every time I made my way to this place, it was there, singing a low, warbling song. It didn't appear to have a mate and I wondered at the sweet melody it was able to make despite its lonely existence. Many were the times I had sat and listened to its sweet, wordless music and I had come to feel a strange affinity with the little creature. We seemed to have a lot in common. We both liked that particular part of the woods, and shared an interest in singing and, perhaps most important of all, neither of us had a mate. The only difference was that she was happy and able to sing in spite of it all, whereas I was miserable and, on that particular day, quite angry.

I had tried so hard not to give in to my feelings that morning, but, as I sat with my back against the bark, I found myself once again raising my bitter arguments to God. Why, I asked Him, yet again, was it all right for everyone else to have a companion to share their lives with, but it wasn't for me? The whole idea had been His in the first place, so why did he expect me to live the way He did? Looking up, I reflected on the beauty all around me; the sunlight glinting through the tangled web of branches overhead and glistening on the water, just yards from where I sat. But I was unable to enjoy it

233

fully, for, in contrast with my surroundings, I felt ugly and screwed up inside.

For quite some time, I sat listening to the sounds of nature all around me, feeling as if I were the only person in the whole of the universe. I became so caught up in my web of solitude and self-pity that I hardly noticed when the sun had ducked behind a cloud and the bird had stopped singing. But, gradually, I noticed that everything seemed to have become very still and quiet, and even the rippling water close by seemed to make only the slightest of sounds. Then, in the ever-deepening silence that followed, I recalled my conversation with Ted, years ago.

"Did you just stop being angry?" I so clearly remembered asking him. Once again, I saw his face, with that warm, rosy glow shining through the sallowness of his pale complexion and his blue spectacles sparkling like diamonds.

"No, Lindsey," I could almost hear him say. "There was a very important step I had to take first."

Acceptance. I rolled the word round in my mind, like the silver ball in the small game I had played with on Uncle Tom's back step. I had tried so hard to make it land in the tiny hole, barely big enough to hold it, but had always been unable to make it stick. It was the same now, with that uncertain word.

Could I ever accept the fact that the Lord might require me to be single for the rest of my life, I wondered? Slowly, I began to weigh up what it would mean if I did. I could have taken up any of the offers made to me during my early days at the solicitor's office, but I had chosen not to because of what I believed. Could I really give up the thought of ever having someone of my own, and of ever experiencing that kind of love that seemed commonplace and permissible for most of the world's population? And even if I could, would I one day look back on my long, lonely life and wish I had had a family of my own? Then, reluctantly, I thought back to my experience with Hal and was able, for the first time, to see it for what it had really

234

been. At the time, I had convinced myself that I was in love with him, but now, upon reflection, I realised that it was not Hal that I had been in love with, but love itself. I had wanted a boyfriend, just like all the other girls at college. I had enjoyed the way he had made me feel, but now I was certain I had never really been in love with *him*. It had been a difficult situation at the time, but what I was faced with now was far more intense. Now it wasn't just a case of giving up a boyfriend. Now, I was weighing up the whole question of why I was a woman at all.

God had, in the beginning, created a woman for a man and now He was asking me to give up the very thing I thought I had been created for. Once again, I remembered the struggle it had been to let go of my career and ambition. At the time, it had been one of the hardest things I had ever had to do, but what I was faced with now made that experience seem like a picnic. Now, after years of striving, it no longer mattered to me what I did, what mattered more than anything was what I was. And, like it or not, I was a woman – God Himself had made it that way!

I sat for quite some time, turning the whole thing over in my mind, until all my colourful hopes and dreams spun round so quickly that the colours finally blended into one and I knew, deep down inside, that there was only one possible thing to be done. I looked up, squinting against the glare of the cloud-covered sun. Right in front of me, growing close to the water's edge, stood another large tree. It was not yet in leaf, but heavily budded, promising that, in a short space of time, it would be covered in a glorious green mantle.

"Lord," I prayed silently, "remember how You turned up and appeared to Gideon when he sat under that oak tree, centuries ago? He was in a pretty rough situation, but You turned up and gave him the strength to do what he had to do. I'm not sure this is an oak tree, but I suppose I feel a bit like he must have felt. This is the most difficult thing I've ever had to do." I paused for a moment, wondering if I would be falling into the category of "tempting God", but eventually concluded that I might as well continue as He knew the innermost thoughts of my heart anyway.

"It would be so much easier, Lord, if you turned up now – I mean in a physical form, and spoke to me." I thought for a moment about how silly my request would have sounded if spoken audibly. But, on the other hand, I had seen visions before now, surely this wasn't too ridiculous or, indeed, difficult, a request for Him to comply with.

"If only you said *something* to encourage me," I continued silently, "it would be so much easier to do what you want me to do." I had closed my eyes whilst praying and, after a few moments, I slowly opened them, hoping to see, if not the Lord Himself, at least a fairly reasonable representative. He didn't even have to be wearing a bright, dazzling robe, a plain white one would do, just as long as he had a message for me. But the clearing was thoroughly devoid of heavenly ambassadors. Not even the tip of a flaming sword was apparent and I sighed in defeat. The silent pigeon tipped its head on one side and fixed me with one piercing eye, vaguely reminiscent of Jim when he was at his most disconcerting.

"Okay, Lord, I guess you win," I sighed. "I suppose it would be a bit too easy if you turned up right now. I suppose I wouldn't need any faith if you did it that way, would I?"

So the time had come to take that all-important step that Ted had spoken of several years ago and that I had, unknowingly, stored away for this very moment. But, even though I knew what had to be done, I didn't feel a bit like doing it. I thought back to Derek's experience of giving thanks, when his wife had died, and remembered how he had done it in spite of himself, and then I remembered Jim's words about Jacob. If ever I could have identified with the ancient Patriarch, it was now. He had found himself alone, on the banks of the Jabbok, having lost everything he had ever worked for, face to face, alone with God. It wasn't nearly so dramatic a setting as Jabbok, and I had never felt more as if God had hidden His face, far from being right there with me. But there was nothing else to be done.

"Lord," I began hesitantly, after quickly looking round to make sure no one was listening. "I don't feel a bit like doing this, and I suppose you know that anyway. But I want you to know that I accept the fact that you won't ever allow me to get married." I thought for a moment. Maybe that was a bit strong, after all, when Abraham had been willing to give up Isaac, hadn't the Lord stepped in and stopped him doing it? Maybe he just wanted me to be *willing* not to get married and, once I had convinced Him I was, maybe He would allow me to after all. Maybe I should rephrase my sentence. But it was no use, I knew, more clearly than ever, what He wanted me to do. I drew a deep breath and spoke to Him again.

"I know I could be wrong about that, Lord, and that you might let me one day. But I think you want me to make the commitment as if you really have said 'no' for ever, otherwise, it would only be a conditional acceptance." I thought once again of all that I was accepting, and all that I would be letting go of and then, quickly, in case I changed my mind, I made my acceptance complete by adding some final words, spoken by the Lord Himself, so long ago.

"Not my will, but Thine be done." It took all the strength I possessed to say them and, far from feeling better, as Ted had, I felt completely shattered. On the whole, however, I felt it had been quite a rousing performance that warranted at least a short guest appearance by my heavenly Master. But, even then, He was all the more conspicuous by His absence.

I opened my eyes and gazed around me at the unruffled normality of the quiet surroundings. No one had even been aware of the heart-rending, life-changing decision that had been made that day beside the sparkling waters of those peaceful woods. All at once, there was a flapping of wings and the little pigeon flew off into the distance. I watched until it was out of sight then, digging my hands deep into my pockets, decided it was time that I, too, headed for home.

19

"So yours is the impossible task of keeping Sue under control?" asked the tall, blond and exceedingly handsome young man who stood with his arm around my office junior. At last, I was face to face with her beloved, blue-eyed boyfriend, and he was every bit as dishy as she had led me to believe.

"I'm afraid so, Tony," I said, smiling. "And I think it's going to turn me grey by the time I'm thirty!"

Sue pouted reproachfully. "Oh, come on, Lindsey, I'm not *that* bad, am I?"

"No, not really. Actually, Tony, you could do a lot worse."

"Yeah, well I agree with you there," he said, gazing at her admiringly. Sue looked down at the floor as a faint flush crept over her face.

"Is it okay if we go off then?" she asked shyly.

"Yes, I'll be fine. I promised Mr Brayne I'd hang on for him."

"Mr Brayne? What's he want?"

"He's moving away, down to my neck of the woods actually. Wants to pick up some papers we've been holding for him. He said he could only make it during the lunch hour."

"Oh, well, in that case, here's some reading matter." She handed me a glossy teenage magazine and grinned. "I'm not sure it's exactly your scene, but it's better than nothing." I glanced at the smiling faces of obscure teeny-bopper idols, displaying rows of dazzling white teeth and silently agreed with her statement. However, it had been a very sweet gesture and I accepted it graciously.

"It looks great," I said enthusiastically. "Thanks. Have a nice lunch – and watch her with the chips, Tony, she's got a passion for them." They both laughed and left the office arm in arm. As the door swung softly shut behind them I sighed and then returned to the pile of papers on my desk.

It was roughly a month since I had taken the great step of acceptance in the woods, that chilly Saturday morning and, since then, I had never mentioned the question of marriage to the Lord again. It wasn't that I didn't want to, but simply because I had cold-bloodedly decided that He had nothing further to say on the subject and if He didn't wish to discuss it further, neither should I. The main benefit derived from the experience was that I was able to concentrate more fully on other things and had begun to take a greater interest in my work. Mr Parker had been so impressed with my new enthusiasm that he had felt confident enough to take a week's holiday, leaving me to hold the fort. It was quite a demanding responsibility, but, nevertheless, I found myself actually enjoying the challenge.

I glanced at the clock and saw that twenty-five minutes stood between me and my appointment with Mr Brayne. I couldn't leave the office until he had been and had arranged to take a late lunch hour. With nothing else to fill in the time, I decided I would flick through Sue's magazine after all.

As I turned the pages one by one, I found myself transported back to my turbulent teenage years, when I had bought the same magazine myself. In fact, I was quite amazed that it was still in existence. The basic layout was the same, with the usual cartoon-style romances, and their inevitable happy endings, the beauty tips, fashion information and problem page. The only differences were in the names and faces it now contained. After glancing through it apathetically for a few minutes, I was about to close it up when I noticed one small face that I was certain I had seen before. Picking up the magazine, I peered at it more closely for, although it was vaguely familiar, the face it reminded me of had belonged to someone I thought had been younger and much happier-looking. Upon closer inspection, my suspicions proved to be correct.

There, staring blankly back at me, with an expression of utter misery, was the wife of the sad singer who had influenced me so much. As I studied her unsmiling face, I remembered how this very woman had caused me to shake an angry fist at God. Together, she and her superstar husband had summed up everything I felt the Lord was withholding from me and I had told Him so in no uncertain terms. At the time, it seemed as if he had ignored my challenge, but in reality, I had been too deaf to hear the answer He had actually given. Now, as I read the small article beneath the sad picture, I was almost unable to take in what it said. The couple had now split, in a bitter, heart-rending divorce.

When I looked again at the clock on the wall, only seven minutes had elapsed since I had picked up the magazine, but during those few, significant minutes, God had begun to revolutionise my thinking and, consequently, my life. During those minutes, I began to see even more clearly than when I had fasted, that loneliness had roots far deeper than the natural eye could see. The sad singer had been a lonely man, on the inside. Getting married had not changed what he was, it had merely made him a married lonely man. For a few moments, it was as if the clouds had shifted, allowing a single beam of brilliant sunlight to pierce through the gloom of an overcast day. For the first time, I realised that my loneliness existed on the inside too, and that it was from the inside that its healing had to take place.

I continued staring at the glossy pages on my desk, but seeing nothing, my mind elsewhere, listening at last to the voice I wanted most in the world to hear. I had always believed He had nothing to say. Only then did I realise that He had been wanting, all along, to say so much, but I had always been unable to listen. Years ago, He had wanted to tell me that a relationship with Hal would not have solved the problem that had far deeper roots than I would then have believed. As I looked back, I was able to admit that I would have expected a lot more from him than he would have been able to give, and perhaps he had sensed it too. Now I could understand that marriage would not have solved the problem and that a natural man could only have satisfied my surface needs for a time. Far from holding out on me, the Lord had actually stopped me entering a relationship that would have proved inadequate to meet my real needs.

During those seven, priceless minutes, the first few notes of a new melody rang out from the darkened stage that had once been my mind; clear, concise and shortly to be joined by many others until they finally swelled into a rich chorus of majestic beauty – the song had already begun.

Just then, my glorious revelations were interrupted by the trilling of the door-bell, which I knew would be followed moments later by a knock at my office door. Hastily, I slid the magazine under the pile of filing and stood up in readiness. Just as predicted, the awaited knock came and, at my bidding, a tall, professional-looking man stepped into the office.

"Good afternoon, Mr Brayne. You've come for your decree nisi," I smiled, holding out a brown envelope with his name inscribed across the front.

"My decree . . . ?" He looked a little dazed and I smiled sympathetically.

"Your divorce certificate, Mr Brayne," I said quietly.

"Oh . . . oh yes. Well . . . thank you – and thank you for staying open for me."

"That's quite all right, and I hope things go well for you now that . . . "

"Yes, well, I'm just glad it's over, that's all." He shook my hand and made a pretence at smiling.

"Goodbye, Mr Brayne," I smiled back.

A few moments later, the door swung shut behind him and I returned to the filing on my desk. I flicked through it quickly, finding a home for each sheet of paper and had just reached the bottom of the pile, where lay the divinely-deposited, glossy magazine as Sue burst through the door. She smiled wryly at supposedly catching me red-handed.

"Hmm," she grinned. "So you liked the old teeny-bopper magazine then?"

"Actually, Sue," I said, smiling, "you won't believe this, but I thought it was great!" Her mouth dropped open in surprise.

"You did? But I thought . . . "

"Anyway, I'm off to lunch now. Nothing too terrible should happen while I'm out and I'll phone anyone back this afternoon." I paused for a moment. "Well, anyone except Mr Rogers. I'm leaving *that* one for Mr Parker to deal with himself." She grinned and nodded knowingly.

"Serves him right too. He should have dealt with it when you mentioned it to him." I smiled and disappeared into the teeming masses outside, my newest thoughts still rolling around in my mind and the first beginnings of something like hope rising inside me.

As the next few months unfolded, my new insight remained fresh in my mind, as did the step of acceptance that I had taken. But even though something had very definitely taken place deep inside me, I was a little perturbed that none of it had seemed to make too much difference to the feelings on the surface. Although I had never mentioned the question of marriage to the Lord again, I still felt lonely and isolated and had been convinced that He would, by now, have begun to do something about changing such emotions. To my surprise, however, He began His work in some completely different areas of my life. This work was so subtle that, at first, I hardly realised there was any connection between it and my current problems, but it all started with a few verses from the good book.

Ever since that Saturday morning, years ago, when I had returned home with my first Bible, I had hungrily devoured page after page and had read it from cover to cover more than once. Now, as I continued with this exercise, I found myself bumping into scriptures that I had read many times before, but which had never seemed quite as meaningful as they did now. All of them seemed to have one thing in common: they were all concerned with my physical being. There was the one that informed me that my body was the "Temple of the Holy Spirit", while others told me that I was to "Glorify God in my body, and in my spirit", which were God's, and even that I was "bought with a price" and wasn't "my own". Everywhere I looked, the message rang out loud and clear: my body wasn't my own, to do with as I pleased, as I had been guilty of declaring so many times of late. Instead, it belonged to God and He was interested, not just in the hidden realms of spirit and soul, but in this very tangible, physical expression of my life.

Gradually, I realised that my feeling of not belonging had affected not only my mind and emotions, but my outward appearance too. I had thought no one was particularly interested in how I looked, or even behaved, and if they weren't, neither was I. Now there was no hiding from the truth that stared me so blatantly in the face. I was His temple, the place where He had chosen to live and, quite frankly, far from being a suitable dwelling-place for this majestic Being, I had provided Him with a tumble-down shack of a place that was badly in need of renovation. Now I saw how bad a testimony I had been and why it was that not many people had seemed convinced when I had told them of the wonderful new life that was available to them upon accepting Christ. A cursory glance at my own life would have been enough to convince them that they were doing just fine, and perhaps even a little better without Him.

One by one, I turned the thoughts over in my mind, like pages of an enchanting novel, of which each chapter was better than the last, and I wondered into what kind of glorious culmination all the loose and seemingly unrelated ends would eventually be drawn. As the story that was my very own unfolded I began to see that the drab, despondent image I had created did not stop even at my physical appearance, but was also apparent in the kind of atmosphere I had, unknowingly, created around me. As I dwelt on this latest concept, an incident from my early days in the north of England returned to my mind.

It had happened one Friday evening, when the washing-machine at Albert Avenue had broken down and I had been forced to take my weekly wash to the local launderette. It was warm and deserted and strewn with an assortment of newspapers and I settled down quite happily to read the latest headlines. My blissful state didn't last for very long however. Not five minutes into the *Daily Mail*, I noticed, with extreme irritation, that the door was being pushed open by a familiar figure. It was Jake, the local tramp, who roamed the streets every day, in all weathers, and seemed to exist solely on his findings in the local litter bins or hand-outs from those who felt sorry for him. I had often seen him sitting in the launderette as I made my way home in the evenings, but had never encountered him at such close quarters before. Now, as he sat just a few feet away, I couldn't help noticing what a miserable, wretched bundle of humanity he was.

Despite his obvious lack of finance, he smelt heavily of drink, his clothes were less than clean and an air of hopeless failure hung about him, like floating cobwebs in a dusty attic. I remembered how some of his depressing attitude had rubbed off on me, dragging me down and making me feel, to some degree, how he must have felt himself. Once out in the fresh, evening air, I had been able to forget the incident, but now I remembered so clearly the atmosphere that he had brought with him and how tangible, how powerful it had been. Now I realised that I had been guilty of doing the same thing.

My clothes were clean, but they were drab and depressing, and everything about their shapeless protectiveness gave out unmistakeable signals. They advised would-be visitors to keep out and made the atmosphere I created around myself as drab and depressing as my appearance. The more I thought about it, the more I could see how true it was. At home, I had kept myself to myself, not bothering to speak to any of the other residents except Miss Peters. At work, I had always thought Mr Parker officious and stand-offish, and wondered why he would never condescend to address me by my Christian name. And at the fellowship, I had always expected people to reach out to me and include me into their lives.

Viewing myself as from a great distance, I was able to see that I had created around myself a cold, hard, professional exterior and had become a past master at holding other people at arm's length. Now I could see how hard they had tried, but, after a few times of bumping their noses against the solid brick walls I had built around myself, they had all but given up. Could it be, I now wondered, that it was not other people, but I, myself, that had created the cold, clinical and lonely world in which I existed?

They were scattered, unstructured thoughts and I felt certain I was not immediately grasping their full significance. But, for the time being, I stacked them carefully on the shelf of my sub-conscious store-cupboard, like a set of new tools, awaiting the right time for them to be put to use.

The only other noteworthy event that took place during those enlightening months was that I became irresistibly drawn to an attractive item in a shop window which I passed every day on my way home from work. Such was my obsession with it that I felt I would have no peace of mind until it became mine. One Saturday morning, I handed the cash over to the shop assistant and walked out with it in my possession at last. Hardly stopping to examine it more closely, it was immediately put to use and, a short while later, I stood panting outside Jim's gate, having turned up in acceptance of their invitation to lunch. Jim, who had been clipping the front hedge, stopped immediately and looked up at me with a rather puzzled expression on his face. Usually, it was him that caused me to be lost for words and I noticed, with a fair amount of satisfaction, that this time, the roles had been reversed.

"Lindsey, what on earth . . . ?" I struggled for a moment

to catch my breath and felt my face glowing with exertion.

"I . . . I've run . . . all . . . the way," I panted breathless. Jim's brow furrowed in confusion and I couldn't help giggling.

"This is my new tracksuit," I explained, breathing more easily. "I only bought it this morning. Like it?" Jim nodded, still looking slightly mystified.

"It's very nice, Lindsey, but why . . . ?" I stepped inside the gate and removed a small bag from my shoulders.

"I'll tell you later," I laughed. "Mind if I have a shower?"

"No, not at all, come in." We walked into the house together, much to Sally's surprise on seeing my flushed face and uncharacteristic get-up.

"Lindsey! What on earth have you done to yourself?" she asked in amazement.

"It's okay," said Jim humorously. "It's all under control. Lindsey wants a shower." Sally laughed.

"Okay, tell me later. Lunch'll be about quarter of an hour."

"Quarter of an hour!" I gasped. "I'll never make it in time."

"Not if you stand there talking," muttered Jim drily. I laughed and raced up the stairs. Ten minutes later, I appeared, feeling greatly refreshed and tingling all over from my athletic escapade.

"Why are you on the run, Lindsey?" asked George, when we sat down to lunch. "Is someone after you?" I glanced quickly at Jim and Sally, who seemed just as curious as George, but were making a famous job of concealing the fact.

"Well, sort of, George," I replied mysteriously.

"Is it the police?" asked Jessica, with wide eyes. "There's someone in my book that was running away 'cause the police were after him."

"No, Jessica, it's not the police."

"Now come on," interrupted Sally. "Let's get this lunch eaten, you can talk to Lindsey afterwards."

"Yes," muttered Jim, without looking up from his plate.

"After *we've* talked to her!" We all laughed and set about devouring our lunch.

"So why *are* you running?" asked Sally as we sat out in the garden later. Eagerly, I began to recount what the Lord had recently shown me about being His temple and taking care of my physical body because it was His. They listened attentively and a look of relief swept over them both.

"Praise the Lord," muttered Jim under his breath. I looked at him enquiringly.

"Well, we were all getting a little concerned about you, Lindsey," he explained. I looked down at the ground, feeling suddenly ashamed of myself. They had all tried so hard to encourage me to take more interest in myself and smarten up my appearance, but I had always lacked the incentive and advised myself that there was no point in it anyway. Now, at last, I was able to see things from a different perspective.

"I've only just realised how much it matters," I continued. "And that what people see on the outside is a reflection of how I am on the inside." Jim nodded.

"Yes, that's very true."

"Anyway, I'm going to run every morning before work as I don't have to be there till nine-thirty." Sally raised her eyebrows.

"All right for these part-timers," she said sarcastically. I looked at her and grinned.

"And I'm going to stop eating all that greasy junk food and things in between meals too. It was just so convenient, especially as this 'part-timer' doesn't usually get home till seven in the evening." Sally laughed. "I thought I could have a proper meal out at lunchtime and then have something a bit more nutritious in the evening."

"Well, it can only do you good, Lindsey," smiled Jim. "Not just naturally, but because you're doing it in obedience to Him – and the outcome of obedience is always good."

Jim was right and, over the next few months, a gradual change began to take place. Of course, there were still times when my feelings of isolation and loneliness would get the better of me, but my life had already begun to take a new direction. True to my word, I ran faithfully every morning; four miles during the week and five on Saturdays – on Sundays I allowed myself a morning off! In addition to this, I ate a much healthier diet and after a while, noticed that my formerly sallow-looking complexion had regained that vibrant, rosy glow for which I had been notorious as a child. But, without a doubt, the thing that gladdened my heart the most was that my hair had begun to lose its severe boyish look. It had always grown much faster than the normally accepted half an inch a month and was now well below my collar. As the layers grew out, I noticed that they turned up into little curls, giving the whole style a much softer, more feminine look.

Gradually, I began to take an interest in myself again. This task was made easier by the knowledge that the Lord was interested in me, even if I was a single person and I began to feel happier about myself than I had been for a very long time. It wasn't the same, bubbly happiness that I had experienced on the night of my conversion, or even at times when I had been with Hal, but it was somehow deeper, richer and more meaningful. Best of all, it stemmed not from the fact that everything seemed to be going my way, but from the fact that, at last, I was listening to Him again and being obedient to what He spoke to me day by day.

In spite of the obvious, all-round improvement I was slightly bothered by a vague, niggling sensation in the back of my mind. For a while, I had been conscious that there was yet one more step to be taken in order to make my obedience complete, but, in a funny kind of way, it frightened me. Taking this vital step would mean finally letting go of everything that, for me, had come to typify safety and security, and embracing instead I knew not what. I felt tenuously suspended, like some novice trapeze artist, desperate to make the exhilarating leap to the opposite swing, but having first to let go of the one I was holding and being, for a few, terrifying moments, suspended in thin air. It would not be an easy step to take and I tried to project it as far into the future as possible. However, it became obvious one morning that it could not be put off for very much longer.

I had just returned home from an enjoyable Christmas spent with Jim and Sally with three days of my official Christmas holiday left. This, I had decided, would be an excellent time to carry out an early spring clean of my room and my first plan of action was to wash the curtains. Balancing precariously on the arms of my easy chair, I began unclipping the hooks one by one, but had not got very far into the task when a strange thing happened. As I reached up for the next hook, my skirt swivelled round, dropped two inches and settled on my hips. I looked down in surprise, but assumed that the button had come off – *that*, I advised myself, was the price one paid for putting on weight – since it had been a severe test of my skill and dexterity to arrive at my present position, I decided to continue with the task in hand and to deal with the skirt afterwards.

A few moments later, the curtains lay in a heap on the floor and I carefully made my descent in order to examine the skirt. I swivelled it round, fully expecting to see a bundle of loose ends where the button had come off or, worse still, a split, somewhere in the region of the zip, but, to my great amazement, the button was still intact and the zipper completely done up. The skirt, however, still hung on my hips and utterly refused to remain around my waist, no matter how many times I hitched it up. Of course, it was only to be expected that as my diet altered, so would my weight, but the expectation didn't make it any less exciting when, at last, it began to happen.

Without further ado, I rushed downstairs to the bathroom and pulled out the scales that Miss Peters had kindly donated for common use upon purchasing a new pair of electronic ones for herself. Hardly daring to breathe, I stepped slowly on to them, allowing the needle to creep gradually forward, pound by pound. A moment later, it stopped and my heart sank. They were obviously broken and registered my weight as being half a stone less than it should have been. Feeling more than a little deflated, I stepped off and allowed the needle to spin back to its original position. I thought I would set it correctly and give it one more try. After a few seconds, the needle had settled and I blinked in surprise as it had landed fairly and squarely on the nought. Reluctant to raise my recently shattered hopes again, I tapped the scales a few times with my toe, but each time the needle returned to the same place. A sudden thrill of excitement raced through me as I stared at the little red marker. Then, hurriedly, almost in case they changed their mind, I stepped on to the scales once again. Sure enough, they informed me that I was half a stone lighter than when I had used them last.

Hardly able to contain my excitement, I rushed back to my room and began trying on all my clothes. Thinking back, I *had* noticed that they had become a little more comfortable recently, but I had put this down to the fact that long use had stretched the fabric. Now there was no mistake about it, they were all far too big and my grand spring clean was postponed whilst I got busy with a needle and thread and took in all the waistbands. The jumpers, I decided, would be all right and didn't look any bigger or baggier than they had always done. This task accomplished, I returned to my cleaning with renewed vigour, feeling on top of the world.

Over the week that followed, I wondered, several times, whether I had taken my skirts in enough as they still seemed very loose and I couldn't possibly believe I had lost more weight already. By Saturday, after a week of hitching them up in vain, I could contain my curiosity no longer and made for the scales as soon as I got up. The suspense was almost unbearable as I watched the needle creep forward, almost expecting it to tell me the worst. A moment later, however, I gasped in delight as a further four pounds were unaccounted for. Thrilled beyond words, I rushed excitedly up the stairs, almost bumping into Miss Peters. It was funny, I thought quickly, how she seemed to have a strange ability to always be in the right place at the right time. I flashed her a dazzling smile and wished her a good morning.

"Same to you, dear," she said, returning my smile. "You look happy today, had some good news?" I nodded vigorously.

"Yes, I've lost eleven pounds!"

"Goodness me, I wouldn't smile about it, dear. Where did you have it last?"

"On my hips, I think." She broke into an aged, silvery laugh and I noticed again how much younger her face looked when she smiled.

"Oh, I see, it's those kind of pounds, is it? Well, congratulations, dear." She glanced surreptitiously in all directions, as if we were at a crowded cocktail party, surrounded by any number of foreign spies, rather than on the stairway of a quiet, seemingly deserted house. Then, leaning forward, she employed her characteristic, confidential tone of voice.

" . . . and I must say, dear, your hair looks *so* much prettier now that it's got a bit longer." I felt myself blushing and smiled at her shyly.

"Oh, thanks, Miss Peters . . . I'm growing it long again." She patted my shoulder and nodded.

"Good for you, dear. I've never cut mine – a woman's crowning glory, you know." I smiled admiringly at her grey bun and nodded.

"Yes, I think so too."

"Anyway, I must let you get on. I was just on my way to . . . just on my way." I smiled sweetly and decided not to give away the fact that I had already suspected her of a little harmless snooping, as was her wont, and continued my dash up the stairs.

Once safely in my room, I flopped down on my easy chair and tried to sort out the jumble of mixed emotions that spun round in my mind. I was ecstatic about the fact that I had lost weight, although this would not have been at all apparent, due to the concealing nature of the clothes that had become my trade-mark over the past few years. But, on the other hand, that strange, compelling uneasiness returned once more. In the light of these recent events, it was obvious that I could put off my next step no longer. After making a quick phonecall, I continued with my usual Saturday routine. Then, at roughly three o'clock, I grabbed my coat and headed for the other side of town.

— 20 —

Jim, nonchalant as ever, sat back in his chair, hands folded behind his head and nodded calmly. Apart from a slight twinkle in his eyes, he displayed no other emotion. Had he not been a Christian, I could easily have imagined him lolling on a street corner, clad in trench-coat and trilby, blowing blue rings of smoke into the air from a large cigar. He was Mr Cool personified and, if I hadn't known him better, I might have thought him uninterested. Sally, as always, was quite the opposite, expressive and forthright and, if ever opposites attracted, this was certainly true in their case. She sat cross-legged in a large armchair, jerking one foot up and down until her slipper almost bounced off the end, at which point, she would quickly curl her toes back and catch it just in time. Each time she completed this exercise, my tension mounted so that when it finally did fall to the ground, I almost fell off my chair in sympathy.

"Well," she said, leaning forward to retrieve the fallen slipper. "We'll come on one condition." I raised my eyebrows and shrugged.

"What's that?"

"That you take our advice and . . . "

"You do as you're told," finished Jim with half a smile and Sally nodded. I pursed my lips and sighed, knowing that they were fully justified in setting such conditions. Of all the folks at the fellowship, they had tried the hardest to encourage me out of my widow's weeds and into something bright and feminine, but I had always shrugged off their advice, and not always in the best of spirits. Now I had shared with them that terrifying next step which I had tried so hard to put off.

"I've lost so much weight," I explained, "that I'm going to have to buy new clothes. But the thing is," I continued, feeling suddenly self-conscious, "I feel as if the Lord wants me to break out of the mould I've put myself in – you know, the 'frumpy spinster' look." They both nodded as I continued. "It's going to be so difficult, though, because I know that, left to my own devices, I'm going to end up buying all the same things again. I don't think I've got the nerve to buy anything really different and in any case, I wouldn't know if it really suited me or not. That's why I thought of asking you and Barbara to come with me," I finished, looking at Sally.

It had been a very humbling step for such a proud person as myself to take and, as I had waited for Sally's response, I indeed felt as if that moment of suspension in thin air had arrived. Now, as she agreed to go with me, it seemed as if that opposite trapeze was within my grasp at last.

"Okay, I promise," I said, referring back to their conditions. Jim stretched his arms out in front of him and looked up at the ceiling.

"Right then," he said briskly. "What about one Saturday next month? The sales should be really good by then." As he spoke, and I realised that it really was all going ahead, I suddenly began to panic.

"Well, I haven't asked Barbara yet," I said, clutching at any straw that might delay the terrifying expedition for just a little while longer.

"She won't mind," said Sally, getting up and pushing her feet into her slippers.

"But shouldn't I ask her first, just in case . . . "

"She won't mind," repeated Sally emphatically and then turned to Jim.

"Looks like you'll be playing nurse-maid then, Jim." Jim sank back into his chair with a look of exaggerated despair.

"Oh no, Sally, George and Jessica on my own, for a whole day?"

"Exactly," she said, with a bright smile.

"But Sally, how can you do this to me?"

"Quite easily," she said, bending over to kiss him quickly. "Who was it wanted eight?" Jim groaned and looked at me accusingly.

"See what you've got me into, Lindsey," he muttered in defeat.

"Anyway," continued Sally as she headed for the door, "Ken's going to be at a loose end, so maybe he could give you some moral support." We all laughed and a date was eventually set approximately four weeks ahead. On the appointed day, I was already at Jim and Sally's house when Ken and Barbara arrived.

"Hi, mate," called Ken, with a sympathetic wink at Jim.

"Am I glad to see you," replied Jim, who was up to his elbows in washing-up water with George and Jessica running circles round him. "Got any ideas for these two?"

"Yes," replied Ken. "A couple of strait-jackets in the boot." We all laughed, leaving Ken to explain to Jessica what a "straight" jacket was. Then, after a quick cup of coffee, we set off promptly in order to get a full day's shopping in.

As Sally and Barbara fastened their seat-belts, I sat in the back seat, unsure whether I felt more nervous or excited. When we stopped at the lights, I suddenly leaned forward, clutching the back of Sally's seat.

"Sally," I said sheepishly, "I'm nervous."

"Nervous!? What on earth have you got to be nervous about? I wish I could get the kind of 'word from the Lord' that you get!"

"Me too," agreed Barbara. "Could do with a new wardrobe myself."

"But the thing is," I continued, ignoring their hilarity, "it's just that . . . well, I've dressed like this for so long . . . what if I end up looking really stupid?"

"Well, one thing's for sure," commented Barbara drily, "you won't end up looking half so stupid as you sound.

Ever heard of a little thing called 'faith'? It'd make a nice change from all this negative stuff." I flopped back into my seat as she turned to smile at me.

"Okay, I won't say any more," I muttered and looked out of the window.

As we turned the corner, I noticed a young girl on the pavement, vaguely reminiscent of Jessica and my thoughts drifted back to Jim and Ken. Secretly, I had been wondering why they had thought we would be out for the whole day, as I felt sure we would be back well before lunchtime. After the first hour, however, I began to see how mistaken I had been. We had trudged through endless shops and boutiques, only to leave again, empty-handed. Without variation, I had turned my nose up at everything Sally and Barbara had suggested and had gravitated towards the tweed skirts and baggy jumpers. By eleven o'clock, I had had enough.

"Sally, why don't we give up and go home?" I whimpered as we stood on the kerb. "Maybe this wasn't such a good idea after all."

"Give up? We haven't even started yet. Come on, we can cross now." Reluctantly, I followed them across the road, doing my best not to pout and revert to the immature and childish behaviour that usually got the better of me at times like this. A few moments later, we stood in the women's department of a local chain store, and I began half-heartedly flicking through a rail of skirts.

"You're looking at the wrong size, Lindsey," advised Barbara from across the floor. I examined the size marker and frowned.

"No, it's okay," I informed her. "These are all size fourteen."

"Like I said," she replied firmly, steering me away from my rail. "You're looking at the wrong size." I sighed helplessly. This was turning out to be anything but the nice little shopping expedition I had imagined. But, there again, since fixing our date, I had lost even more weight. The total gone was now almost two stone and I tipped the scales at my ideal weight of seven stone twelve, so maybe it was just possible that I might be a size smaller.

"Okay, where are the size twelves then?" Sally, who had apparently not been paying too much attention, suddenly grabbed my arm.

"You're a size ten, Lindsey," she said decisively. I gasped in horror.

"Sally, I've never taken a size ten in my life, not even before I put on all that weight."

"Look Lindsey, not only have you lost a great deal of weight, but you've also been exercising, which means you're much more toned up than you were back then. You're a size ten and you've got to change your mind about yourself. C'mon, over here." She was holding a shimmery blouse, in some nondescript colour, in her other hand. It had black buttons and a black neck-tie and didn't look too startling. At least she'd got the colour right, I told myself, but once again, I was wrong.

"Excuse me," she said, addressing an obliging sales assistant. "Have you got this in red?" I shuddered as she spoke. Red was the colour I would have worn years ago, to the school discos and it always reminded me of how depressed I had felt afterwards. I had hardly worn it since leaving school and considered it far too bright and flashy, and definitely not me.

"Yes," smiled the assistant. "What size is madam?"

"Twelve," I said definitely.

"Ten," replied Sally and Barbara simultaneously. I huffed quietly and scowled at Sally who was successfully ignoring me, whilst Barbara dived behind a rail of skirts, doing her best not to smile.

"Madam is a size ten," said Sally sweetly to the confused assistant.

"Right, I won't be a minute then." As she disappeared, Sally began to hum a little tune to herself and then turned to smile at me.

"Hungry?" she asked brightly. "We'll stop for lunch in a minute." I pursed my lips a little tighter in order to stop myself from smiling, but it was no use and I broke into a reluctant laugh.

"Sally, sometimes you make me so cross," I protested indignantly.

"Yeah," she sighed. "Jim kind of says the same thing." At that moment, the assistant re-appeared, holding a replica of the nondescript blouse in a rather glorious shade of scarlet.

"Hmm . . . very nice," murmured Sally. "Er . . . thank you."

"My pleasure," smiled the assistant and disappeared again. Sally held the blouse up against me and looked at it with her head on one side.

"Yes, it suits you very well – hang on to it." She stretched out my arm and draped the blouse over it. "Now, where's Barbara got to?"

"Over here," came her familiar voice. "I've got the skirt." She held up a black pencil skirt, that looked so short, I suspected it would have only just been a modest length on Jessica. And, to top it all, it was in that infernal size ten!

"Yes, that's great," said Sally enthusiastically. "Now, what's over here?"

Over the next half hour, the heap of clothes draped over my arm had grown so large that I was almost relieved when we headed in the direction of the fitting-room. The assistant handed me a large, plastic tag, with the number of items blazoned across it and I was just about to disappear through the entrance with Sally in tow, when she stopped us.

"I'm sorry," she said pleasantly enough. "But we don't allow anyone else in with the customer."

"That's okay," said Sally. "Just put the stuff on and come out here and show us, Lindsey." I glanced quickly round the shop floor, where scores upon scores of bored men were standing around, obviously waiting for their wives or girlfriends to appear in their latest acquisitions. The thought of having to appear myself and prance around in front of all those people was quite terrifying.

"But Sally," I whispered, "what about all these people?"

"What about them?" she asked calmly.

"They'll all stare at me," I said, feeling yet again like an embarrassed schoolgirl, rather than a young woman in her mid-twenties.

"Well, I suppose we could ask them all to go home for half an hour."

I scowled again and disappeared down the long corridor of curtained cubicles as Sally called after me.

"Don't forget to put the shoes on as well, so we can get the skirt length right."

Once inside my cubicle, I drew the curtain sharply and noted, with slight irritation, that it didn't quite cover the doorway. But what did it matter, I asked myself? I was going to look stupid enough in a moment, so I might just as well get on with it. I sat down on the small stool, undid my sensible flat lace-up shoes and examined my new ones. They were made of black patent leather and were so shiny that I could literally see my face in them. The heels were two inches high and the toes culminated in a delicate point. I thought them quite dainty, but had grave doubts about how practical they would be. Once I had put them on and assured myself that I would get used to them in time, I turned my attentions to the scarlet blouse.

As I removed it from the hanger, I noticed how soft and shiny it was in contrast to the plain cotton blouse I had just removed. In spite of myself, I couldn't help liking how it felt against my skin and spent several moments just running my hand up and down my arm, letting its smooth silkiness glide across my palm. It was like nothing I had ever owned before as, in my former student days, I had always gone for the casual look and had practically lived in jeans.

All of a sudden, I remembered that Sally and Barbara would be waiting for my grand appearance and I hurriedly removed the black skirt from its hanger. I pulled it on quickly, almost willing it not to fit so that I could change it for a larger size, but to my utter amazement, it slid easily over my hips and the button did up perfectly. Even so, it was short, far too short, I decided, but in reality, it only just cut across my knees. I bent over and lifted the hem, hoping that if they persuaded me to be stupid enough to buy it I could at least let it down when I got home, but my idea was soon shattered. It was machined right on the very edge, with no spare material whatsoever. I sighed and straightened up, catching sight of myself in my new attire for the first time.

I had never considered myself to be pretty, any more than I had considered myself to be sweet as a child. My nose was all the wrong shape and my face was far too round, and even if I *had* been a good-looking kid years ago, I certainly didn't think I was now. Indeed, to my mind, only those girls with the classic, high cheekbones of the *Vogue* fashion model could be considered pretty, not those with round faces like mine. But, nevertheless, there was something that even I found attractive about the young woman that stared back at me from the full-length mirror on the wall. I remembered so well the pathetic, sallow-skinned and overweight creature that had confronted me in the bathroom mirror at Albert Avenue some time ago and could hardly believe that the person I now looked at had been hidden underneath all along. My face was slightly flushed from bending over and my hair, now well down on my shoulders, was thrown forward, looking full and feminine again at last. I turned sideways, almost unable to believe that this slim, efficient-looking person was really me. In a few, short moments, I had changed from a frumpy spinster into a bright, smart young woman and I could hardly believe my eyes.

"Lindsey?" Barbara's voice rang down the curtained corridor and I suddenly jolted back to reality. Grabbing my handbag, I made my way nervously towards the entrance, hoping that no one would pay too much attention. As I peered round the doorway, I caught sight of Sally, propping the wall up with one shoulder and staring calmly at the hordes of bargain-hunters that pushed and jostled all around her. Barbara was nowhere in sight.

"Sally," I hissed as quietly as possible. She turned quickly and looked me up and down. "What about this then?" Before she could answer, a wolf-whistle rose from somewhere to my left and I spun round to see the culprit. One of the formerly bored men seemed to have brightened up considerably and stood with one thumb pointing at the ceiling.

"That's the outfit, love," he grinned. "Suits you really well."

Sally smiled wryly. "Well, how much more confirmation do you need?"

I knew I had turned the same colour as the blouse, but somehow it didn't matter.

"Hey, that looks really nice, Lindsey," said Barbara, who had re-appeared. "Go and try the rest on." Feeling much happier, I disappeared back into the fitting-room and tried on the next outfit that had been draped over my arm.

The skirt was white, with all-round knife pleats and looked very clean and crisp. The blouse was jade, with tiny white daisies peppered all over it, each with a small, black eye. I noted in passing that it would look just as good with the black skirt as it did with the white one. When I emerged the second time, the wolf whistling man had vanished, leaving Sally and Barbara to convince me of how nice this outfit looked. And so, after a potentially disastrous beginning, it looked as if our shopping expedition was going to be a success after all. At roughly two o'clock, we stopped for lunch and, several purchases later, made our way wearily home.

"Thanks for coming," I said sincerely as we pulled up in Albert Avenue. Barbara said nothing, but simply smiled.

"Well, just make sure you wear it all," cautioned Sally. I jumped out of the car with countless plastic carrier bags, bulging as if they would split at any moment.

Once inside, I mounted the stairs with lightning speed, hoping desperately that I wouldn't bump into Miss Peters "just on her way", which, thankfully, I didn't. Puffing slightly, I closed the door behind me, dropped the bags on my bed and set about making a cup of coffee. Once my caffeine level had been sufficiently boosted, I began to unpack my acquisitions one by one. This task was executed slowly, and with the greatest of care, as if the articles were made of glass and as I laid out the soft, shimmery blouses and pretty skirts on my bed I suddenly felt ashamed of myself all over again.

"Lord, I'm sorry," I said quietly. "I've been so stupid. I thought nobody cared or was interested in me, but Sally and Barbara have spent the whole day being interested. But, more than that, *You're* interested, it was You who really made all this possible."

As I surveyed the new clothes, laid out so carefully on my bed, I was reminded, yet again, that I was not "my own", but His and that He cared about every detail of my life, even down to what I wore and what I did with my physical body. I might be a single person, but He cared about me as much as a husband cared about his wife. Knowing this had at last given me the incentive to take an interest in myself and feel it was all worthwhile.

When I woke up the following morning, the first thing I set eyes on was a large black rubbish sack, containing most of my old clothes, although I had decided to keep just a few. This was not because I wasn't thrilled with my new wardrobe, but simply because, underneath it all, I was still very nervous about the whole thing. Supposing I got cold feet at the last minute and couldn't bring myself to wear my new clothes. I had felt self-conscious enough in the shop, just trying them on, but now the thought of actually having to wear them every day was somehow quite terrifying. In the end, I decided to keep a few of my best old clothes just in case. The others I was going to take to a local charity shop on Monday morning.

After a hot shower, I dressed slowly in the white skirt and jade blouse and put on a necklace that Sally had persuaded me to buy. Even in my younger days, I had never worn jewellery and had always considered it a little over the top, but now, in spite of myself, I had to admit it did add a certain something to the outfit. As a finishing touch, I wove my shoulder-length hair into a neat French braid and secured the end with a brightly coloured band. Then, feeling very nervous, I made my way down the stairs and waited for Ken to arrive. Not much later, his familiar green car pulled up and he leaned out of the window.

"Good morning," he said, smiling broadly. "I'm looking for a certain Miss Fairweather. Does she live around here?" I blushed and smiled sheepishly at him.

"Ken, stop it, it's bad enough without comments like that."

"Just ignore him, Lindsey," advised Barbara. "You look lovely."

"I never said she didn't," protested Ken as I slid into the back seat and glanced at my watch.

"Hey, we're a bit late, aren't we?" I asked, partly because I thought we were, but mainly in order to change the subject.

"Yes," said Barbara drily. "Ken cut himself shaving this morning."

Ken sniggered. "Well, someone told me I would have to pick up a very attractive young woman this morning, so I had to look my best." Barbara raised her eyebrows and shot me a sympathetic smile over the back of her seat.

In actual fact, I was quite glad that we were going to be late, as this would mean that the meeting would be well under way by the time we arrived and no one would immediately notice my new look. I would most definitely make for a seat in the back row and perhaps that way I would manage to remain inconspicuous until the meeting was over. My clever scheming, however, did not account for a certain young lady in the row in front of me. She sat with both arms draped over the back of her chair and admiration shining out of her soft brown eyes.

"Jessica, turn round!" commanded Sally, for the third time. The little girl reluctantly obeyed, but couldn't help fidgeting and half turning her head at regular intervals. At the end of the meeting, she was the first person to voice her opinion on the "new Lindsey".

"Lindsey, Lindsey!" she squealed, bounding up to me and throwing her arms around my waist. "You look like . . . like a princess!" I picked her up and whirled her round in the air, causing her to squeal again in delight. A few moments later, I set her safely back on the ground and held on to her until she was steady on her feet.

"Know what, Jessica?" I asked happily. "I *feel* like one!"

So, my first, grand appearance as a "new person" had gone better than I had expected, but the following morning proved a little more difficult. Just the thought of facing Mr Parker and Sue with my new look was totally unnerving. I had decided to arrive in good time and to be seated at my desk, as innocently as possible and was hoping neither of them would take too much notice. However, I might just as well not have bothered.

"Wow!" gasped Sue as she strolled through the door. "What's up, got a man in your life at last?" I thought for a moment before answering. She had quite often told me that I was "unusual" and "full of surprises" and I decided now to live up to my reputation.

"Yes, Sue," I smiled, "there is a man in my life." A look of sheer amazement filled her eyes.

"Really? What's his name?"

"You wouldn't believe me if I told you." Before she could question me further, Mr Parker strutted through the door and stopped dead in his tracks.

"Hmm . . . er . . . yes, good morning, Miss Fairweather," he muttered fuzzily. "You look very . . . er . . . smart. Yes, that's it, very smart." I could feel my face flushing, but managed to thank him for the compliment before he had quite disappeared through the heavy oak door. Sue let out a low whistle.

"Bet that's the first time he's ever given a woman a compliment," she said scathingly.

She could have been right, and certainly, it was the

first he had ever given me as a person, but such compliments were not confined to Mr Parker. After only a short while, the steady stream of admirers returned. Of course, I never allowed my relationship with them to go beyond platonic friendship, but their flattering attention helped me immensely in the task of regaining my self-esteem and pleasure in being a woman. I might be single for the rest of my life, I concluded, but I certainly didn't have to look down on myself because of this fact. I could be just as worthwhile as married women and I was to realise this more and more as time went on.

But hard though it had been to change my outward appearance, making a similar change on the inside proved to be infinitely more difficult. Sometimes, in spite of the significant progress that had been made, I still felt lonely and wished that I were married. It was then that my attitude was once again reflected in my appearance and I would fish out the old clothes I had kept. Even though they were now far too big for me, when I just couldn't face being the "new Lindsey", it was strangely comforting to hide behind their shapeless protectiveness for a while. But, surprisingly enough, it was actually the bad days that proved, even more definitely, that something inside me really had been changed. Even as I went to wallow in my self-pity once again, there was something that just wouldn't let me do it. I couldn't just let myself go any more, much as I would have liked to. I didn't have a husband, it was true, but I belonged to Someone who had loved me enough to give His very life for me. In view of this, I couldn't any longer indulge my feelings, I had a responsibility to take care of myself, for Him. Of course, it wasn't easy to do it at first, but as I began to determinedly obey that inner voice, an amazing thing happened. I began to understand that the feeling of isolation and loneliness itself was able to lead me into a deeper and more meaningful relationship with the Lord than I had yet experienced.

Even during my most difficult struggles, I had always prayed (except, of course, during the days that had preceded my week of fasting), but my prayers had become very polished and "professional". I had always tried to say the right things, things I felt the Lord wanted to hear, even when this had meant saying the opposite of what I really felt. Ridiculous though it was, I had convinced myself that one couldn't really be honest with the Lord. One had to say what was right and proper and respectful – He was, after all, God. But He was also my Father and Friend, an all-seeing, omnipresent God, who knew the innermost thoughts of my heart better than I knew them myself. One day, despite trying hard to maintain my perfect, submissive attitude, my feelings got the better of me and my polished, professional prayers had flown out of the window. Before I knew it, I was pouring out to Him the inner depths of my heart. I didn't use any of the right phrases to describe how I felt, and I didn't leave anything out. I had kept it all to myself for long enough, I decided, and if I couldn't tell Him, who could I tell?

How long it was before I was finally through, I wasn't quite sure, but the result was surprising. I had thought I would feel at least a little condemned for talking to God in such an open, honest way, but I didn't. Instead, I felt relieved and released, rather like a child might feel after climbing up on to Dad's lap and having a really good cry. The problems might still be there, but I had shared them, they weren't just mine any more and I didn't have to cope with them alone. Furthermore, I realised that it didn't matter to Him if I *was* down, and that He certainly didn't mind if I told Him so. He loved me regardless and actually wanted me to share it all with Him. This wasn't just so that I could wallow in self-pity for a while, but simply so that once I had been open and honest with Him about what my real problem was, He could begin to show me some open and honest solutions.

As this new understanding developed still further, I found myself actually grateful for the times when I felt down and realised how right Jim had been. The "dizzy, sunny days of God's apparent blessing" were wonderful, but there was something even more wonderful about coming to Him when I *didn't* feel blessed. Indeed, it was then that I discovered how strong and able He was to help me through a situation that I once would have found impossible to cope with. Something very special happened inside me during those times and I often reflected that, had it not been for the down days, I might never have come to know what a faithful Friend He could be.

Not only did He listen, He also spoke and gradually the answers to those difficult times became apparent. On the days when I felt like hiding behind my old clothes again, I deliberately did the opposite of what I wanted to do. If convenient, I would go for an extra run and have a refreshing shower when I got home. Then I would make a point of putting on my best clothes and take extra time over blow-drying my hair. This alone made me feel physically better, but they were also symbolic actions, my way of telling the Lord (and myself) that I really didn't want to be the old me any more. And when the exercise was complete, I went a step further.

As I had begun to pray honestly about myself, so I had also begun to pray honestly about other people and consequently had begun to see them in a much more honest way too. In times past, I had been convinced that they didn't have any problems and that only I had been called upon to suffer in a particular way. But gradually, I began to see that they had their trials too. Despite her happy disposition, Sally also carried her own particular burdens. Barbara often grieved over an un-saved son and the others in the fellowship were not, by any means, exempt from their own personal struggles. Whenever I was tempted to lick my wounds and give in to my self-pity, it was these things that I deliberately remembered. Then I would get on my knees and pray for them as honestly as I prayed for myself.

At other times, I would remind myself of all the things the Lord had done for me and as I did, so many people came to mind that were in far worse circumstances than myself. There were those faithful souls in communist Russia and Red China, suffering unspeakable persecution, simply because they dared to name the name of Christ. And then there were those a bit closer to home, like Mrs Barton, the partially-sighted widow downstairs, or some of the probate widows I had come to know through my work and who had invited me to visit them.

As I took up their invitations, and began to reach out to others in a practical or spiritual way, I was overjoyed at the great sense of fulfilment that this exercise always produced. At first, it was a little difficult to do for others what I had always expected others to do for me, but as time went on, I realised that I actually wanted to bring pleasure to other people. I *liked* listening to Miss Peters' endless prattle, because, underneath her starchy exterior, I sensed that she too was lonely and needed someone to talk to. And, as my attitude towards other people changed, so did their attitude towards me. People of all ages and backgrounds would invite me to visit them and I was as thrilled to realise that they actually wanted me around as I had been when I had first taken Ben's small, silky paw into my hand and received his token of acceptance. As I reflected on these things one evening and realised how much happier I was, I also realised that, had it not been for my own struggles, I might never have become concerned for anyone except myself.

But, best of all, I sang. During my seven-day fast, I had, once again, discovered the transforming power of music. In my younger days, it had been the wrong kind of power, inspired by the wrong source. But the music I now played and sang was praise and worship to God, which praise He was said to inhabit. Whenever I got my guitar out and began to sing, I never failed to find release from my introspection and self-pity. How well my Bible advised me that the "garment of praise" was the perfect antidote for the "spirit of heaviness".

Before very long, the old Lindsey had become a thing of the past. I didn't think like her, speak like her, or even look like her any more, and no one was more overjoyed about this than me. And, even if I did have the occasional bad day, I was able to view it objectively and after a while, those difficult days became valuable experiences from which I learned so much. In the end, I decided that the old Lindsey really had gone for good and that I didn't want to behave like her ever again. One day, I got together every remaining item of my old clothing and took it all to the local Scout jumble sale. It was the most exhilarating thing I had ever done and I walked out of their hall feeling ten foot tall. At last, I had let go and caught hold of that opposite trapeze and it felt wonderful!

21

So began the dramatic change I would never have dreamed possible and I traced it back to the cold-blooded step of acceptance I had taken on that bleak January morning in the local woods. Now, eighteen months later, I was amazed at what had transpired and, my heart overflowing with gratitude, I decided once more to visit my favourite place and thank the Lord for what He had done.

Upon arriving, one thing was evident: the woods had undergone the same degree of transformation as I had. Back then, in early spring, everything had looked bleak and barren, but now it was almost summer and new life was apparent everywhere. Little wild flowers had sprung up in the most surprising places and the warm breeze blew my hair gently across my face. As I reached my favourite spot, I looked up at the tree, beneath which I had hoped so desperately for the Lord to appear. It was now covered with a rich green mantle of leaves, proving that it was an oak tree after all, just like the one Gideon had sat under, all those centuries ago. It might well have been coincidence, but I allowed myself the luxury of believing that it had been planted there, just for me. The Lord really had been there all along, even though I had believed the complete opposite.

The only change that saddened me slightly was that, although the woods were now full of chirping, brightly-coloured birds, the little grey pigeon was nowhere to be seen. I never saw it again and often wondered what had become of it. Maybe it, too, had discovered a new life and ceased to be the solitary being it once was. I missed it terribly but knew, deep down inside, that some day, all former things would pass away, but that the new would be infinitely more glorious, despite the pain of present loss.

At this point in my life yet another loose end was tied up when my bell rang early one Saturday morning. Wondering who it could be at such an unearthly hour, I rushed downstairs to find an unfamiliar man standing a little nervously on the doorstep.

"Er . . . Lindsey? Lindsey Fairweather?" he asked uncertainly.

"Yes," I replied, slightly mystified, but he volunteered no further information. Unsure exactly what was expected of me, I studied him in blank silence for a few moments as the vague notion that I had seen him somewhere before crossed my mind. Then, quite suddenly, I gasped in amazement, wondering how I could have been so blind. There was no mistaking the deep-set eyes and high, rounded forehead, echoed so perfectly in my own features.

"Dad!" I whispered under my breath, hardly able to take in what was happening. He nodded silently and seemed to tremble just a little as he spoke.

"I . . . I wanted to come and see you," he volunteered hesitantly.

Still wondering if I was awake or dreaming, I continued to stare silently at the unfamiliar man who was "Dad". Many times I had thought about what I would do if we ever met up again. In the back of my mind, I wondered if I might flare up in anger and lash out at him with many bitter questionings. But, as I studied his sad eyes and furrowed brow, I saw a person who had condemnation enough for himself, without me adding any to it. Much to my own surprise, I felt nothing but pity for this man, who had obviously been punished by his own guilt as much as I had been by mine years ago.

"Would . . . would you like to come in?" I asked eventually. He nodded silently, without smiling and stepped into the hallway. Feeling completely out of my depth,

I searched frantically for something to say, but eventually he broke the silence himself.

"Lindsey," he began in a tremulous voice. "I know I've no right to disturb you like this but . . . " He looked down at the ground, obviously struggling to maintain his composure. "I just had to see you again," he said huskily. "I've often thought about my little girl." I swallowed hard and looked up at him as tears came to my eyes, completely at a loss as to what I should do. He did the same for a few moments and then stepped forward and, taking his "little girl" into his arms, held her as if he were never going to let go. Years ago, I would have stood, stiff as a board, completely unable to respond, but as I willingly yielded to his embrace, I was conscious, once again, of how faithful the Lord had been in healing those deep, inner scars.

After what seemed like hours, he eventually let go and held me at arm's length, studying my face, just as Mum had at our grand reunion. It was an awkward few moments and, for once, I was actually glad of being interrupted by Miss Peters.

"Oh, hello, Lindsey," she said, looking at Dad, rather than me. Dad quickly dropped his arms and took a step backwards.

"Oh, Miss Peters, I . . . this is my Dad," I stammered. She shook his hand and smiled warmly.

"Yes, of course," she beamed. "I could tell immediately. Your daughter is a charming young lady," she advised him confidentially. I blushed and laughed with embarrassment.

"And that's definitely an exaggeration," I said humorously, at which they both laughed and the ice was broken at last.

"Anyway," finished Miss Peters, "I must let you get on. I expect you've lots to talk about." We both smiled and nodded as she disappeared out of the front door.

"Well," I said, as brightly as I could, "shall we go for a walk somewhere?" Dad smiled again.

"Yes, that would be nice, Lindsey."

"I won't be a minute then," I said and dashed up the stairs to get a coat.

"I'll take you the long way," I told him as we stepped out on to the pavement. "There's some nice woods at the back of here." He nodded, but said nothing. In fact he seemed to spend more time studying my face than actually talking and I was quite relieved when we eventually reached my favourite spot.

"Shall we sit down for a bit?" I asked, indicating the large, gnarled tree that lay on its side. Dad nodded and positioned himself next to me on the ivy-covered seat. For a few moments, we sat in awkward silence, rather like a courting couple, finding themselves alone together for the first time. Then, slowly and silently, his hand reached out for mine.

"Lindsey," he said quietly, in that same, tremulous voice, "I've thought about you so much over the years and wondered how you've grown up. I always worried that you might have been damaged in some way by what happened." I looked up at him and smiled.

"Well, I suppose I was for a while, but I'm not any more. Things have turned out okay." He squeezed my hand a little tighter and then looked up with a faint smile that contained some kind of emotion, although I wasn't quite certain what it was.

"They really have," I finished earnestly. He nodded silently.

"Yes, love, it seems as if they have. You were a frightened young child when I saw you last, but now, you really are a charming young woman."

As we began to talk and the conversation flowed more easily, it was as if the missing pieces of a jig-saw puzzle were one by one fitted into place. He hadn't been the unconcerned, uncaring person I had always thought he was. Indeed, he had wanted to make contact with me many times over the years that had followed his disappearance. But he really hadn't known how to, just as I hadn't known how to make contact with Mum as a child. Our paths could not have taken us in more differing directions, but we had, in one sense, travelled the same road.

About an hour later, I stood once again on a station platform, trying to negotiate yet another emotional farewell. Truly I had never regained my initial affection for trains and station platforms! Eventually, the train clattered noisily down the line and our unexpected meeting was over. After a few minutes of vigorous waving as it dragged slowly away, I turned and walked out of the station, feeling lighter than I had ever felt in my life, as if I had unloaded as much emotional weight as I had physical weight. Now it seemed as if that familiar black cloak, that had settled upon my shoulders so long ago, had at last been cast aside, just as my old clothes had been and the outward changes were echoed again and again through the inner chambers of my mind and soul.

As the next few months passed, I became more content and happy than I had ever been in my life. Furthermore, I tried to make other people happy too, and the results were sometimes quite astounding. One incident, in particular, I would always remember, and the recollection of it would never fail to bring a smile to my face.

On my way to work, I had noticed some sweetly-scented freesias in the local florist's window and could just see them in a particularly gloomy corner of Mr Parker's office. Before I could stop myself, I had bought a large bunch and presented it to a dumbstruck Sue. She could hardly believe her eyes or ears when I told her who they were for, but once the initial shock had worn off, she gladly helped me fish out an old copper vase into which the blooms were placed. Once positioned on Mr Parker's musty shelf, we waited with baited breath to see what his reaction would be. Five minutes later, he shuffled slowly in as usual, muttered a sombre "good morning" and disappeared into his office. A few seconds later, he re-appeared, looking rather puzzled and informed me that there had been a "slight error". Someone, he claimed, must have sent me some flowers and they had got into his office by mistake. Whereupon, I confessed to my crime, which had the astonishing effect of causing him to smile at me, probably for the first time since my interview. Later that day, he also advised me that I could, for ever after, call him Frank. This, I did quite willingly and was rewarded by the fact that, thereafter, he addressed, not only myself, but Sue as well, by our first names. From that day forward, a similarly dramatic change took place at work and Frank was often to be found chatting or laughing with us in our front office during slack moments. The whole place had become brighter and happier and even my relationship with Sue climbed up a notch.

In the past, I had often been irritated by her constant prattle about her beloved boyfriend, but now I made a point of listening as attentively as I could and tried to appear as enthusiastic about Tony as she was herself. This had obviously meant more to her than I realised as, when they eventually broke up, it was me, the "professional spinster" that she chose to confide in.

"I just feel so lonely sometimes," she told me one day. "Don't you?" As I was, at the time, checking through a will I had just typed, I was only vaguely aware of what she was saying and responded quite casually.

"Hmm? Oh ... er ... yeah, sometimes."

"I suppose it's different for you though," she continued. "With all your friends and everything." I shook my head slowly, paying a little more attention.

"I'm afraid it doesn't always work like that, Sue. Sometimes having a lot of people around you doesn't guarantee that you won't feel lonely. In fact, it sometimes makes it worse, having all those happy 'attached' people around you when you're on your own in the middle of it all." She leaned forward and rested her chin in her hands, obviously interested.

"Well, I suppose you pray, or read your Bible or something then?" By now I was aware that the conversation was going to be a bit longer than I had expected. I whipped the steadily curling will out of my machine and turned to face her.

"Sometimes I do, but you know, even that doesn't always help." She gasped in surprise at my unexpected confession.

"Well, what *do* you do then?" I tipped my head on one side and smiled.

"Well, you won't believe this, Sue," I said warily, "but I polish my shoes." Her eyes widened in surprise.

"Polish your shoes!? What's that got to do with it?"

"Well, I don't always mean literally, it's more of a principle really."

She shook her blonde, curly head and frowned.

"You've completely lost me now."

"Well, it's like this: Whenever I felt down or lonely, or anything else like that, I used to end up sitting around moping, not wanting to do anything except feel sorry for myself." She nodded.

"Yeah, I know the feeling."

"Well, one day, I worked out how much time I actually spent sitting around, doing nothing but feeling sorry for myself, and I was horrified at how much of my life I was actually wasting. If I spent only ten minutes a day, for one week, just moping, that's over an hour of my life that I could have done something constructive with. And I can assure you, it used to be a lot more than ten minutes a day! Anyway, one evening, I felt really down and in the end, I heaved all the shoes out of my wardrobe and polished every single one of them till they shone like glass!" She laughed.

"And it stopped you feeling down?"

"Well, to some small degree, yes. I suppose it did take my mind off the immediate problem, but that wasn't why I did it. I decided that there was precious little I could do to change how I felt, so I thought I would at least do something constructive with the time. That day, it happened to be polishing my shoes, but gradually, I built up a reserve of odd jobs that I never quite got round to doing and whenever I hit one of those bad days, I would attack one of them and put all my energy into doing it." She shrugged her shoulders doubtfully.

"Sounds awfully like escapism to me." I shook my head again.

"Actually, I think it's quite the opposite. Escapism is trying to pretend the problem isn't there by burying yourself in something else, maybe an activity, or something worse, like drugs or alcohol, but what I was doing was saying, in effect: 'Okay, the problem's there, and I'm not trying to pretend it isn't, all I'm trying to do is to make the time I have as profitable as I can, while I feel like I do'." Her wrinkled brow had smoothed out and as she appeared to be listening, so I continued.

"The thing is, Sue, down days don't last for ever and I knew that sooner or later I'd feel good again and want to go out with my friends and enjoy myself, and I knew I'd feel all the better for knowing that I didn't have a closet full of dirty shoes, or a long list of things that I simply had to get round to doing. It may only have helped slightly with the emotional side of things at the time, but it helped a lot on the practical side and it meant that the good days were even better." Her expression was noncommittal and I wasn't sure that she was a hundred per cent convinced. However, I did notice that she arrived at work the following Monday with a completely new hairstyle.

"Looks really nice," I told her.

"Yeah," she mumbled, looking down at the floor. "Well, I suppose it was my way of 'polishing my shoes'." We both laughed and it was obvious that it had worked for her too.

As the next three years flew quickly past, my life took on a greater stability than I had yet experienced. Even though I had not achieved the glamorous career I had so much wanted, there was, nevertheless, something very fulfilling about being just where the Lord wanted me. I found myself looking forward to each day at the office, wondering what new experiences were in store and even praying for the people I met there each week. Many of them were probate clients who had recently experienced the loss of a loved one and my heart went out to them. To me, they weren't just numbers in a filing system, but hurting, desperate people, sometimes quite obviously unable to cope with the tragedy that had recently touched their lives. As they poured out far more than estate details, I listened attentively and realised, once again, how blessed I was myself. And as I continued to find my feet in the something else that the Lord had, after all, lined up for me, life became more fulfilling and worthwhile than I had ever believed it could be. None of it had gone the way I had hoped and planned that it should. The Lord had not miraculously changed all my situations around to suit me, but *I* had changed and that once faint glimmer of hope had grown infinitely brighter, lighting up my pathway and leading me in the way of everlasting life.

My changed attitude was not confined only to my work and personal struggles. It also affected my relationship with the folks at the fellowship as I continued to realise that they, too, experienced trials and troubles, just as I did. The fact that they were married didn't guarantee that they never felt down about things as I had so often believed. Indeed they did, quite frequently and I soon came to realise that there were areas in their lives that they, too, would rather have changed. The truth confronted me more clearly each day, that we were all just clay upon the Potter's wheel, each one being fashioned and formed into the vessel of honour that only we could be. The instruments used by the Master Potter were sometimes vastly different, but they were, ultimately, wielded by the same hand. Knowing this enabled me to relate to them again, without feeling threatened or inferior because I was single. I came to understand that I, too, was a worthwhile person and had as much to contribute as they did. No longer did I have to slink off whenever a corporate activity was suggested. Now I wanted to be there, playing my part, and realising that, at last, I had found the place where I belonged. Everything we did together was now a joyful experience for me, but there was one particular incident that I was certain would stay with me for as long as I lived.

Ever since that disastrous hike through the local woods, I had remained true to my word and never again participated in this activity. One day, however, Ken suggested another woodland ramble and, as the others gave their enthusiastic agreement, I felt a sudden twinge of panic. Although the Lord had accomplished so much in my life, I couldn't help wondering how I would cope with this situation. Even now, I could still remember gazing wistfully at the romantic couples, disappearing into the distance during the last walk I had gone on and now I was faced with a nerve-racking decision. Either I could revert to being my old self and come up with some excuse for not going, or I could step out in faith and allow the Lord to hold me up. In the end, nervous though I was, I knew in my heart of hearts that I had no choice but to go along.

After lunch the following Saturday, we set off in the direction of those familiar woods and began the afternoon's activities with a game of football. This, in itself, got things off to a good start as playing football was hardly a good time for couples to become "smoochy". But eventually, the game ended and the walk proper began. As always, we started off together, but after a few minutes, the children ran off and the couples gravitated towards each other as usual. Some wandered off ahead of me, whilst others lagged behind until the distance between myself and the two romantic parties increased. Once again, I found myself alone, just as I had on the last walk.

"Well, Lord," I sighed, "I guess it's just the two of us!"

Digging my hands into my pockets, I began to wander down one of the narrow, winding pathways, waiting expectantly for that familiar feeling of self-pity to engulf me. But it never did. Instead, as I continued to stroll through the vast woodlands, I began to dwell on the beauty all around me; the birds singing, the sun glinting off the shimmering waters, and the occasional glimpse of a squirrel, with its floating, silver feather of a tail, bobbing along behind him. And as I smiled contentedly at the scenic surroundings, I remembered the One who had made it all. Then, just as on the night of my conversion, I became aware that I wasn't alone. He walked there with me, just as He had ever since that night, and even before. All the many things I wanted to say to a physical companion, I could say to Him and He would listen and respond. Suddenly, the situation I had dreaded so much turned out to be an experience I would always want to remember. At last, I had found the Friend I had been searching for all my life. Of course, He was also special to so many others, but that didn't stop Him being personal to me as well. He would always be with me, no matter where I went and, at last, I knew that I need never be lonely or frightened again.

22

I turned the pages of my old diary and couldn't help laughing to myself. There, in rather scrawly shorthand, were the thoughts and feelings of someone completely the opposite of the person I now was. I found it difficult to believe how depressed and angry I had once been and could only marvel afresh at all that the Lord had done for me. Of course, there were still many imperfections that needed to be ironed out, but they were no longer the cause for undue concern that they once had been. If the Lord had been able to heal those areas of my life and personality that had seemed beyond redemption, I was now perfectly confident that He could take care of the rest. This was particularly true when it came to the question of marriage.

Being single was one thing I had thought I would never come to terms with. It had seemed to me that even the Lord could not provide the answer to the desperate need I had felt for a human companion, but He had exceeded all my tenuous expectations. Now, as I looked back over the many years of agonising I realised at last just how beneficial the situation had been. So many times I had asked the question "Why?", just as Derek had, and equally as many times there had seemed to be no answer. Now, however, it all seemed so perfectly clear. Through this very dealing, I had found the Lord in a way that I might not have done, had I easily found a husband. By going through this very struggle, I had learned to trust Him, even when it seemed He was working against me, to obey Him when it seemed ridiculous to do so, and to follow Him, when I had felt like turning around and walking another way. By doing so I had not only found Him, I had, in a sense, found myself. At last, that great longing I had felt while talking to Ted years ago, had been fulfilled. I was a whole person, just as he had been, despite his outward circumstances. I was, as the Bible so aptly put it: "Complete in Him", even though I was a single person. Of course, I was still human enough to like the idea of getting married, and kept my mind open to the possibility, but it was no longer the desperate need it had once been. Instead, I was able to give myself completely to the Lord's current plan for my life and noticed a growing seriousness in my overall commitment. Each day, as I went about my work, I prayed that my life would count, in however small a measure, for Him, and this desire was shared by our group as a whole. It seemed that a fresh wind of His spirit had begun to blow upon our fellowship and, as I found myself caught up in its stirring currents, yet another new chapter in my life began to unfold.

In recent years, the small Nursery run by Ken and Barbara had expanded to the point where they had needed to buy larger premises. As they had asked Mr Parker to handle the conveyancing for them, I had been one of the first of our number to view the property and had instantly fallen in love with it.

Situated in five acres of picturesque lawns, woodlands and water gardens, the old Vicarage provided a spacious dwelling that was to become a welcome retreat to so many in future years. But, beautiful though the building was, the grounds were what really captivated my imagination. There, in a perfect blend of sweeping curves and symmetrical lines, was captured that mysterious, old-fashioned beauty only to be found in the rambling estates and cottage gardens of long ago. As we wandered into the shrubbery, I could just see the smiling, rosy-cheeked milk-maid, drawing water from the ancient wishing-well, or young children, sailing paper boats on the shimmering lake where a family of mallards were taking an energetic bath. Then, as we proceeded from the formality of the rose garden, with its razor-sharp edges, to the unstructured wildness of the woods, I couldn't help smiling in sheer delight. There, across the luminous carpet of bluebells would often flash the white fluffiness of a rabbit's tail as it dived into its burrow, scattering twigs and causing nearby robins to cheep in indignation. But, delighted though I was, there was one thing that had bothered me ever since we had arrived and I was very glad when Ken prompted my question.

"Well?" he smiled. "What d'you think of it, Lindsey?"

"It's beautiful," I replied, sincerely. "But . . . "

"But?" he echoed enquiringly.

"Well, if it's going to be a Nursery, won't it be a bit of a shame to rip it all up and turn it into potting sheds and green-houses and all the rest of it?" Ken shook his head and smiled.

"We're not intending to do that," he said firmly.

"You're not? But how're you going to have a Nursery without . . . ?"

"Show you," he said simply, and led us out of the woods and up a fairly steep hill.

"Thing is," he advised me as we walked, "the Nursery isn't the most important part of it. We both feel this is quite a different venture altogether." I nodded as I listened and wondered why the fleeting notion that I had walked up this hill before had suddenly crossed my mind.

"Over the past few years," continued Ken as I drew my thoughts back to the subject in hand, "we noticed that people weren't so much coming to buy plants as they were to have a cup of coffee and a chat. Then, as we started praying about new premises, we felt the Lord was wanting us to provide, not just a bigger Nursery, but a place where people could come, bring the family or friends, and just get away from it all for a while."

I nodded again. "Well, this is certainly a beautiful place for doing that, but it still doesn't explain about the green-houses and all the rest of it."

Ken smiled. "Ah, you'll see in a minute," he said mysteriously.

Just then, we emerged at the top of the pathway and

were confronted with a large plantation of some kind. It was a vast field of brittle, brown stalks, as tall as myself, that stretched to the boundaries of the property. I looked at Ken and Barbara feeling rather non-plussed.

"What's this?" I asked eventually.

"Raspberry fields," volunteered Barbara with a chuckle. "Apparently the vicar was crazy about raspberries! They haven't been tended for years though, which is why they're so overgrown."

"And this is the answer to your question, Lindsey," finished Ken. I gazed at the huge, flat area in front of us and then turned to look behind us. As I did, the penny dropped.

"Oh, I see," I exclaimed. "Potting shed and greenhouses and all the commercial stuff up here. Woodlands form a natural screen and the gardens on the lower level are kept intact." They both nodded.

"Exactly," said Ken. "This place is just perfect for the dual purpose. People can enjoy the peace and tranquillity of the gardens and then, if they do want to buy plants, they can stroll through the woods, up the hill and into the Nursery proper." As he began to unfold the vision that the Lord had given to them for the new premises, I found myself becoming as excited as they were about it.

"Of course, the shop will have to be down in the main car-park," continued Ken. "But the old coach house lends itself to the purpose very well without destroying the 'olde worlde' look of the place."

"Sounds great," I said enthusiastically. "It's going to be a real hit!"

And so it was. In no time at all, word had spread about this enchanting oasis on the outskirts of town and people of all ages and backgrounds began to pour through the gates. They ranged from the young mother with children to the retired pensioner, or the solitary plant collector to the mini-buses full of children from the local schools for the handicapped. Whoever they were and wherever they came from, they always received a warm welcome and inevitably went home and told their friends about it.

But, not only did it draw the general public, it also began to absorb more and more people from the fellowship itself as the larger venture obviously necessitated a larger workforce. Rick joined forces with Ken and Barbara and became their official landscaper. His first assignment was to carry out some intensive landscaping on the more run-down areas of the Nursery and, with this as his advertisement to visiting customers, his services were soon in great demand.

"Don't care what you do with it," his prospective customers would often tell him, "just create a little piece of your Nursery in my garden, and I'll be happy!" And so he did, and so they were – happy enough, in fact, to pass his name to many others who were also touched by the beauty and serenity of the Nursery and wanted him to re-create some of the same atmosphere in their own gardens.

And then there was Jim. Some time earlier, he had folded up his accountancy business, retaining only a few personal clients, and had gone into partnership with Ken and Barbara. One of the rooms in the top of the old coach house had been converted into an office, from which he handled the administration with Barbara acting as his personal secretary. This was something of a new venture for her, as her only experience of office work was what little there had been connected with the previous Nursery. However, being of a ready mind and willing heart, she soon settled into her new role and executed her responsibilities with expert efficiency. Jim was always full of praiseworthy comments about this, although Ken found the situation a little distressing at times.

"Crazy, absolutely crazy!" he muttered as he burst into the office one morning, dabbing his nose with a delicate pink tissue.

"Hi, Ken," called Jim cheerfully. "What's up? Can't afford to buy decent hankies these days?" Ken stopped with the tissue half way to his pocket and sighed.

"Oh yeah, can afford 'em all right. Trouble is, she keeps 'filing' things. Everything's got to have a special place these days, even the hankies. Can't find any of 'em. Sometimes I'm afraid to stand still too long in case she files me as well!"

"Better move then," came Barbara's voice from behind him. "I'm just about to start a filing session any minute now!" Ken groaned as she kissed his forehead and made his way to the door.

"I'm going," he said, jerking his thumb in the general direction of the potting shed. "At least there aren't any filing cabinets out there!"

Although they laughed, Barbara's flair for office work had, in reality, been of great benefit to them both. It meant that Jim had needed to spend less and less time in the office himself, leaving her to handle everything except the more complicated bookwork, and had become increasingly involved in the practical and physical work of the Nursery. Often, he was to be found on the end of a spade or wheelbarrow, helping Rick with the landscaping, or discussing development plans with Ken as they strolled round the grounds with clip-boards and pens. In no time at all, he had become as able a plantsman as Barbara had a secretary.

I, for my part, could hardly stay away from the place. It wasn't too far from Albert Avenue and, if I took a certain route home, I would actually walk past it and see the coach house lights on if Barbara was still working in the office. I spent as much time there as I could, as did the others, and after a while, it seemed to have become a kind of permanent "open house". Every time I turned up, there were certain to be several others from the fellowship there as well and we had some precious, memorable and sometimes quite hilarious times together. In addition to this, I stayed at the Vicarage almost every weekend and became quite involved in the practical, outdoor work myself. It seemed that I was extra-specially happy when I was out in the fresh air, talking to customers or helping the others with the propagation or maintenance. The wide open spaces and dappled woodlands seemed to echo the breadth and depth freedom I now felt within myself. No longer was

I closed up and bound in my former chains of guilt and loneliness. I could relax, walk, or even run in the vast, open spaces of glorious liberty that knew no bounds.

They were some of the happiest days I could remember since the early days of my conversion. Indeed, I wouldn't have minded if things had stayed just as they were for ever, but the Lord, obviously, had quite different ideas. Only three short years after the Nursery was set up, He began to unfold the next part of His plan. One night, in spite of all that had been accomplished in the area of my emotions, I found it more than a little difficult to keep my composure.

At last, after so many years, the "right time" had come for Ken and Barbara to realise their calling to South America. In the setting up of the new Nursery, I had begun to hope that they would forget about their former longing to be missionaries. I had pushed the thought of their leaving to the back of my mind, which made it all the more painful when it surfaced once more. Struggling to hold back the tears, I glanced round the room and realised that I didn't need to. Most people there seemed to be wrestling with the same feelings and I noticed that even Jim found it necessary to dab his eyes once or twice during the meeting.

It had been a bitter-sweet gathering as we reminisced on the "old days" and all that Ken and Barbara had put into the fellowship since it had begun. Derek, who was leading the meeting that night, had re-lived the events so beautifully that I was almost relieved when it was all over. By the end of the evening, I was so overcome with emotion that I felt completely unable to watch them saying their tearful farewells. Instead, I crept quietly out of the door and waited in the back of Ken's car for what would be the last time. After a while, with the last goodbye obviously said, they joined me and we sped off towards Albert Avenue.

There was so much I wanted to say on that final, heart-breaking journey, but I suddenly felt the same as I had on that cold, station platform, so many years ago. Just as it had been then, with Mum and Uncle Tom, I couldn't begin to express the many things I wanted so much to say. And, as we turned the final corner, and Ken stepped on the brake pedal, I wished, more than anything, that I could have stopped time in its tracks, just as his car had stopped in the road outside my house. A moment later, all three of us stood on the pavement in that same painful silence until Ken finally spoke.

"Well, Lindsey," he said softly, "I guess we have to say goodbye now." I nodded and tried to smile, but was unable to hold back the tears any longer. Suddenly, he stepped forward and gave me a big hug. Barbara did the same thing a moment later, and I noticed that her most endearing quality of being able to quickly withdraw was completely missing tonight. Instead, she held on to me for quite some time as I wept quietly on her shoulder. Then, as she stood back and Ken drew his arm around her waist, I noticed that tears glistened in their eyes too.

"I'm going to miss you so much," I said, dabbing my eyes with a handkerchief that was far too small to be of any real use.

"We'll miss you too, Lindsey," said Ken softly. "You've come a long way."

"Well, only because of people like you," I replied tearfully.

We stood in silence again for another few seconds, unable to find adequate words to leave with each other after so many years of friendship. Then Ken suddenly withdrew his arm from Barbara's waist and jumped into the car. Barbara followed suit and wound down her window as he started up the engine.

"We love you, Lindsey," she whispered into the moonlit night.

"I love you too," I said, smiling through my tears and waved vigorously as they sped off down the road, even though I knew that they couldn't see me doing so.

— 23 —

Heaving a sigh of relief, I slid the blue folder back into its sleeve and pushed the drawer shut – at last, I had finished. The documents were ready, the strong room locked and the key deposited in Frank's safe. As the clock in the square outside struck seven, I remembered Sally's words about part-timers. Most people would be sitting in some cosy living room, watching television, or enjoying their evening meal together by now, but it would be a while before I got home, let alone had something to eat. But it wasn't so bad, and in fact, much better than it used to be. Over the years, I had gradually managed to curb Frank's habit of leaving things to the last minute, and usually got away at a more civilised hour. However, there were still the occasions when he forgot things, such as this important and very early appointment scheduled for the following morning. I had only been informed of it myself that afternoon and had spent the rest of the day preparing the necessary documents. To make matters worse, Sue, who would normally have taken care of the more routine work, was on holiday, leaving me to cope with it all alone. By the time I grabbed my coat and let myself out of the front door, I felt completely shattered. In view of this, I wondered why it was that I decided to take the more scenic, but definitely longer way home. It was the route that went past the Nursery and I often used it on a normal day. Why I should choose it tonight of all nights was a complete mystery, but for some reason, I felt almost obliged to do so.

As I turned off the busy main road and started down a more rural lane, the building came into view. Even from a distance, I could see the coach house light, blinking like a solitary, bright star, through the dense woodlands that surrounded the house. A few seconds later, I reached a fork in the road and stopped. Usually, I took the path to the left and continued on to Albert Avenue, but tonight, I turned right instead and walked down the familiar driveway.

Shortly after Ken and Barbara had left, Jim and his family had moved into the Vicarage and continued to run the Nursery, but it soon became obvious how much the couple were missed. Not only had we lost great friends and spiritual leaders, on the business side of things we were also missing two invaluable members of staff. Much of the responsibility had fallen on Jim's shoulders, who once again found himself heavily entrenched in the office work. Often, when I called round to see them, he would be in the coach house, surrounded by mountains of paperwork, or painstakingly typing an estimate with two fingers. In addition to this, Rick and the others had come to rely on him quite heavily for guidance in the practical work of the Nursery and he would frequently be called away from the office to advise on some matter or other. To make up for lost time, he would often work late into the evening and be missing from the usual gatherings that still happened at the Vicarage. His absence was noticed by all of us, but seemed to be taking its toll, most of all, on Sally.

"Thought we'd see more of him now that we're actually living on site," she confided one day. "But seems to me that we see less of him now than before." Her comments had struck a deep chord inside me, for I had been as concerned as the others about the situation. Now, as the tell-tale light informed me that Jim was working late, yet again, I realised why I had taken that particular route home.

Instead of pushing through the back door into the house when I reached the top of the driveway, I carried on down into the main car-park and up the stairs to the office. As I quietly pushed open the door, my suspicions proved correct. Jim was seated at his large desk, his newly acquired g glasses perched on the end of his nose and bits of paper strewn everywhere. I closed the door behind me with a loud click, hoping to attract his attention, and succeeded.

"Lindsey!" he exclaimed in surprise. "What are you doing here?"

"I could almost ask you the same thing," I said, perching on the edge of the window-sill. "Don't you ever stop working?"

"Oh, I was just finishing a bit of paperwork."

"A bit! Looks like you could start a recycling plant with this lot." He laughed wearily and removed his glasses, enabling me to study his classic, aquiline features, just as I had at that first meeting. He had been a good decade younger then, with jet-black hair and those ever-piercing blue eyes. The latter, I knew, would never lose their intensity, but in other ways, it was quite a different Jim that confronted me now. His expression, slightly more defined by deeper lines, and the hair at his temples, now quite grey, made him look much softer and definitely less disconcerting. I folded my arms and smiled wryly as he began an explanation.

"Yeah, I suppose there is rather a lot. Seems to have all got on top of me since Barbara left. Funny how you never really appreciate how much a person does until they're not there to do it any more." We both fell silent for a moment and then, to my own surprise, I found myself speaking.

"Jim, I've been thinking," I began warily. He looked up at me enquiringly, but said nothing.

"It's just that . . . well, you seem to be working so hard since Barbara left." He put his head on one side and smiled just a little.

"You mean I didn't work hard before?"

"No, of course not," I said earnestly. "But . . . well, I can type, you know." He nodded calmly.

"Yes, Lindsey, I think I'm aware of that."

"And do shorthand and . . . other things." Again he nodded and I noticed that playful gleam of laughter in his eyes.

"Well, the thing is, Jim, I find it so difficult to go back to work on a Monday morning after spending the weekend here. It's like I'm leaving part of me behind every time I go back and I was only wondering if . . . if you would let me work for you instead." I stopped for a moment as that usual unnerving silence ensued.

"I mean, I've learnt a lot about Nursery work already – I even know the difference between a weed and a plant now," I continued wryly. Jim smiled, obviously remembering the time when I had pulled up one of the more choice specimens in the garden and hurled it triumphantly on to the compost heap. "And I could help you with all this stuff," I finished, waving a hand over his desk as if it were some kind of magic wand. He rested his chin in his hand and tapped the side of his face with his fingers. I looked up at him, hoping to read something vaguely encouraging in his expression, but apart from that playful sparkle in his eyes, he remained as noncommittal as ever. Suddenly, it occurred to me that I had made a terrible mistake. Maybe he would think I was accusing him of inability or inefficiency, or, conversely, that I was trying to impress him with my own capabilities. All at once, I wondered if I should just apologise and ask him to forget the whole thing. Just as I was about to speak again, however, he quenched my fears in his own, inimitable way. Suddenly sitting bolt upright, he pursed his lips and folded his arms.

"Hmm . . . I wondered how long it would take," he muttered with a sly smile. I frowned and wondered what I was supposed to make of this statement.

"Well, it's obvious, isn't it?" he volunteered eventually. "I've been able to see you working here for quite some time, I just wanted to hear you say so yourself, that's all." I let out a deep breath and smiled with relief.

"Really?" I exclaimed enthusiastically. "Well, that's really great. When do I start?"

"Tonight if you like," he said, indicating the jumble of papers on his desk with a laugh. I laughed too and we then embarked upon one of our typical conversations, during which I would become more and more excited and he would respond with characteristic coolness. We might have continued talking for quite some time, had it not been for the high-pitched bleep of his wristwatch.

"Hey, Jim," I gasped, "I'm sorry, I've held you up even more now."

"That's okay," he grinned. "I'll just leave this lot for my new secretary to sort out later." I laughed again as he got up and opened the door for me.

"Staying for dinner?" he asked casually. I nodded vigorously, as nothing could have been more appealing at that moment than the thought of Sally's home cooking.

The following Monday, I reluctantly handed my notice in to Frank. Excited though I was about my next step, I couldn't help feeling sad at the prospect of leaving his employment. Over the years, he and Sue had become great friends to me and I knew I would miss them terribly.

"Hmm ... yes, well ... er ... goodbye, Lindsey," muttered Frank on the final day. "And ... of course you're welcome to visit us ... if, of course, you'd like to, that is and ... "

"Of course I'd like to," I said sincerely. "And you must come to the Nursery – both of you," I said, glancing at Sue who was keeping very quiet. "I'll give you a guided tour myself." They both smiled and promised to take up my invitation then, to my great surprise, Sue stepped forward and gave me a hug.

"Bye, Lindsey," she said quickly. "Thanks for everything." I looked at them both for a few moments longer, wishing I really didn't have to leave and then shook hands with them.

"Well, goodbye," I said eventually. "Thanks for having me." Then I left the office for the last time to embark upon the something else that the Lord had planned for me after all.

The first three months were spent entirely in the office with Jim, learning the inner workings of the business. This included not only the administration for the Nursery and landscaping business, but also the book-keeping and accounts. In addition to this, I also handled the mail-orders, bookings from local societies for slide-shows and guided tours of the Nursery and applications for the national flower shows at which we regularly exhibited.

The work was varied, interesting and stimulating, and even more so because I had developed a first-hand knowledge of the products we were marketing. As time went on, I found myself increasingly drawn into the practical work of the Nursery, just as Jim had been. During slack periods in the office, I would don a pair of boots and one of Rick's jackets and help with the seed-sowing or potting and gradually found myself spending more and more time outside.

Of course, there was still a lot of paperwork to be done, but Jim and I had worked it out to a fine art. We spent one complete day a week in the office, keeping up to date with correspondence and accounts. The rest of the administration work we managed to integrate into what we were doing outside. I took to carrying my note-pad and pencil wherever I went and it wasn't unusual for me to take dictation whilst propped up against a mountain of peat bales. Then, when I had come to a sensible stopping point in whatever I was doing, I would dash up to the coach house and type up my notes. At other times, I would speak to people on Jim's mobile phone whilst helping Rick with the landscaping, and the "office" in which I arranged to meet with reps and advertisers usually turned out to be the humble potting shed, but none of them seemed to mind.

Such a fluid and varied structure gave me a great sense of freedom and being my own boss and I enjoyed my work more and more as time went on. Occasionally it crossed my mind, especially when I was building a rock garden with Rick or on the back of a lorry, unloading compost, that it was a far cry from the glamorous career I had so firmly set my mind on as a youngster. But it didn't matter in the slightest. It was enough to know that I was in the right place, doing the right thing, and this knowledge did me good in every way.

I became stronger and healthier than I had ever been and old friends that called in to see me often remarked on how well I looked. In summer, I was frequently asked where I had gone to obtain such a "gorgeous tan", but few people really believed I had got it at work. And in winter, as my face tingled in the fresh, bracing air, I stopped to spare a thought for those poor people, huddled in their centrally-heated offices, who were unable to enjoy the scenic surroundings which I was fortunate enough to work in every day. But the benefits were not just physical, being in the right place did me good emotionally and spiritually too and one day, I stumbled upon something that turned out to be a source of great enjoyment.

Singing continued to provide for me a tremendous release, doing for my soul what running did for my body, but I never felt able to really let myself go in my room at Albert Avenue for fear of disturbing the residents. It wasn't a great problem, but I was overjoyed when the solution presented itself, quite unexpectedly, one day at work.

In a secluded corner of the garden, like a giant bubble, stood a rather space-age greenhouse. It was a domed construction, made up of numerous triangles of glass, webbed together with slim, metal strips. The over-all effect was quite dramatic, especially when the sun lit up its many facets, making it glisten and gleam like a giant precious stone. For me, it was a near-perfect representation of what I imagined the classic UFO might look like when grounded. I could quite easily see it inhabited by little green men, or something similar, but it contained, instead, such mundane and ordinary objects as a few garden chairs, a small table and some glossy magazines. Customers often congregated there during the day, enjoying the sun and reading, but when they had gone, I used it myself for quite a different purpose. It was something I had discovered when I had gone over to renew the magazines one morning.

As usual, I had been singing to myself as I walked and continued as I stepped through the sliding doorway. Immediately, I was arrested by the efficiency of the acoustics, which made even my mediocre, contralto voice sound fairly reasonable and a plan began to unfold in my mind. Here, in this secluded part of the garden, I could sing to my heart's content, without fear of disturbing anyone.

It seemed such a good idea that I put it into action the very next day. At lunchtime, armed with my guitar and songbook, I sneaked into the glass dome and spent half an hour in abandoned praise. From that day forward, many of my lunch hours were spent singing in this rather unconventional concert hall, and experiencing some of the most releasing and inspiring times of praise and worship I had ever known.

So it was that at last, after years of striving, I was happy. The Lord had done things for me that I could never have done for myself and another experience one day at the Nursery was a graphic revelation of just how faithful He had been over the years that had followed my first encounter with Him.

It was a Friday morning in late September and I had just opened up the shop when a car roared into the car-park and a man in a grey suit jumped out.

"Hi, Lindsey," he shouted as he slammed the door behind him with more than necessary gusto. "S'pose you're still buying from the opposition then?" I laughed and nodded as I recognised him as my favourite sales rep.

" 'Fraid so, Tim," I grinned. "You'll have to drop your prices a bit if you want to do some trade with us." He laughed and leaned one elbow on the counter by the till.

"Well, in that case, maybe you can sell me something instead."

"Oh yes?" He nodded.

"Wallflowers – got any?"

"Yes, stacks. How many do you want?" He pursed his lips and thought for a moment.

"How much are they?"

"To you, Tim, ten for a pound." He smiled at my supposed favouritism, but then I continued, "To anyone else – ten for fifty pence." We both laughed and then he suddenly straightened up.

"Well, I'm sorry, but you'll have to drop your prices a bit if you want to do some trade with me," he replied, mimicking my tone to perfection. After a few more minutes of laughter and friendly banter, he eventually settled on the grand total of forty wallflowers at ten for a pound, with a generous discount of ten per cent.

"Where are they?" he asked, looking round quickly.

"Up the top," I replied, waving a hand in the direction of the concealed greenhouses. "We do them open ground – don't get so root-bound that way."

"Oh, I see."

"I'll have to dig them up for you," I continued. "It'll take a minute, so why don't you have a wander round?" He smiled and nodded.

"Okay, I haven't had a chance to do that yet – always too busy arguing with you!" I laughed again and went off to find a bucket.

Since starting work at the Nursery, I had climbed the hill to the greenhouses many times. I was so familiar with its bumps and curves that I could walk up it in almost pitch darkness without stumbling, but, on that bright, autumn morning, there was something strangely new about it. Once again, the trees on each side of the sloping pathway had been set on fire with the golden, glowing colours of the season. Robins peeped and darted in and out of the dense undergrowth while the resident squirrels jumped effortlessly from branch to branch overhead. Slowly, I began to feel a strange, stirring harmony with the beauty all around me. A moment later, I found myself singing and swinging my bucket to and fro as I walked briskly up the hill. My pace began to quicken as I realised what a happy person I had become but then, quite suddenly, I stopped. As I did, it seemed as if all creation held its breath and stood on tip-toe to witness what was taking place. All at once, I had remembered walking up this hill for the first time with Ken, and having the distinct feeling that

I had been there before. Now, as I stood immobilised, at a point where past and present were eternally fused together, I at last knew why that strange feeling had come upon me. As I looked down at myself, and realised that I was wearing a roll-neck jumper, blue trousers and green wellington boots, that long-forgotten vision I had seen as a child came rushing back to my mind. As it did, I could hardly contain the excitement that swept over me in great, gushing waves. It had come true, at last, right there, before my very eyes. Everything about me, my clothes, my surroundings, and that inner joy I had hardly dared to believe could be mine, was exactly as I had seen it all those years ago. As Derek might well have told me, it had, indeed, "taken time" for the vision to be fulfilled. There had been steep hills and deep valleys in between. Periods of confusing darkness and others of dazzling light, but none of it had been a mistake, none of it had been wasted. It had all been worth it in the end.

"Lord," I told Him as I started off again, "I don't regret a single mile."

Hodder Christian Paperbacks: a tradition of excellence.

Great names and great books to enrich your life and meet your needs. Choose from such authors as:

Corrie ten Boom
Charles Colson
Richard Foster
Billy Graham
Michael Green
Michele Guinness
Joyce Huggett
Francis MacNutt
Catherine Marshall
Jim Packer
Adrian Plass

Jackie Pullinger
David Pytches
Mary Pytches
Jennifer Rees Larcombe
Cliff Richard
John Stott
Joni Eareckson Tada
Colin Urquhart
David Watson
David Wilkerson
John Wimber

The wide range of books on the Hodder Christian Paperback list include biography, personal testimony, devotional books, evangelistic books, Christian teaching, fiction, drama, poetry, books that give help for times of need – and many others.

Ask at your nearest Christian bookshop or at your church bookstall for the latest titles.

SOME BESTSELLERS IN HODDER CHRISTIAN PAPERBACKS

THE HIDING PLACE by Corrie ten Boom

The triumphant story of Corrie ten Boom, heroine of the anti-Nazi underground.

"A brave and heartening story."

Baptist Times

GOD'S SMUGGLER by Brother Andrew

An international bestseller. God's Smuggler carries contraband Bibles past armed border guards to bring the love of Christ to the people behind the Iron Curtain.

"A book you will not want to miss."

Catherine Marshall

DISCIPLESHIP by David Watson

". . . breath-taking, block-busting, Bible-based simplicity on every page."

Jim Packer

LISTENING TO GOD by Joyce Huggett

A profound spiritual testimony, and practical help for discovering a new dimension of prayer.

"This is counselling at its best."

Leadership Today

CELEBRATION OF DISCIPLINE by Richard Foster

A classic on the Spiritual Disciplines.

"For any Christian hungry for teaching, I would recommend this as being one of the most challenging books to have been published."

Delia Smith

RUN BABY RUN by Nicky Cruz with Jamie Buckingham

A tough New York gang leader discovers Christ.

"It is a thrilling story. My hope is that it shall have a wide reading."

Billy Graham

CHASING THE DRAGON by Jackie Pullinger
with Andrew Quicke

Life-changing miracles in Hong Kong's Walled City.

"A book to stop you in your tracks."

Liverpool Daily Post

BORN AGAIN by Charles Colson

Disgraced by Watergate, Charles Colson finds a new life.

"An action packed story of real life drama and a revelation of modern history as well as a moving personal account."

Elim Evangel

KNOWING GOD by J I Packer

The biblical portrait that has become a classic.

"(The author) illumines every doctrine he touches and commends it with courage, logic, lucidity and warmth . . . the truth he handles fires the heart. At least it fired mine, and compelled me to turn aside to worship and pray."

John Stott

THE HAPPIEST PEOPLE ON EARTH by Demos Shakarian with John and Elizabeth Sherrill

The extraordinary beginnings of the Full Gospel Business Men's Fellowship.